THE COW

"I hate you!"

Jace smiled. "D_____ hate
to think you we_____ unrequited love for me.
But if you change your mind, honey, you know
where my room is," he added for good measure.
"Just don't expect marriage. I know how badly you
need a meal ticket. But," he said, as he opened the
door, "it won't be me."

PASSION FLOWER

"I want you to leave," he said.

"Yes, I know," Jennifer said on a soft little sigh.
"When?"

"At the end of the week."

So soon, she thought miserably? "Do you hate
me?"

Rett turned around slowly, and his eyes slashed at
her. "I could hate you," he said harshly. "If I didn't
want you so damned much."

AFTER THE MUSIC

"I'm not gentle," Thorn said abruptly. "There's
never been a woman who could make me gentle.
But I could lose my head with you, so keep a few
yards away from me while you're here, okay? It
would be hell living with myself if I seduced a
virgin."

Dear Reader,

Diana Palmer has long been a favourite of Silhouette readers and it is with great pleasure that we bring you this collection of three superb novels in one volume.

Back by popular request, these are some of the earliest books Diana ever wrote, and two have never been published in Great Britain before. Don't miss the opportunity to catch up on all three stories now.

We know you will enjoy her special brand of humour and warm emotional tension. To all of her fans present, past and future—we wish you happy reading.

Do take the time to write and let us know how you enjoyed your Diana Palmer Collection.

Jane Nicholls
Silhouette Books
PO Box 236
Thornton Road
Croydon
Surrey
CR9 3RU

DIANA PALMER

COLLECTION

THE COWBOY AND THE LADY

PASSION FLOWER

AFTER THE MUSIC

*First published in Great Britain in 1993
by Silhouette Books, Eton House, 18-24 Paradise Road,
Richmond, Surrey TW9 1SR*

Diana Palmer Collection	© *Silhouette Books 1993*
The Cowboy and the Lady	*First published in Great Britain 1983 as a Silhouette Desire* © *Diana Palmer 1982*
Passion Flower	© *Diana Palmer 1984*
After the Music	© *Diana Palmer 1986*

*Silhouette and Colophon are
Trade Marks of Harlequin Enterprises B.V.*

ISBN 0 373 59005 9

47/9306

Made and printed in Great Britain

CONTENTS

A Note from Diana Palmer

Dear Reader,

In late 1979 I finally got up enough nerve to send a manuscript to Silhouette Books, and in early 1980 they accepted my first book.

The Cowboy and the Lady was my first Silhouette Desire novel and Jace is my favourite of all the heroes I've ever created. Amanda was very much on the defensive with him, and it was obvious to me from the beginning that she was going to have a difficult time with him.

I also enjoyed creating Thorn in *After the Music* because he was a hard-headed businessman who learned that there are things more important than making money. He wasn't at all hard on the eyes, though! Sabina and Thorn played so beautifully against each other that the book practically wrote itself.

Everett in *Passion Flower* was a renegade. He sort of flowered from a really spiny cactus plant, and he seemed to suit the rugged Texas terrain where he thrived.

I prefer writing books with Western settings. There is something timeless about a vast plain where men struggle against nature itself to carve a life—or an empire—for themselves. The men who tamed the West were a special breed. I have enjoyed recreating that pioneer spirit in modern-day cattlemen, in heroes who are, I hope, a little larger than life. If their virtues are slightly magnified, it is to compensate for the flaws of modern society, which are also magnified. Romance fiction offers a brief escape from the pain and pressure of modern life, taking you into a world where the human spirit can be noble and strive for a higher, richer existence. My characters aren't completely true to life—but then, perhaps that's their appeal.

I hope you enjoy this special collection.

Diana Palmer

THE COWBOY
AND THE LADY

To Frances Thompson and family

1

They were at a standstill, the tall man and the willowy young blonde, poised like boxers waiting for an opening.

"Never!" she repeated, her brown eyes throwing off sparks. "I know we need the business, and I'd do anything for you—within reason. But this isn't reasonable, and you know it, Terry Black!"

He drew a weary breath and turned to the window overlooking San Antonio's frantic late morning traffic, his hands rammed into his pockets, his thin shoulders slumping dejectedly.

"I'll be ruined," he said softly.

She glared at his back. "Sell one of your Cadillacs," she suggested.

He threw her an irritated glance. "Amanda...!"

"I was Mandy when I came in this morning," she reminded him, tossing back her long, silver blond hair with a smile. "Come on, Terry, it isn't all that bad."

"No," he agreed finally, "I guess it isn't." He leaned back against the wall beside the huge picture window and let his eyes drift over her soft, young curves, lingering where her beige shirtwaist dress made a straight line across the high, small curve of her breasts. "He can't really dislike you," he added absently. "No man with blood in his veins could."

"Jason Whitehall doesn't have any blood in his veins," she said. "He has ice water and a dash of aged whiskey."

"Jason didn't offer me the account. His brother Duncan did."

"Jace owns the lion's share of the corporation, though, Terry," she argued. "And he's never used an advertising agency, not ever."

"If the Whitehalls want to sell lots in that inland development project they're working on in Florida, they'll have to use one. And why not us?" he added with a boyish grin. "After all, we're the best."

She threw up her slender hands. "So you keep telling me."

"We need the account," he persisted. His thin, boyish face grew thoughtful. "Do you realize just how big the Whitehall empire is?" he asked, as if she'd never heard of it. "The Texas ranch alone covers twenty-five-thousand acres!"

"I know," she sighed, and her soft brown eyes were sad with memory. "You forget, my father's ranch adjoined the Whitehalls' before—" She broke off. "Anyway, it's not as if you couldn't go by yourself."

He looked briefly uncomfortable. "Uh, I'm afraid I can't do that."

She blinked at him across the luxurious carpeted room with its modern chrome-trimmed furniture. "I beg your pardon?"

"It's no deal unless you come along."

"Why?"

"Because we're partners," he said stubbornly, his lower lip thrusting forward. "And mostly because Duncan Whitehall won't discuss it without you. He's considering our agency because of his friendship with you; how about that? *He* came looking for *us*."

That was strange. She and Duncan had been friends for many years, but knowing how his brother felt, it was odd that he'd insist on her presence for business.

"But Jace hates me," she murmured, wide-eyed. "I don't want to go, Terry."

"Why does he hate you, for heaven's sake?" he asked, exasperated.

"Most recently," she admitted, "because I ran over his quarter-million-dollar bull."

"Come again?"

"Well, I didn't actually do it; Mother did, but she was so afraid of Jace that I took the blame. It didn't endear me to him, either; he was a grand champion."

"Jace?"

"The bull!" She folded her arms across her chest. "Mother can't accept the fact that the old days, when we had money, are gone. I do. I can stand alone. But she can't. If she wasn't able to visit Marguerite at Casa Verde for several weeks a year, and pretend nothing has changed, I'm not sure she could manage." She shrugged. "Jace hated me anyway, it just gave him a better reason to let him think I crippled the animal."

"When did all this happen?" he asked curiously. "You never mentioned it after your trip... of course, you looked like death warmed over for a couple of weeks, and I was head over heels with that French model...."

She smiled. "Exactly."

He sighed. "Well, it doesn't change things, anyway. If you don't go with me, we forfeit the account."

"We may forfeit it anyway, if Jace has his way," she reminded him. "It's only been six months. I promise you he hasn't gotten over it."

His pale eyes narrowed. "Amanda, are you really afraid of him?"

She smiled wanly. "I didn't realize it showed."

"That's a first," he observed, amused. "You aren't the shrinking violet type, and I've seen that sweet temper of yours a time or two in the past year." His lips pursed. "Why are you afraid of him?"

She turned away. "Now, there, my friend, is a question. But I'm afraid I don't have an answer."

"Does he hit?"

"Not women," she said. "I've seen him deck a man though." She winced at the memory.

"Over a woman?" he fished, grinning.

She averted her eyes. "Over me, actually. One of the Whitehalls' hands got a little too friendly with me to suit Jace, and he gave him a black eye before he fired him. Duncan was there, too, but he hadn't got his mouth open

before Jace jumped in. Trying to run my life, as usual,"
she added unfairly.

"I thought Jace was an old man."

"He is," she said venomously. "Thirty-three and
climbing fast."

He laughed at her. "Ten whole years older than you."

She bristled. "I can see what fun this trip is going to
be."

"Surely he's forgotten the bull," he said comfort-
ingly.

"Do you think so?" Her eyes clouded. "I had to watch
Jace shoot him after the accident. And I'll never forget
how he looked or what he said to me." She sighed.
"Mother and I ran for our lives, and I drove all the way
home in a borrowed car." The skirt of her dress swirled
gracefully around her long, slender legs as she turned
away. "It was a lot of fun, with a sprained wrist, too, I'll
tell you that."

"Don't you believe in burying the hatchet?"

"Sure. So does Jace—about two inches deep at the
peak of my forehead. . . ."

"How about if you go home and pack?" he suggested
with a grin.

"Home," she laughed softly. "Only you could call
that one bedroom efficiency apartment a home. Mother
hates it so; I suppose that's why she spends her life visiting old friends." Visiting. There was another word for it,
sponging, and Jace never tired of using it. If he'd had any
idea that Beatrice Carson, not her daughter, had steered
that car broadside into Duke's Ransom, he'd have
thrown her out for good, despite all his mother's fiery
protests.

"She isn't at the Whitehalls' place now?" Terry asked
uneasily, visions of disaster clouding his pale eyes.

Amanda shook her head. "It's spring. That means the
Bahamas." Beatrice had a schedule of sorts about where
she visited and when. Right now she was with Lacey
Bannon and her brother Reese. But Marguerite
Whitehall's turn was coming up soon, and Amanda was

already afraid for her. If Beatrice let anything slip about that stupid bull while she was on the ranch....

"Maybe Duncan will protect me," she murmured wistfully. "Since it was his idea to drag me out to Casa Verde. And I thought he was my friend," she groaned.

Terry toyed with a stack of photographs on his neat desk. "You're not really sore at me, are you?"

She shrugged. "I don't know yet. But if Jace turns thumbs down on the account, don't blame me. Duncan should have let you handle it. I'll only jinx you."

"No, you won't," he promised. "You won't regret it."

She glanced at him over her shoulder with a wry smile. "That's exactly what Mother said when she coaxed me into going to Casa Verde six months ago. I hope your predictions are more accurate than hers were."

Late that night, she sat curled up in her comfortable old armchair long after the prime time shows had gone off, watching a news program that she didn't really see. Her eyes were on a photograph in an album, a color snapshot of two men: one tall, one short; one solemn, one smiling. Jace and Duncan, on the steps of the big Victorian mansion at Casa Verde with its green trim and huge white columns and sprawling wide front porch scattered with heavy rocking chairs and a swing. Duncan was smiling, as usual. Jace was openly glaring at the camera, his dark, hard face drawn into a brooding scowl, his eyes glittering like new silver under light. Amanda shivered involuntarily at that glare. She'd been holding the camera, and the glare had been for her.

If only there were some way out of this trip, she thought wildly. If only she could lock the door and put her head under the pillow and make it all go away. If only her father were still alive to control Beatrice. Bea was like a child, backing away from reality like a butterfly from an outstretched hand. She hadn't even protested when Amanda took the blame for hitting the bull and brought Jace's wrath onto her head. She sat right there and let her daughter take the responsibility for it, just as she'd let her take the responsibility for dozens of similar incidents.

And Jace had been given reason to hate her mother long before that accident. But Amanda was too tired to think about that, too. It seemed that she spent her life protecting Bea. If only some kind, demented man would come along and marry her vivacious little headache and take it away to Alaska, or Tahiti, or lower Siberia....

She took one last look at the Whitehall brothers before she closed the album. Now why had Duncan insisted that she come with Terry? They were partners in the ad agency, but Terry was the senior partner and he had the lion's share of experience. She frowned. Of course, Marguerite liked her, and she might have put a bug in Duncan's ear. She smiled. That must be the explanation.

She leaned back in the chair and closed her eyes while the newscaster blared away about a recent murder in the city. His voice began to fade in and out, and before she realized it, she was fast asleep.

2

*

Amanda watched the Victoria airport loom up on the horizon as the pilot of the air taxi banked for his final approach. This part of Texas was no stranger to her. It had been her home before she settled in San Antonio, where she'd gone to college. She'd spent her childhood here, among cattlemen and businessmen and bluebells and a historical legacy that could still make her heart race.

She clenched her hands in her lap. She loved this state, from its western desert fringes to the lush portion of eastern Texas they were now flying over. From Victoria, it was only a short drive to the Whitehall ranch, Casa Verde, and the small community called Whitehall Junction that had sprung up at the edge of the massive property Jace Whitehall had accumulated.

"So this is your hometown?" Terry asked as the small plane touched gently down on the runway with a brief skidding sound before the wheels settled.

"Yes, Victoria," she laughed, feeling her childhood again as she remembered other trips, other landings. "The friendliest little city you've ever seen. I've always loved it here. My father's people settled in this area when it was still dangerous to go riding without a gun. One of Jace's ancestors was a Comanche," she added absently. "It was his uncle who owned Casa Verde. Jace's father, Jude Whitehall, inherited it when the boys were very young."

"You became good friends, I gather?" he asked.

She flushed. "On the contrary. My mother didn't even want me to associate with them. They were only middle class at that time," she added bitterly, "and she never let them forget it. It's a miracle that Marguerite ever forgave her. Jace didn't.''

''I begin to see the tip of the iceberg,'' he chuckled.

They climbed down out of the plane and Amanda drank in the clean air and sun and endless horizon beyond the Victoria skyline.

''No small town, this,'' Terry said, following her gaze.

''The population is sixty thousand or so,'' she told him. ''One of my grandfathers is buried in Memorial Square. That's the oldest cemetery here, and a lot of pioneer families are buried there. There's a zoo, and a museum, and even a symphony orchestra. Not to mention some of the most delightful concerts—the Bach Festival Concerts are held in June. And there are some old mission ruins—''

''I only made a comment,'' he interrupted, laughing. ''I didn't ask for a community profile.''

She smiled at him. ''Don't you want to know that it's located on the Guadalupe River?''

''Thank you.'' He shaded his eyes against the sun. ''Who's going to meet us?''

She didn't want to think about that. ''Whoever's got time,'' she said, and hoped that ruled out Jace. ''Ordinarily, Duncan or Jace would probably have flown to San Antonio after us. They've got two planes, and they're both pilots. They have their own airstrip and hangars, but it's spring,'' she said, as if that explained everything.

He blinked. ''Come again?''

''Roundup,'' she said. ''When they cull and brand and separate cattle. The ranch manager bears the brunt of the responsibility for it, but Jace doesn't turn over all the authority to anyone. He likes to keep his eye on the operation. And that means Duncan has to double up on the real estate interests and the other companies while Jace is occupied here.''

''And time is short,'' Terry said, pressing his lips together. ''I didn't think about that, or I'd have been willing to wait until next month. The thing is,'' he sighed, ''we really need this account. Business hasn't been all that good during the winter, the economy's in such a slump.''

She nodded, but she wasn't really hearing him. Her eyes were glued to the road leading to the airport, on a silver Mercedes speeding toward them. Jace drove a silver Mercedes.

"You look faintly terrified," Terry remarked. "Recognize that car, do you?"

She nodded, feeling her heartbeat triple as the car came closer and pulled up in front of the terminal. The door swung open and she breathed a sigh of abject relief.

Marguerite Whitehall came toward them in a dressy pink pantsuit and sandals, her white hair faultlessly arranged, her thin face beaming with a smile.

"It's lovely to see you again, dear," she told Amanda as she hugged her, wrapping her in the delicious scent of Nina Ricci and pressed powder.

"It's good to be here," she lied, meeting the older woman's dark eyes. "This is Terrance Black, my partner at the advertising agency in San Antonio," she introduced him.

"You're very welcome, Terrance," Marguerite said courteously. "Duncan explained the offer you've made. I do hope Jace will go along with it. It's just good business sense, but my eldest has some peculiar ideas about... things," she said with an apologetic smile at Amanda.

"I'm anxious to talk with Duncan about the account," Terry said with a smile.

"He isn't here right now, I'm sorry to say," came the polite reply. "He had to fly to San Francisco this afternoon on some urgent business. But Jace is home."

Amanda felt something give way inside her, and she fought back the urge to leap back aboard the plane and go home. Instead, she followed the two of them to the car and allowed herself to be placed in the front seat with Marguerite while Terry loaded their bags and got in the back seat.

"The weather's nice," Terry commented as Marguerite headed the sleek little car toward the city.

"But dry this year," Marguerite sighed. She didn't go into the various ways droughts played havoc with a ranch. Amanda already knew, and it would have taken the better part of an hour to explain it to someone who wasn't familiar with cattle.

"I'm looking forward to seeing the ranch," Terry volunteered.

Marguerite smiled over her shoulder at him. "We're rather proud of it. I'm sorry you had to take a commercial flight. Jace could have come after you, but Tess was with him, and I didn't think you'd care for her company," she added with a wry glance at Amanda.

"Tess?" Terry probed.

"Tess Anderson," Marguerite replied. "Her father and Jace are partners, with Duncan of course, in that real estate venture in Florida."

"Will we have to consult him about the account as well?" Terry asked.

"I shouldn't think so," the older woman replied conversationally. "He always goes along with whatever Jace says."

"How is Tess?" Amanda asked quietly.

"Just the same as always, Amanda," came the haunted reply. "With one hand reaching out toward Jace eternally."

Amanda remembered that. Tess had always been a step away from him, since they were in their teens. Jace had offered to take Amanda to a dance once—a mysterious offer that Amanda had refused in silent terror. Tess had got wind of it, and given Amanda the very devil, as if it had been her fault that Jace asked her.

"Tess and Amanda were at school together," Marguerite told Terry. "In Switzerland, you know."

It seemed like a hundred years ago. Amanda's family had lost everything when Bob Carson was caught with his financial fingers in a crooked land deal. The shock of discovery had caused a fatal heart attack, and he'd died leaving his stunned wife and daughter to deal with the monumental disgrace and debt. By the time the creditors were satisfied there was nothing left. Jace had offered to help. Amanda still blushed when she remembered exactly how he'd presented the cold-blooded proposition to her. She'd never told anyone about it. But the memory was still with her, and she'd always believed her refusal had fanned Jace's contempt.

After the ranch went on the auction block, Amanda had carried her journalism degree to Terry Black's office, and the association rapidly became a partnership. The job kept the wolf from the door, when Bea wasn't on a marathon spending spree and so long as she imposed on her wealthy friends with long visits. The sacrificing was all on Amanda's part, not on her mother's. Bea liked pretty clothes and shoes, and she bought them impulsively, always apologizing for her lapses and bursting into tears if Amanda was stern with her. Every day of her life Amanda thanked God for time payments. And every other day, she wondered if Bea was ever going to grow up.

"I said, how's Bea?" Marguerite prompted gently, breaking into her weary musings.

"Oh, she's fine," Amanda said quickly. "With the Bannons this season."

"The Bahamas," Marguerite sighed. "Those lovely straw hats and musical accents and blistering white beaches. I wish I were there now."

"Why not go?" Terry asked.

"Because the first time Mrs. Brown was fussy about Jason missing breakfast, he'd fire her," came the tight reply, "and this is the only time I've ever been able to keep a cook longer than three months. I'm standing guard over this one."

Terry looked out the back window uncomfortably. "He sounds a little hard to please," he laughed nervously.

"It depends on the mood he's in," Marguerite said. "Jason can be very kind. He's always easy to get along with when he's asleep. The only time we have problems is when he's awake."

Amanda laughed. "You'll scare Terry to death."

"Don't worry, now," Marguerite promised. "Just make sure he hasn't been near the cattle when you approach him, Terry." She frowned slightly. "Let's see,

Sunday evenings are fairly safe, if nothing's broken down or if...."

"We'll talk to Duncan first," Amanda promised her colleague. "He doesn't bite."

"He doesn't always have Tess underfoot, either," Marguerite said in a faintly goaded tone.

"Maybe Jace will relent and marry her someday," Amanda suggested.

The older woman sighed. "I had hoped that you might be my daughter-in-law one day, Amanda."

"Be grateful for small blessings," came the smiling reply. "Duncan and I together would have driven you crazy."

"I wasn't thinking about my youngest," Marguerite said with frightening candor, and the look she gave Amanda made her pulse race.

She looked away. "Jace won't ever forgive me for that bull."

"It was unavoidable. You didn't ask the silly bull to crash through the fence."

"Jace was so angry," she recalled, shuddering. "I thought he was going to hit me."

"I always thought he was angry for a quite different reason. Oh, damn," Marguerite added with perfect enunciation when they turned into the long paved driveway that led to Casa Verde. "That's Tess's car," she grumbled.

Amanda saw it, a little Ferrari parked in the circular space that curved around the fish pond and fountain in front of the towering two-story mansion.

"At least you know where Jace is," Amanda said lightly, although her pulse was doing double time.

"Yes, but I knew where he was when Gypsy was alive, and I liked Gypsy," Marguerite said stubbornly.

"Who was Gypsy?" Terry asked the two women, who both had burst into laughter.

"Jace's dog," Amanda volunteered through her giggles.

Marguerite pulled up behind the small black car, and cut the engine. The house was over a century old, but still solid and welcoming, and despite the air-conditioners sticking out of the windows, it retained its homey atmosphere. To Amanda, who loved it and remembered it from childhood, it wasn't a mansion or even a landmark. It was simply Duncan's house.

"Duncan and I used to hang by our heels from those low limbs on the oak tree at the corner of the house," Amanda told Terry as they walked up the azalea-lined path that led to the porch steps. "Duncan slipped and fell one day, and if Jace hadn't caught him, his head would have been half its present size."

"I shudder to think what might have happened," Marguerite said and her patrician face went rigid. "You and Duncan were always restless, my dear. Duncan has the wanderlust still. It's Jace who's put down strong roots."

Amanda's fingers tightened on her purse. She didn't like to think about Jace at all, but looking around that familiar porch brought back a bouquet of memories. And not all of them were pleasant.

"Your son said that we could take a look at the property tomorrow," Terry remarked casually. "I thought I might spend this evening filling his brother in on the way we handle our accounts."

"If you can get Jace to sit still long enough," Marguerite laughed. "Ask Amanda; she'll tell you how busy he is. I have to follow him around to ask him anything."

"At least I can ride," Terry laughed. "I suppose I could gallop along after him."

"Not the way Jace rides," Amanda said quietly.

Marguerite opened the front door and led her two guests inside the house. The entrance featured a highly polished heart of pine floor with an Oriental rug done in a predominantly red color scheme, and a marble-top table on which was placed an arrangement of elegant cut red roses from the massive rose garden that flanked the oval swimming pool behind the house.

A massive staircase with a red carpet protecting the steps led up to the second floor, and the dark oak bannister was smooth as glass with age and handling. The house gave Amanda goose pimples when she remembered some of the Westerners who were rumored to have enjoyed its hospitality. Legend had it that Uncle John Chisholm had once slept within its walls. The house had been restored, of course, and enlarged, but that bannister was the original one.

A small dark maid came forward to take Amanda's lightweight sweater, followed by a small dark man who relieved Terry of the suitcases.

"Diego and Maria." Marguerite introduced them only to Terry, because Amanda had recognized them. "The Lopezes. They're our mainstays. Without them we'd be helpless."

The mainstays grinned, bowed, and went about making sure that the family wasn't left helpless.

"We'll have coffee and talk for a while," Marguerite said, leading them into the huge, white-carpeted living room with its royal blue furniture and curtains, its antique oak tables and upholstered chairs. "Isn't white ridiculous for a ranch carpet?" she laughed apologetically. "But even though I have to keep on replacing it, I can't resist this color scheme. Do sit down while I let Maria know we'll have our coffee in here. Jace must be down at the stables."

"No, he isn't," came a husky, bored voice from behind them in the hall, and Tess Anderson strolled into the room with her hands rammed deep in the pockets of her aqua knit skirt. Wearing a matching V-necked top, she looked like something out of a fashion show. Her black hair was loose and curling around her ears, her dark eyes snapping, her olive complexion absolutely stunning against the blood red lipstick she wore.

"Wow," Terry managed in a bare whisper, his eyes bulging at the vision in the doorway.

Tess accepted the male adulation as her due, gazing at Terry's thin, lackluster person dismissively. Her sharp eyes darted to Amanda, and she eyed the other girl's smart but businesslike suit with distaste.

"Jace is out looking at a new harvester with Bill Johnson," Tess said casually. "The old one they used on the bottoms broke down this morning."

"Bogged down in the hay, I reckon," Marguerite joked, knowing full well there wasn't enough moisture to bog anything down. "Has he stopped swearing yet?"

Tess didn't smile. "Naturally, it disturbed him. It's a very expensive piece of equipment. He asked me to stop by and tell you he'd be late."

"When has he ever been on time for a meal?" Marguerite asked curtly.

Tess turned away. "I've got to rush. Dad's waiting for me. Some business about selling one of the developments." She glanced back at Terry and Amanda. "I hear Duncan is thinking about hiring your agency to handle our Florida project. Dad and I want to be in on any discussions you have, naturally, since we do have a rather large sum invested."

"Of course," Terry said, reddening.

"We'll be in touch. 'Night Marguerite," she called back carelessly. Her high heels beat a quick tattoo on the wood floor. Then the door slammed shut behind her and there was a conspicuous silence in the room.

Marguerite's dark eyes flashed fire. "And when did I give her permission to call me by my first name?"

Terry looked down at his shoes. "Snags," he murmured. "I should have known it seemed too easy."

"Don't fret," Amanda said cheerfully. "Mr. Anderson isn't at all like his daughter."

Terry brightened a little, but Marguerite was still muttering to herself as she left the room to tell Maria to bring coffee to the living room.

Maria brought the coffee on an enormous silver tray with an antique silver service and thin bone china cups in a burgundy and white pattern.

While Marguerite poured, Amanda studied the contents of the elegant display case against one wall. Inside, it was like a miniature museum of Western history. There was a .44 Navy Colt, a worn gunbelt that Jace's great uncle had worn on trail drives, a Comanche knife in an

aging buckskin sheath decorated with faded beads, some
of which were missing, and other mementos of an age
long past. There was an old family Bible that Jace's people had brought all the way from Georgia by wagon train,
and a Confederate pistol and officer's hat. There was
even a peace pipe.

"Never get tired of looking at it, do you?" Marguerite
asked gently.

She turned with a smile. "Not ever."

"Your people had a proud history, too," Marguerite
said. "Did you manage to hold on to any of those French
chairs and silver?"

Amanda shook her head. "Only the small things, I'm
afraid," she sighed, feeling a great sense of loss. "There
simply wasn't any place to keep them, except in storage,
and they were worth so much money…it took quite a lot
to pay the bills," she added sorrowfully.

Terry caught the look on her face and turned to
Marguerite. "Tell me about the house," he said, frowning interestedly.

That caught the older woman's attention immediately, and an hour later she was still reciting tidbits from
the past.

Amanda had been lulled into a sense of security, listening to her, and there was a quiet, wistful smile on her
lovely face when the front door suddenly swung open. As
she looked toward the doorway, she found her eyes
caught and held by a pair almost the exact color of the
antique silver service. Jace!

3

*

Jason Everett Whitehall was the image of his late father. Tall and powerful, with eyes like polished silver in a darkly tanned face and a shock of coal black hair, he would have drawn eyes anywhere. The patterned Western shirt he was wearing emphasized his broad shoulders just as the well-cut denim jeans hugged the lines of his muscular thighs and narrow hips. His expensive leather boots were dusty, but obviously meant for dress. The only disreputable note in his outfit was the worn black Stetson he held in his hand, just as battered now as it had been on Amanda's last unforgettable visit.

She couldn't drag her eyes away from him. They traced the hard lines of his face involuntarily, and she wondered now, as she had in her adolescence, if there was a trace of emotion in him. He seemed so completely removed from warmth or passion.

He was pleasant enough to Terry as he entered the room, shaking hands, making brief, polite work of the greetings.

"You know my junior partner, of course," Terry grinned, gesturing toward Amanda on the sofa beside him.

"I know her," Jace said in his deep, slow drawl, shooting her a hard glance that barely touched the slender curves of her body, curves that were only emphasized by the classical cut of her navy blue suit.

"We're not going to have much time to talk tonight," he told Terry without preamble. "I've got a long-standing date. But Duncan should be back tomorrow, and I'll try to find a few minutes later in the week to go over the whole proposal with you. You can give me the basics over supper."

"Fine!" Terry said. He was immediately charming and pleasant, and Amanda couldn't repress an amused smile, watching him. He was so obvious when he was trying to curry favor.

"How's your mother?" Jace asked Amanda curtly as he went to the bar to pour drinks.

Amanda felt her spine going rigid. "Very well, thanks," she said.

"Who is she imposing on this month?" he continued casually.

"Jason!" Marguerite burst out, horrified. She turned to her guests. "Amanda, wouldn't you like to freshen up? And, Terry, if you'll come along, I'll show you to your room at the same time." She herded them out of the room quickly, shooting a furious glance at her impassive son on the way.

"I don't know what in the world's wrong with him," Marguerite grumbled when she and Amanda were alone in the deliciously feminine blue wallpapered guest room. The pretty quilted blue bedspread was complemented by ruffled pillow shams, and green plants grew lushly in attractive brass planters.

"He's just being himself," Amanda said with more humor than she felt. The words had hurt, as Jace meant them to. "I can't remember a time in my life when he hasn't cut at me."

Marguerite looked into the warm brown eyes and smiled, too. "That's my girl. Just ignore him."

"Oh, how can I?" Amanda asked, dramatically batting her long eyelashes. "He's so devastating, so masculine, so...manly."

Marguerite giggled like a young girl. She sat down on the edge of the thick quilted coverlet on the bed and folded her hands primly in her lap while Amanda hung up her few, painstakingly chosen business clothes. "You're the only woman I know who doesn't chase him mercilessly," she pointed out. "He's considered quite a catch, you know."

"If I caught him, I'd throw him right back," Amanda said, unruffled. "He's too aggressively masculine to suit me, too domineering. I'm a little afraid of him, I think,'' she admitted honestly.

"Yes, I know,'' the older woman replied kindly.

"Tess isn't, though,'' she sighed. "Maybe they deserve each other,'' she added with a mean laugh.

"Tess! If he marries that girl, I will move to Australia and set up housekeeping in an opal mine!'' Marguerite threatened.

"That bad?''

"My dear, the last time she helped Jace with a sale, she had Maria in tears and one of my daily maids quit without notice on the spot. As you saw today, she simply takes over, and Jace does nothing to stop her.''

"It is your house,'' Amanda reminded her gently.

The thin shoulders lifted and fell expressively. "I used to think so. Lately she's talked about remodeling my kitchen.''

Amanda toyed with a button on one of the simple tailored blouses she was hanging in the closet. "Are they engaged?''

"I don't know. Jace tells me nothing. I suppose if he decides to marry her, the first I'll hear of it will be on the evening news!''

Amanda laughed softly. "I can't imagine Jace married.''

"I can't imagine Jace the way he's been, period.'' Marguerite stood up. "For months now, he's walked around scowling, half-hearing me, so busy I can't get two words out of him. And even Tess—you know, sometimes I get the very definite impression that Tess is like a fly to him, but he's just too busy to swat her.''

Amanda burst out laughing. The thought of the decorative brunette as a fly was totally incongruous. Tess, with her perfect makeup, flawless coiffures, and designer fashions would be horrified to hear them discussing her like this.

Marguerite smiled. "I'm glad you don't take what Jace says to heart. You mother is my best friend, and none of what he said is true.''

"But it is," Amanda protested quietly. "We both know it, too. Mother is still living in the past. She won't accept things the way they are."

"That's still no excuse for Jace to ridicule her," Marguerite replied. "I'm going to have a talk with him about that."

"If the way he looked at me was anything to go by, I think I'd feed him and get him drunk before I did that," Amanda suggested.

"I've never seen him drunk," came the soft reply. "Although, he came close to it once," she added, throwing a pointed look at the younger woman before she turned away. "I'll see you downstairs. Don't feel that you have to change, or dress up; we're still very informal."

That was a blessing, Amanda thought later, when she looked at her meager wardrobe. At one time, it would have boasted designer labels and fine silks and organzas with hand-embroidered hems. Now, she had to limit spending to the necessities. With careful shopping and her own innate good taste, she had put together an attractive, if limited, wardrobe, concentrating on the clothes she needed for work. There wasn't an evening gown in the lot. Oh, well, at least she wouldn't need one of those.

She showered and slipped into a white pleated skirt with a pretty navy blue blouse and tied a white ruffled scarf at her throat to complete the simple but attractive looking outfit. She tied her hair back with a piece of white ribbon, and slipped her hosed feet into a pair of dark blue sandals. Then with a quick spray of cologne and a touch of lipstick, she went downstairs.

Terry was the first person she saw, standing in the doorway of the living room with a brandy snifter in his hand.

"There you are," he grinned, his eyes sweeping up and down her slender figure mischievously. "Going sailing?"

"Thought I might," she returned lightly. "Care to swim alongside and fend off the sharks?"

He shook his head. "I suffer from acute cowardice, brought on by proximity to sharks. One of them was rumored to have eaten a great aunt of mine."

With a laugh like sunlight filtering into a yellow room, she walked past him into the spacious living room and found herself looking straight into Jace's silvery eyes. That intense stare of his was disconcerting, and it did crazy things to her heart. She jerked her own gaze down to the carpet.

"Would you like some sherry?" he asked her tightly.

She shook her head, moving to Terry's side like a kitten edging up to a tomcat for safety. "No, thanks."

Terry put a thin arm around her shoulders affectionately. "She's a caffeine addict," he told Jace. "She doesn't drink."

Jace looked as if he wanted to crush his brandy snifter in his powerful brown fingers and grind it into the carpet. Amanda couldn't remember ever seeing that particular look on his face before.

He turned away before she had time to analyze it. "Let's go in. Mother will be down eventually." He led the way into the dining room, and Amanda couldn't help admire the fit of his brown suit with its attractive Western yoke, the way it emphasized his broad shoulders from the back. He was an attractive man. Too attractive.

Amanda was disconcerted to find herself seated close beside Jace, so close that her foot brushed his shiny brown leather boot under the table. She drew it back quickly, aware of his taut, irritated glance.

"Tell me why Duncan thinks we need an advertising agency," Jace invited arrogantly, leaning back in his chair so that the buttons of his white silk shirt strained against the powerful muscles of his chest. The shirt was open at the throat, and there were shadows under its thinness, hinting at the covering of thick, dark hair over the bronzed flesh. Amanda remembered without wanting to how Jace looked without a shirt. She drew her eyes back to her spotless china plate as Mrs. Brown, Marguerite's prized cook, ambled in with dishes of expertly prepared food. A dish containing thick chunks of breaded, fried cube steak and a big steaming bowl of thick milk gravy were set on the spotless white linen tablecloth, along with a platter of cat's head biscuits, real butter, cabbage, a salad, asparagus tips in hollandaise sauce, a creamy fruit salad, homemade rolls, and cottage fried potatoes. Amanda couldn't remember when she'd been confronted by such a lavish selection of dishes, and she realized with a start how long it had been since she'd been able to afford to set a table like this.

She nibbled at each delicious spoonful as if it would be her last, savoring every bite, while Terry's pleasant voice rambled on.

Marguerite joined them in the middle of Terry's sales pitch, smiling all around as she sat in her accustomed place at the elegant table with its centerpiece of white daisies.

"I'm sorry to be late," she said, "but I lost track of time. There's a mystery theater on the local radio station, and I'm just hooked on it.

"Detective stories," Jace scoffed. "No wonder you leave your light on at night."

Marguerite lifted her thin face proudly. "A lot of people use night-lights."

"You use three lamps," he commented. His gray eyes sparkled at her and he winked suddenly, smiling. Amanda, on the fringe of that smile, felt something warm kindle inside her. He was devastating when he used that inherent charm of his. No woman alive could have resisted it, but she'd only seen it once, a very long time ago. She dropped her eyes back to her plate and finished the last of her fruit salad with a sigh.

In the middle of Terry's wrap-up, the phone rang and, seconds later, Jace was called away from the table.

Marguerite glared after him. "Once," she muttered, "just once, to have an uninterrupted meal! If it isn't some problem with the ranch that Bill Johnson, our manager, can't handle, it's a personnel problem at one of the companies, or some salesman wanting to interest him in a new tractor, or another rancher trying to sell him a bull, or a newspaper wanting information on a merger." She glared into space. "Last week, it was a magazine wanting to know if Jace was getting married. I told them yes," she said with ill-concealed irritation, "and I can't wait until someone shoves the article under his nose!"

Amanda laughed until tears ran down her cheeks. "Oh, how could you?"

"How could she what?" Jace asked, returning just in time to catch that last remark.

Amanda shook her head, dabbing at her eyes with her linen napkin while Marguerite's thin face seemed to puff up indignantly.

"Another disaster?" Marguerite asked him as he sat back down. "The world goes to war if you finish one meal?"

Jace raised an eyebrow at her, sipping his coffee. "Would you like to take over?"

"I'd simply love it," she told her son. "I'd sell everything."

"And condemn Duncan and me to growing roses?" he teased.

She relented. "Well, if we could just have one whole meal together, Jason...."

"How would you cope?" he teased. "It's never happened."

"And when your father was still alive, it was worse," she admitted. She laughed. "I remember throwing his plate at him once when he went to talk to an attorney during dinner on Christmas Day."

Jace smiled mockingly. "I remember what happened when he came back," he reminded her, and Marguerite Whitehall blushed like a schoolgirl.

"Oh, by the way," Marguerite began, "I—"

Before she could get the words out, Maria came in to announce that Tess was on the phone and wanted to speak to Jace.

Marguerite glared at him as he passed her on his way to the hall phone a second time. "Why don't you have a special phone invented with a plate attached?" she asked nastily. "Or better, an edible phone, so you could eat and talk at the same time?"

Amanda's solemn face dissolved into laughter. It had been this way with the Whitehalls forever. Marguerite had had this same argument with Jude.

The older woman shook her head, glancing toward Terry with a mischievous smile. "Would you like to explain the advertising business to me, Terry? I can't give you the account, but I won't rush off in the middle of your explanation to answer the phone."

Terry laughed, lifting a homemade roll to his mouth. "No problem, Mrs. Whitehall. There's plenty of time. We'll be here a week, after all."

During which, Amanda was thinking, you might get Jace to yourself for ten minutes. But she didn't say it.

Later, everyone seemed to vanish. Jace went upstairs, and Marguerite carried Terry off to show him her collection of jade figurines, leaving Amanda alone in the living room.

She finished her after-dinner cup of coffee and put the saucer gingerly back down on the coffee table. Perhaps, she thought wildly, it might be a good idea to go up to her room. If Jace came downstairs before the others got back, she'd be stuck with him, and she didn't want that headache. Being alone with Jace was one circumstance she'd never be prepared for.

She hurried out into the hall, but before she even made it to the staircase, she saw Jace coming down it. He'd added a brown and gold tie to the white silk shirt and brown suit, and he looked maddeningly elegant.

"Running?" he asked pointedly, his eyes narrow and cold as they studied her.

4

_____ * _____

She froze in the center of the entrance, staring at him helplessly. He made her nervous. He always had.

"I...was just going up to my room for a minute," she faltered.

He came the rest of the way down without hesitation, his booted feet making soft thuds on the carpeted steps. He paused in front of her when he got to the bottom, towering over her, close enough that she could smell his woodsy cologne and the clean fragrance of his body.

"For what?" he asked with a mocking smile. "A handkerchief?"

"More like a shield and some armor," she countered, hiding her nervousness behind humor.

He didn't laugh. "You haven't changed," he observed. "Still the little clown." His narrowed eyes slid down her body indifferently. "Why did you come back here?" he demanded abruptly, cold steel in his tone.

"Because Duncan insisted."

He scowled down at her. "Why? You only work for Black."

"I'm his partner," she replied. "Didn't you know?"

He stared at her intently. "How did you manage that?" he asked contemptuously. "Or do I need to ask?"

She saw what he was driving at and her face flamed. "It isn't like that," she said tightly.

"Isn't it?" He glared at her. "At least I offered you more than a share in a third-class business."

Her face went a fiery red. "That's all women are to you," she accused. "Toys, sitting on a shelf waiting to be bought."

"Tess isn't," he said with deliberate cruelty.

"How lovely for her," she threw back.

He stuck his hands in his pockets and looked down his arrogant nose at her. There was a strange, foreign something behind those glittering eyes that disturbed her.

"You're thinner," he remarked.

She shrugged. "I work hard."

"Doing what?" he asked curtly. "Sleeping with the boss?"

"I don't!" she burst out. She looked up into his dark face, her own pale in the blazing light of the crystal chandelier. "Why do you hate me so? Was the bull so important?"

His face seemed to set even harder. "A grand champion, and you can ask that? My God, you didn't even apologize!"

"Would it have brought him back?" she asked sadly.

"No." A muscle in his jaw moved.

"You won't...you won't let your dislike of me prejudice you against the agency, will you?" she asked suddenly.

"Afraid your boss might lose his shirt?" he taunted.

"Something like that."

He cocked his head down at her, his hard mouth set. "Why don't you tell me the truth? Duncan didn't invite you down here. You came on your own initiative." He smiled mockingly. "I haven't forgotten how you used to tag after him. And now you've got more reason than ever."

She saw red. All the years of backing away dissolved, and she felt suddenly reckless.

"You go to hell, Jace Whitehall," she said coldly, her brown eyes throwing off sparks as she lifted her angry face.

Both dark eyebrows went up over half-astonished, half-amused silver eyes. "What?"

But before she could repeat the dangerous words, Terry's voice broke in between them.

"Oh, there you are," he called cheerfully. "Come back in here and keep us company. It's too early to turn in."

Jace's eyes were hidden behind those narrowed eyelids, and he turned away before Amanda could puzzle out the new look in them.

"Off again?" Marguerite asked pleasantly. "Where are you taking Tess?"

"Out," he said noncommittally, reaching down to kiss the wrinkled pink cheek. "Good night."

He pivoted on his heel and left them without another word, closing the door firmly behind him.

Terry stared at Amanda. "Did I hear you say what I thought I heard you say?"

"My question exactly," Marguerite added.

Amanda stirred under their intent stares and went ahead of them into the living room. "Well, he deserved it," she muttered. "Arrogant, insulting beast!"

Marguerite laughed delightedly, a mysterious light in her eyes that she was careful to conceal.

"What is it with you two?" Terry asked her. "If ever I saw mutual dislike...."

"My mother once called Jace a cowboy," Amanda replied. "It was a bad time to do it, and she was terribly insulting, and Jace never got over it."

"Jace took to calling Amanda 'lady,'" Marguerite continued. She smiled at the younger woman. "She was, and is, that. But Jace meant it in another sense."

"As in Lady MacBeth," Amanda said. Her eyes clouded. "I'd like to cook him a nice mess of buttered toadstools," she said with a malicious smile.

"Down, girl," Terry said. "Vinegar catches no flies."

Amanda remembered what Marguerite had said about Tess, and when their eyes met, she knew the older woman was also remembering. They both burst into laughter, dissolving the somber mood memory had brought to cloud the evening.

But later that night, alone in her bedroom, memories returned to haunt her. Seeing Jace again had resurrected all the old scars, and she felt the pain of them right through her slender body. Her eyes wide open, staring at the strange patterns the moonlight made on the ceiling of her room, she drifted back to that Friday seven years ago when she'd gone running along the fence that separated her father's pasture from the Whitehalls' property, laughing as she jumped on the lower rung of the fence and watched Jace slow his big black stallion and canter over to her.

"Looking for Duncan?" he'd asked curtly, his eyes angry in that cold, hard face that never seemed to soften.

"No, for you," she'd corrected, glancing at him shyly. "I'm having a party tomorrow night. I'll be sixteen, you know."

He'd stared at her with a strangeness about him that still puzzled her years later, his eyes giving nothing away as they glittered over her slender body, her flushed, exuberant face. She'd never felt more alive than she did that day, and Jace couldn't know that it had taken her the better part of the morning to get up enough nerve to seek· him out. Duncan was easy to talk to. Jace was something else. He fascinated her, even as he frightened her. Already a man even then, he had a blatant sensuousness that made her developing emotions run riot.

"Well, what do you want me to do about it?" he'd asked coldly.

The vibrant laughter left her face, draining away, and some of her nerve had gone with it. "I, uh...I wanted to invite you to my party," she choked.

He studied her narrowly over the cigarette he put between his chiseled lips and lit. "And what did your mother think about that idea?"

"She said it was fine with her," she returned rebelliously, omitting how hard she'd had to fight Bea to make the invitation to the Whitehall brothers.

"Like hell," Jace had replied knowingly.

She'd tossed her silver blond hair, risking her pride. "Will you come, Jason?" she'd asked quietly.

"Just me? Aren't you inviting Duncan as well?"

"Both of you, of course, but Duncan said you wouldn't come unless I asked you," she replied truthfully.

He'd drawn a deep, hard breath, blowing out a cloud of smoke with it. His eyes had been thoughtful on her young, hopeful face.

"Will you, Jace?" she'd persisted meekly.

"Maybe," was as far as he'd commit himself. He'd wheeled the horse without another word, leaving her to stare after him in a hopeless, disappointed daze.

The amazing thing was that Jace had come to the party with Duncan, dressed in immaculately stylish dark evening clothes with a faintly ruffled white silk shirt and ruby cufflinks. He looked like a fashion plate, and, to Amanda's sorrow, he was neatly surrounded by admiring teenage girls before he was through the door. Most of her girl friends were absolutely beautiful young debutantes, very sophisticated and worldly. Not at all like young Amanda who was painfully shy and unworldly, standing quietly in the corner with her blond hair piled on top of her head. Her exposed throat looked vulnerable, her pink lips soft, and her brown eyes stared wistfully at Jace despite the fact that Duncan spent the evening dancing attendance on her. She'd looked down at her green embroidered white organdy dress in disgust, hating it. The demure neckline, puffed sleeves and full, flowing skirt hadn't been exciting enough to catch and hold Jace's eye. Of course, she'd told herself, Jace was twenty-five to her sixteen, and probably wouldn't have been caught dead looking at a girl her age. But her heart had ached to have him notice her. She'd danced woodenly with Duncan and the other boys, her eyes following Jace everywhere. She'd longed to dance just one dance with him.

It had been the last dance, a slow tune about lost love that Amanda had thought quite appropriate at the time. Jace hadn't asked her to dance. He'd held out his hand, and she'd put hers into it, feeling it swallow her fingers warmly. Even the way he danced had been exciting. He'd held her young body against his by keeping both hands at her waist, leaving her hands to rest on his chest while they moved lazily to the music. She could still smell the expensive Oriental cologne he'd been wearing, feel the

warmth of his tall, athletic body against the length of hers
as they moved, sense the hard, powerful muscles of his
thighs pressed close to her even through the layers of
material that made up her skirt. Her heart had gone wild
in her chest at the proximity. New, frightening emotions
had drained her, made her weak in his supporting arms.
She'd looked up at him with all her untried longings plain
in her eyes, and he'd stopped dancing abruptly and,
catching her hand, had led her out onto the dark patio
overlooking the night lights of Victoria.

"Is this what you want, honey?" he'd asked, crushing
her against him with a curious anger in his voice. "To see
how I rate as a lover?"

"Jace, I didn't—" she began to protest.

But even as she opened her mouth to speak, his lips
had crushed down on it, rough and uncompromising,
deliberately cruel. His arms had riveted her to the length
of him, bruising her softness in a silence that had com-
bined the distant strains of music with the night sounds
of crickets and frogs, and the harsh sigh of Jace's breath
with the rustle of clothing as he caught her even closer.
His teeth had nipped her lip painfully, making her moan
with fright, as he subjected her to her first kiss and taught
her the dangers of flirting with an experienced man. With
a wrenching fear, she'd felt his big, warm hand sliding up
from her waist to the soft, high curve of her breast,
breaking all the rules she'd been taught as he touched and
savored the rounded softness of her body.

"It's like touching silk," he'd murmured against her
mouth, drawing back slightly to stare down at her.
"Look at me," he'd said gruffly. "Let me see your face."

She's raised frightened eyes to his, pushing at his hand
in a flurry of outrage and embarrassment. "Don't,"
she'd whispered.

"Why not?" His eyes had glittered, going down
to the darkness of his fingers against the white organdy
of her bodice. "Isn't this why you asked me here
tonight, Amanda? To see if a ranch hand makes love
like a gentleman?"

She'd torn out of his arms, tears of humiliation glistening in her eyes.

"Don't you like the truth?" he'd asked, and he laughed at her while he lit a cigarette with steady fingers. "Sorry to disappoint you, little girl, but I've gone past ranch hand now. I'm the boss. I've not only paid off Casa Verde, I'm going to make a legend of it. I'm going to have the biggest damned spread in Texas before I'm through. And then, if I'm still tempted, I might give you another try." His eyes had hurt as they studied her like a side of beef. "You'll have to round out a bit more, though. You're too thin."

She hadn't been able to find the right words, and Duncan had appeared to rescue her before she had to. She'd never invited Jace to another party, though, and she'd gone to great lengths to stay out of his way. That hadn't bothered him a bit. She often suspected that he really did hate her.

That night, Amanda slept fitfully, her dreams disturbed by scenes she couldn't remember when she woke up early the next morning. She dragged herself out of bed and pulled on the worn blue terry cloth robe at the foot of her bed, her long blond hair streaming down her back and over her shoulders in a beautiful silver-blond tangle that only made her look prettier. She huddled in the robe in the chill morning air that blew the curtains back from the window. She'd opened it last night so that she could drink in the fresh clean country air.

A knock at the door brought her to her feet again from her perch on the vanity bench, and she yawned as she padded barefoot to the door. Her eyes fell sadly to the old robe, remembering satin ones she used to own that had dainty little fur scuffs to match. Her shoulders shrugged. That life was over. It was just a dream, washed away by the riptide of reality.

She opened the door, expecting Maria, and found Duncan grinning down at her, brown-eyed and boyish.

"Good morning, ma'am," he said merrily.

"Duncan!" she cried, and, careless of convention, threw herself into his husky arms. They closed around her warmly and she caught the familiar scent of the spice cologne he'd always worn.

"Missed me, did you?" he asked at her ear, because he was only a couple of inches taller than she was—not at all as towering and formidable as Jace. "Not even a post-card in six months, either."

"I didn't think you'd want to hear from me," she murmured.

"Why not? It wasn't my bull you ran over," he chuckled.

"No, it was mine," came a rough voice from behind Duncan, and Amanda stiffened involuntarily.

Tugging away from Duncan, she shook back her wealth of soft, curling hair and glared at Jace's set face. He was dressed for work this morning, in expensively cut but faded jeans and a gray shirt that just matched his cold, narrow eyes. Atop his head was the old black Stetson.

"Good morning, Jace," she said with chilling sweetness. "So sorry I forgot my manners yesterday. I haven't thanked you for your warm reception."

Jace threw up an eyebrow, and there was something indefinable in the look he gave her. "Don't strain yourself, Lady."

Her face burned. "My name is Amanda or Miss Carson. Or hey, you. But don't call me Lady. I don't like it."

One corner of Jace's hard mouth went up in a taunting smile. "Brave in company, aren't you? Try it when we're alone."

"Make sure your insurance is paid up first, won't you?" she said, smiling venomously.

"Now, friends," Duncan interrupted, "this is no way to start off a beautiful morning. Especially when we haven't even had breakfast."

"Haven't we?" Amanda asked. "Your brother's had two bites of me already."

Jace cocked his head at her and his eyes sparkled dangerously, like sun on ice crystals. "Careful, honey. I hit back."

"Go ahead," she challenged bravely.

"On my own ground," he said with the light of battle kindling in his face. "And in my own time." He looked from Amanda to Duncan. "What came out of the meeting?"

"Jenkins is interested," the younger man replied with a smile. "I think I hooked him. We'll know tomorrow. Meanwhile, has Black explained what the ad agency can do for us on that Florida development?"

"Briefly, but not in any detail," Jace replied. He pulled a cigarette out of his pocket and lit it with steady fingers. His eyes glanced at the gold-plated lighter before he replaced it in his pocket, and Amanda remembered the Christmas his father had given it to him.

"What do you think?" Duncan persisted, his brown eyes questioning Jace's gray ones.

Jace stared back through a haze of smoke. "I'll have to hear more about it. A hell of a lot more."

"Sound like we're in for a long week," the younger man sighed.

"It may be too long for some of us," came the curt reply, and a pair of silvery eyes cut at Amanda. "And if Lady here doesn't get that chip off her shoulder, Black can damned well take his proposal back to San Antonio without my signature on any contract."

Amanda hated him for that threat. It was all the more despicable because she knew he meant it. He'd carry his resentment of her over into business, and he was ruthless enough to deny Terry the account out of sheer spite. Jace never bluffed. He never had to. People always came around to his way of thinking in the end.

"Now, Jace," Duncan began, mediating as always.

"I've got work to do," Jace growled, pivoting on his booted heel. "Come on down to the Kennedy bottoms when you've had breakfast and I'll show you the young bull I bought at the Western Heritage sale last week."

"Can I bring Amanda?" Duncan asked with calculating eyes.

Jace's broad shoulders stiffened. He glanced back angrily. "I'd like to keep this one," he said curtly, and kept walking.

Amanda's face froze. She glared at the long, muscular back with pure hatred. "I wish he'd fall down the stairs," she muttered.

"Jace never falls," he reminded her. "And if he ever did, he'd land on his feet." He grinned down at her. "My, my, how you've changed. You never used to talk back to him."

"I'm twenty-three years old, and he's not using me for a doormat anymore," she replied with cool hauteur.

Duncan nodded, and she thought she detected a hint of smugness in his eyes before they darted away. "Get dressed and come on down," he told her. "I'm anxious to hear about the ad campaign you and Black have worked up."

"Do Tess and her father have to see it, too?" she asked suddenly.

"Tess!" he grumbled. "I'd forgotten about her. Well, we'll cross that bridge later. Jace and I have a bigger investment than the Andersons, so we'll have the final say."

"Jace will side with them," she said certainly.

"He might surprise you. In fact," he added mysteriously, "I'd bet on it. Get dressed, girl, time's a wasting!"

She saluted him. "Yes, sir!"

Later in the day, Duncan took his guests out for a ride around the ranch on horseback, taking care to see that Terry—an admitted novice—got a slow, gentle mount.

The ranch stretched off in every direction, fenced in green and white, with neat barns and even neater paddocks. It was a staggering operation.

"Jace has a computer that can store records on over a hundred-thousand head," Duncan told Terry as they watched the beefy Santa Gertrudis cattle graze, their rich red coats burning in the sun. "We're fortunate enough to be able to run both purebred and grade cattle here, and we have our own feedlot. We don't have to contract our beef cattle out before we sell them; we can feed them out right here on the ranch."

Terry blinked. Ranch talk was new to him, but to Amanda, who knew and loved every stick and horn on the place, it was familiar and interesting.

"Remember how that old Brahma bull of your father's used to chase the dogs?" Amanda asked Duncan wistfully.

He nodded. "Mother always threatened to sell him for beef after he killed her spaniel. When Dad died, she did exactly that," he added with a shake of his head. "Over a hundred-thousand dollars worth of prime beef. We actually ate him. A vindictive woman, my mother."

"Didn't Jace try to stop her?" Amanda asked incredulously.

"Jace didn't know about it," he chuckled. "Mother dared me to open my mouth. And he was off the property so much checking on the other ranches, he didn't notice an animal was missing."

"What did he do when he found out?"

"Threw back his head and laughed," Duncan told her. Both eyebrows went up. "All that money...!"

"Strange how different Jace is with you," he remarked. "He's the easiest man in the world to get along with, as far as the rest of us are concerned."

Amanda turned away from those probing eyes and looked out across the range. "Did you mention something about showing us the new bull?" she hedged.

"Sure. Follow me," Duncan grinned.

It was roundup at its best, and hundreds of calves were being vetted in a chuted corral with gates opening into paddocks on all four sides. In the midst of the noise, bawling cattle, dust, yelling cowboys and blazing sun was Jace Whitehall, straddling the fence, overseeing the whole operation. His interest in ranch work had never waned, even though he could have gone the rest of his life without ever donning jeans and a work hat again. He was rich now, successful, and his financial wizardry had placed him in a luxurious office in a skyscraper in downtown Victoria. He didn't have to work cattle. In fact, for a man in his position, it was unusual that he did. But then Jace was unconventional. And Amanda wondered if he hadn't really enjoyed ranch work more before it made him wealthy. He was an outdoor man at heart, not a desk-bound executive.

He caught sight of Amanda at once, and even at a distance, she could feel the ferocity of his look. But she straightened proudly and schooled her delicate features to calmness. It wouldn't do to let Jace know how he really affected her.

"Don't let him rattle you, Mandy," Duncan said under his breath. "He picks at you out of pure habit, not malice. He doesn't really mean anything."

"He's not walking all over me anymore," she returned stubbornly. "Whether or not he means it."

"Declaring war?" he teased.

"With all batteries blazing," she returned. She put up a hand to push a loose strand of her silvery hair back in place.

"I came to see the calves," Duncan called to his brother.

Jace leaped gracefully down from the fence and walked toward them, pausing to tear off his hat and wipe his sweaty brow on the sleeve of his dusty shirt. "Did you need to bring a delegation?" he asked, staring pointedly at Amanda and Terry.

"We did think about hiring a bus and bringing the kitchen staff," Amanda agreed with a bold smile.

Jace's glittering silver eyes narrowed. "Why don't you come down here and get cute," he invited curtly.

"Grass allergy," she murmured. "Dust, too. Horrible to watch."

Duncan chuckled. "Incorrigible child," he teased.

"How do you stand the dust and the heat?" Terry asked incredulously. "Not to mention the noise!"

"Long practice," Jace told him. "And necessity. It isn't easy work."

"I'll never complain about beef prices again," Terry promised, shading his eyes with his hand as he watched the men at work sorting and tagging and branding.

"Hi, Happy!" Amanda called to an old, grizzled cowboy who was just coming up behind Jace with his sweaty hat pushed back over his gray hair.

"Hello, Mandy!" the old cowboy greeted her with a toothless grin. "Come down to help us brand these little dogies?"

"Only if I get a nice, thick steak when you finish," she teased. Happy had been one of her father's foremen before....

"How's your mama?" Happy asked.

Amanda avoided Jace's mocking smile. "Fine, thanks."

Happy nodded. "Good to see you," he said, reading the hard look he was getting from Jace. "I'd better get back to work."

"Damned straight," Jace replied curtly, watching the older man move quickly away.

"It was my fault, Jace," Amanda said quietly. "I spoke to him first."

He ignored her soft plea. "Show Black the Arabians," he told his brother. "They're well worth the ride, if he thinks his anatomy will stand it," he added with an amused glance at Terry, who was standing up in the stirrups with a muffled groan.

"Thanks, I'd love to," Terry said through gritted teeth.

Jace chuckled, and just for a moment the hard lines left his face. "Don't push it," he advised the younger man. "It's going to be tough walking again as it is. Plenty of time."

Terry nodded. "Thanks," he said, and meant it this time. "I'll pass on the horses today."

"We'll head back, then," Duncan said, wheeling his mount. "Amanda, race you!" he called the challenge.

"Hold it!" Jace's voice rang out above the bawling cattle.

Amanda stopped so suddenly that she went forward in the saddle as a lean, powerful hand caught at the bridle of her mount and pulled him up short.

"No racing," Jace said curtly, daring her to argue with him as he averted his gaze to Duncan. "She's too accident prone."

Duncan only looked amused. "If you say so."

"I'm not a child," Amanda protested, glaring down at the tall man.

He looked up into her eyes, and there was a look in his that held banked down flames, puzzling, fascinating. She didn't look away, and something like an electric shock tore through her body.

Jace's firm jaw tautened and abruptly he released the reins and moved away. "If Summers calls me about that foundation sale, send somebody out to get me," he told Duncan, and then he was gone, striding back into the tangle of men and cattle without a backward glance.

Duncan didn't say a word, but there was an amused smile on his face when they headed back to the house, and Amanda was glad that Terry was too concerned with his aching muscles to pay much attention to what was going on around him. That look in Jace's eyes, even in memory, could jack up her heart rate. It wasn't contempt, or hatred. It was a fierce, barely contained hunger, and it terrified her to think that Jace felt that way. Ever since her disastrous sixteenth birthday party, she'd kept her distance from him. Now, finally, she was forced to admit the reason for it, if only to herself. Fastidious and cool, Amanda had never felt those raging fires that drove women to run after men. But she felt them when she looked at Jace. She always had, and it would be incredibly dangerous to let him know it. It would give him the most foolproof way to pay her back for all his imagined grievances, and she wouldn't be able to resist him. She'd known that for a long time, too.

She glanced back over her shoulder at the branding that was proceeding without a hitch in the corral. If Jace hadn't been there, Amanda would have loved to stay and watch the process. It was fascinating to see how the old hands worked the cattle. But Jace would have made her too nervous to enjoy it. She urged her mount into a trot and followed along behind the men.

Terry didn't move for the rest of the afternoon. He spread his spare body out in a lawn chair by the deep blue water of the oval swimming pool, under a leafy magnolia tree, and dozed. Amanda sat idly chatting with Duncan at the umbrella table, sipping her lemonade, comfortably dressed in an aged ankle-length aqua terry cloth lounging dress with slit sides and white piping around the V-necked, sleeveless bodice. She could no longer afford to buy this sort of thing and the dress was left over from better days. Her feet were bare, and her hair was loose, lifting gently in the soft breeze. All around the pool area, there were blooming shrubs and masses of pink, white and red roses in the flower gardens that were Marguerite's pride and joy.

Her eyes wandered to the little gray summer house farther along on the luscious green lawn, with its miniature split rail fence. It was a child's dream, and all the family's nieces and nephews and cousins had played there at one time or another.

"What do you really think of the campaign we've laid out?" Amanda asked Duncan.

"I like it," he said bluntly. "The question is, will Jace? He's not that keen on the real estate operation, but even so he's aware that it's going to take some work to sell the idea of an apartment complex in inland Florida. Most people want beachfront."

She nodded. "We can make it work with specialty advertising," she said quietly. "I'm sure of it.'

Duncan smiled at her. "Are you the same girl who left here a few years ago, all nervous glances and shy smiles? Goodness, Miss Carson, you've changed. I noticed it six months ago, but there's an even bigger difference now."

"Am I really so different?" she mused.

"The way you stand up to Jace is different," he remarked drily. "You've got him on his ear."

She flushed wildly. "It doesn't show."

"It does to me."

She looked up. "Why did you insist that I come with Terry?" she asked flatly.

"I'll tell you someday," he promised. "Right now I just want to sit and enjoy the sun."

"I think I'll go help Marguerite address invitations to her party." She rose, willowy and delightful in the long dress, her bare feet crushing the soft grass as she walked and her long hair tossing like silver floss in the breeze.

Duncan let out a long, leering whistle, and she smiled secretly to herself, pulling off her sunglasses as she walked, to tuck them into one of the two big pockets in the front of the dress.

She went around to the back entrance, where masses of white roses climbed on white trellises. Impulsively, she reached out to one of the fragrant blossoms just as a truck came careening around the house and braked at the back steps.

Jace swung out of the passenger seat, holding his arm where blood streamed down it through the thin blue patterned fabric.

"Go on back," Jace called to the driver. "I'll get Duncan to bring me down when I patch this up."

The driver nodded and wheeled the truck around, disappearing at the corner of the house.

Amanda stared dumbly at the blood. "You're hurt," she said incredulously, as if it was unthinkable.

"If you're going to faint, don't get between me and the door," he said curtly, moving forward.

She shook her head. "I won't faint. You'd better let me dress it for you. I don't think it would be very easy to manage one-handed."

"I've done it before," he replied, following her through the spotless kitchen and out into the hall that led to the downstairs bathroom.

"I don't doubt it a bit," she returned with a mischievous glance. "I can see you now, sewing up a gash on your back."

"You little brat," he growled.

"Don't insult me or I'll put the bandage on inside out." She led him into the bathroom and pulled out a vanity bench for him to sit on. He whipped off his hat and dropped it to the blue and white mosaic tile on the floor.

While she riffled through the cabinet for bandages and antiseptic, his eyes wandered over her slender body moving down the soft tangle of her long hair to the clinging aqua dress. "Water nymph," he murmured.

She looked down at him, shocked by the sensuous remark, and blushed involuntarily.

"What have you been doing, decorating my pool?" he asked when she turned back to run a basin of water and toss a soft clean cloth into it.

"I've been listening to Terry moan and beg for a quick and merciful end," she replied with a faint smile. "You'll have to take off your shirt," she added unnecessarily.

He flicked open the buttons with a lazy hand, his eyes intent on her profile. "Tess would be helping me," he remarked deliberately.

"Tess would be on the floor, unconscious," she retorted, refusing to be baited. His flirting puzzled her, frightened her. It was new and exciting and vaguely terrifying. "You know blood makes her sick."

He chuckled softly, easing his broad, powerful shoulders out of the blood-and-dust-stained garment, dropping it carelessly on the floor.

She turned with the washcloth held poised in her slender hand, her eyes drawn helplessly to the bronzed, muscular chest with its mat of curling black hair, to the rounded, hard muscles of his brown arms. She felt her heart doing acrobatics inside her chest, and hated her own reaction to him. He was so arrogantly, vibrantly male. Just looking at him made her weak, vulnerable.

His glittering silver eyes narrowed on her face. "You're staring," he said quietly.

"Sorry," she murmured inadequately, feeling her whole body stiffen as she leaned down to bathe the long, jagged gash above his elbow. "It's deep, Jace."

"I know. Just clean it, don't make unnecessary remarks," he bit off, tensing even at the light touch.

"It needs stitches," she said stubbornly.

"So did half a dozen other cuts, but I haven't died yet," he replied gruffly.

"I hope you've at least had a tetanus shot."

"You're joking, of course," he said tightly.

He was right, it was ridiculous to even think he wouldn't have had that much foresight. She finished cleaning the long gash and turned to get the can of antiseptic spray.

"Spray the cut, not the rest of me," he said, watching her shake the can and aim it.

"I ought to spray you with iodine," she told him irritatedly. "That," she added with an unkind smile, "would hurt."

He lifted his arrogant face and studied her narrowly. "You wouldn't like the way I'd get even."

She ignored the veiled threat and proceeded to wind clean, white gauze around the arm. "I wish you'd see a doctor."

"If it starts to turn green from your amateurish efforts, I will," he promised.

Her eyes flashed down at him and found, instead of menace, laughter in his dark, hard face. "You make my blood burn, Jace Whitehall!" she muttered, rougher than she meant to be as she tied the bandage.

"Revealing words, Miss Carson," he said gently, and watched the color run into her cheeks.

"Not that way!" she protested without thinking.

Both dark eyebrows went up. "Oh?"

She turned and started to put away the bandages, refusing to look at him. It was too dangerous.

"From riches to rags," he commented, a lightning eye appraising the age of her aqua dress. "Can't your partner afford leisure clothes for you?"

She stiffened. "He doesn't buy my clothes."

"You'll never make me believe it," Jace replied coldly. "Those suits you wear didn't come out of anybody's bargain basement. The latest fashion, little girl, not castoffs, and you don't make that kind of money."

"Can't I make you understand that they're old?" she cried, exasperated. "I bought clothes with simple lines, Jace, so they wouldn't be dated!"

He flexed his shoulders as if the conversation had wearied him, and reached over to retrieve his shirt from the floor. "Nice try, Lady."

"I wish you wouldn't call me that," she said through her teeth. "Why can't you be like Duncan and just accept me the way I am without believing every horrible thing you can imagine about me?"

His eyes cut into hers. "Because I'm not Duncan. I never was." His jaw clenched. "Do you still want him? Is that why you came with Black?"

She threw up her hands. "All right. Yes, I want him. I'm after his money. I want to marry him and steal every penny he's got and buy ermine for all my friends! Now, are you satisfied?"

One dark eyebrow lifted nonchalantly. "I'll see you in hell before I'll see you married to my brother," he said without heat.

Her eyes involuntarily lingered on his broad chest, on the hard, unyielding set of his face that never softened, not even when he was in a gentler humor.

"Why do you hate me so?" she asked quietly.

His eyes darkened. "You damned well know why."

She dropped her gaze. "It was a long time ago," she reminded him. "And it isn't a pleasant memory."

"Why not?" he growled, his hand crumpling the shirt in his lap. "It would have solved your problems. You'd have been set for life, you and that flighty mother of yours."

"And all I'd have had to sacrifice was my self-respect," she murmured gently, glancing up at him. "I won't be any man's mistress, Jason, least of all yours."

He looked as if she'd slapped him, his eyes suddenly devoid of light. "Mistress?" he growled.

She lifted her chin proudly. "And what name would you have put on our relationship?" she challenged. "You asked me to live with you!"

"With me, that's right," he threw back. "In this house. My mother's house, damn you! Do you think her sense of propriety would have allowed anything less than a conventional relationship between us? I was proposing marriage, Amanda. I had the damned ring in my pocket if you'd stayed around long enough to see it."

Death must be like this, she thought, feeling a sting of pain so poignant it ran through her rigid body like a surge of electricity. Marriage! She could have been Jason Whitehall's wife, living with him, sharing everything with him . . . by now, she might have borne him a son. . . .

Tears misted her eyes and, seeing them, a cruel, cold smile fleetingly touched his chiseled lips.

"Feeling regret, honey?" he asked harshly. "I was on my way to the top about then. We were operating in the black for the first time, the first investments I'd made were just beginning to pay off. But you didn't stop to think about that, did you? You took one long look at me and slammed the door in my face. My god, you were lucky I didn't kick the door down and come after you."

"I expected you to," she admitted weakly, her eyes downcast, her heart breaking in half inside her rigid body. "I wouldn't even have blamed you. But you looked so fierce, Jason, and I was terrified of you physically. That's why I ran."

He stared at her. "Afraid of me? Why?"

She put the repackaged gauze back into the medicine cabinet. "You were very rough that night at my birthday party," she reminded him, blushing at the memory. "You can't imagine the secret terrors young girls have about men. Everything physical is so mysterious and unfamiliar. You were a great deal older than I was, and experienced, too. When you asked me so coolly to come and live with you, all I could think about was how it had been that night."

There was a long, blistering silence between them.

"I hurt you, didn't I?" he asked quietly, his eyes intent on her stiff back. "I meant to. Duncan told me that you only invited me out of courtesy, that you hated the sight of me." He laughed shortly. "He'd added a rider to the effect that you didn't think I'd know what to do with a woman."

She turned back toward him, the shock in her eyes. "I didn't tell him why I invited you," she said. Her head lowered. "The other part…I was teasing. Isn't it true that we sometimes joke about the things that frighten us most?" she mused. "I was frightened of you, but I used to dream about how it would be if you kissed me." She turned away. "The dreams were…a little less harsh than the reality." She shrugged, laughing lightly to mask her pain. "It doesn't matter anymore. They were girlish dreams and I'm a woman now."

"Are you?" he asked, rising to tower over her in the small room, moving closer and smiling sarcastically at the quick backward step she took. "Twenty-three, and still afraid of me. I won't rape you, Amanda."

She flushed angrily. "Must you be so insulting?"

"I didn't think you could be insulted," he said coolly, his eyes stripping the clothes from her. "Poor little rich girl. What a comedown. How old is that thing you're wearing?"

"It covers me up," she said defensively.

"Barely," he replied. His eyes narrowed. "Mother mentioned something about buying you some clothes while you were here. Apparently she's seen more of your wardrobe than I have. But don't be tempted, honey," he added with a narrow glance. "I don't work like a field hand to keep you and that mother of yours in silks and satin. If you need clothes, you see to it that Black furnishes them, not Mother."

Her lower lip trembled. "I'd rather go naked than accept a white handkerchief that your money paid for," she said proudly.

"No doubt your boyfriend would prefer it, too," he said curtly.

"He's my partner!" she threw at him. "Nothing more."

"He's not much of a horseman, either," he added with a half-smile. "If he couldn't handle that tame mount Duncan put him on, how does he expect to handle you?"

She turned away. "What would you do for pleasure if I wasn't around to insult?" she asked wearily.

"Speaking of the devil, where is he?"

"Out by the pool with Duncan, discussing the account." She glanced at him icily. "Not that it's going to do any good. You'll just say no."

"Don't presume to think for me, Amanda," he said quietly. "You don't know me. You never have."

She licked her dry lips. "You don't let people get close to you, Jason."

"Would you like to?" he asked coolly.

"I don't think so, thanks," she murmured, turning. "You've had too many free shots at me already."

"Without justification?" he queried, moving closer. "My God, every time you come here there's another disaster."

"I didn't mean to hit the bull," she said defensively. "And you didn't have to yell...."

"What the hell did you expect me to do, get down on my knees and give thanks? You could have been killed, you crazy little fool," he growled.

"That would have suited you very well, wouldn't it?" she burst out. She turned away, just missing the expression on his face. "I meant to apologize, but I sprained my wrist and I couldn't even talk for the pain."

"You sprained your wrist?" Her eyes exploded. "And you drove from here to San Antonio like that? You damned little fool...!"

"What was I supposed to do, ask you for a ride?" she threw back, her brown eyes snapping at him. "You'd already shot the bull, I thought you might turn the gun on me if I didn't make myself scarce!"

She whirled and started out the door, ignoring his harsh tone as he called her name.

He caught up with her in the hall, catching her arm to swing her around, his eyes fierce under his jutting brow. With his shirt off, and that expanse of powerful bronzed muscles, he made her feel weak.

"Where do you think you're going?" he asked.

"To seduce Duncan by the pool," she said sweetly. "Isn't that why you think I came?"

"You'll never marry him." The threat was deliberate, calculated.

"I don't have to marry him to sleep with him, do I?" she asked with a toss of her long, silvery hair. "What's the matter, Jace, does it bother you that your brother might have succeeded where you failed?"

It was the wrong thing to say. She only got a second's warning before he started after her, but it was enough to make her turn and run. There was a peculiar elation in rousing Jace's temper. It made her feel alive, lightheaded.

She ran into the living room and whirled to shut the door behind her, but she was too slow. Jace easily forced his way in, catching the door with his boot to slam it shut behind him, closing the two of them off from the world.

He stood facing her, his silver eyes blazing under his disheveled hair, his face hard and frankly dangerous, pagan-looking with his broad, bronzed chest bare, its pelt of dark hair glistening with sweat.

"Now let's see how brave you really are," he said in a voice deep and slow with banked down anger as he began to move toward her.

She backed away from him slowly, all the courage ebbing away at the look on his face. "I didn't mean it," she said breathlessly. "Jace, I didn't mean it!"

The desk caught her in the small of the back, halting her as effectively as a wall, and he closed the gap quickly, his hands catching her upper arms in a vicelike grip that hurt.

"Don't," she pleaded, wincing. "You're hurting me!"

"You've been hurting me for years," he said in a rough undertone, his eyes blazing down into hers as he jerked her body against the hard, powerful length of his and pinned her to the desk in one smooth motion. "Has Duncan had you? Answer me!"

"No!" she whispered. "He's never touched me that way, never, Jace, I swear!"

She watched some of the strain leave his hard face even as she felt the tension grow in the powerful muscles of his legs where they pressed warmly into hers. His hands shifted around to her back. She wasn't wearing a bra under the terry cloth dress, and she could feel his bare chest against her soft breasts through the thin fabric. The intimacy made her tremble.

He looked down at her, where her slender hands were pressed lightly against the mat of hair over his bronzed skin, and she was aware of the heavy, hard beat of his heart against the crushed warmth of her breasts.

"Is there anything but skin under this wisp of cloth?" he asked in a taut undertone. "I might as well be holding you in your underclothes."

"Jace!" she burst out, embarrassed.

"No, don't fight," he warned shortly when she tried to struggle away from him. His hands moved slowly, caressingly on her back, easing down below her waist to hold her tightly against the hard muscles of his thighs.

"Doesn't Black ever make love to you?" he asked curiously, watching the reaction in her flushed face, her frightened eyes. "You're too nervous for a woman who's used to being touched."

"Maybe I'm nervous because it's you," she burst out. Her fingers clenched together where they were forced to rest against his chest, as she fought not to give in to the longing, to run her hands over his cool flesh. Her nostrils drank in the faint scent of cologne and leather that clung to his tall body.

"Because it's me?" he prompted, eyeing her.

She bit her lower lip nervously, all too aware of the privacy the closed door provided. "The last time, you hurt," she murmured.

"The last time you were sixteen years old and I was mad as hell," he reminded her. "I meant to hurt you."

"What did I do," she asked miserably, "except make the mistake of having a huge crush on you?"

He was so still, she thought for a moment that he hadn't heard her. His hands pressed into her soft flesh painfully for an instant, and a harsh sigh escaped from his lips.

"A crush on me?" he echoed blankly. "My God, you ran the other way every time I looked at you!"

"Of course I did, you terrified me!" she burst out, her eyes wide and dark and accusing as they met his. "I knew you and Mother didn't get along, and I thought you disliked me the way you did her. You were always and forever snapping at me or glaring."

His eyes ran over her face lightly, lingering pointedly on her mouth. "I suppose I was. I got the shock of my life when you invited me to that party."

She searched his hard face. "Why did you come?" she asked softly.

His shoulders lifted and fell heavily. "I don't know," he admitted. "I was out of my element in more ways than one. I'd had women by then, I was used to females a hell of a lot more sophisticated than the crowd that surrounded me that night."

A surge of inexplicable jealousy ran riot through her body as she stared up at him. "So I gathered," she grumbled.

One dark eyebrow went up. "And how would you have known? You were obviously a virgin. I remember wondering at the time how many boys you'd kissed. You didn't even know enough to open your mouth to mine."

She lowered her eyes to his chest before he could see the embarrassed flush that spread down from her cheeks.

"I'd never been kissed by anyone," she said quietly. "You were...the first. You were almost the last, too," she added with an irrepressible burst of humor. "I was scared silly." Her eyes glanced up and down again. "It was a terribly adult kiss."

He lifted a lean hand and tilted her face up so that he could study it. "Did I leave scars on those young emotions?" he asked gently. "All I could remember about it later was the way you trembled against me, the softness of your body under my hands. I had a feeling I'd frightened you, but I was too angry to care. If I'd known the truth..."

"It probably wouldn't have made much difference," she put in. "I...get the feeling that you're not a gentle lover, Jason."

"Do you?" He drew her slowly up against him again, feeling the sudden tension in her body as his hands spread around her waist and trapped her there. "Maybe it's time I did something about that first impression."

"Jason, I don't think..." she began nervously.

"Shh," he whispered, bending his dark head. "We won't need words...it's been so long, Amanda," he murmured as his mouth brushed hers, his teeth nipping at her lower lip to make it part for him before his warm mouth moved on hers with a slow, lazy pressure that knocked any thought of resistance out of her mind. His arms swallowed her gently, folding her into his tall, powerful body while he taught her how much two people could tell each other with one long, slow kiss.

She could hardly believe it was happening, here in broad daylight, in the living room where they had sat like polite strangers the night before and never even touched.

It was almost like going back in time, to her sixteenth birthday party, but the kiss he'd given her then was nothing like this. He was easy with her, gentle, coaxing her mouth to open for him, to admit the deep, expert penetration of his tongue. The silence was only broken by the rough whisper of their breath as they kissed more and more hungrily. Her hands caressed his hair-roughened chest with an ardor that came not from experience, but from longing. She felt the need to touch, to explore, to learn the contours of his body with her fingers. She could feel the length of him, warm against her, and she trembled with the force of the new sensations he was arousing with the slow, caressing motions of his hands.

She felt his fingers move to the zipper at the front of the terry cloth dress with a sense of wonder at his expertise. He was already beginning to slide it down when her nervous fingers caught at his and stilled them.

He drew back a breath, his eyes narrow and glittering with silver lights, his mouth sensuous, slightly swollen from the long, hard contact with hers.

"I want to look at you," he said huskily. "I want to watch your face when I touch you."

Shudders of wild sensation ran down her body like lightning. She realized with a start that she wanted his eyes on her, the touch of those hard fingers on her bare skin. But through the fog of hunger he'd created, she still remembered what the situation was between them. Jason was her enemy. He had nothing but contempt for her, and allowing him this kind of intimacy was suicide.

"No," she whispered tightly.

He lifted his face, looking down his arrogant nose at her. "Are we going to pretend that this is another first?" he asked curtly. "Sorry, honey, I'm an old fox now, and wary of woman-traps. I know one when I see one."

She tried to get away in a flurry of anger, but he held her effortlessly. "Let go of me!" she cried. "I don't know what you're talking about!"

"No?" he returned coldly. "You're full of tricks all right, Amanda, but don't think you'll catch me. Deliberate provocation can be dangerous, and you'd better think twice before you try it again. Next time, I'll take you," he said harshly, watching the shock darken her eyes, "and teach you things about men you never knew."

"I wouldn't let you!" she burst out.

"Why not?" His eyes were faintly insulting as he released her abruptly. "Women like you aren't all that particular, are they? Why not me, Amanda?"

"I hate you!" she whispered unsteadily, and at the moment, she meant it. How dare he make insinuations about her?

He only smiled, but there was no humor in his look. "Do you? I'm glad, Amanda, I'd hate to think you were dying of unrequited love for me. But if you change your mind, honey, you know where my room is," he added for good measure. "Just don't expect marriage. I know how badly you and your mother need a meal ticket. But, honey," he said, as he opened the door, "it won't be me."

He went out, closing the door behind him.

5

*

She went to her room to freshen up, and bathed her hot cheeks in cold water. She held a cold cloth to her lips as well, hoping that might make the bruised swelling go down. Bruised. Her eyes closed, her heart turned over, in memory. Her mind went back to the day Jace had approached her with his earth-shattering proposition.

It had been a day much like this one, sunny and warm, and Amanda had been alone when she'd heard a car drive up in front of the house. She'd gone onto the porch as Jace took the steps three at a time. He was dressed in denims, and had obviously been out working with his hands on the ranch. He'd stopped just in front of her, oddly irritated, sweeping the black Stetson off his dark head. His silver eyes had glittered down at her out of a deeply tanned face.

"You look like death on a holiday," he'd commented gruffly, tracing the unusually thin lines of her slender body with eyes that lingered. "How's it going?"

She'd drawn herself erect, too proud to let him see what a burden it all was—her father's death, Bea's careless spending, the loss of their assets, the disgrace—and met his eyes bravely.

"We're coping," she'd said. She even forced a cool smile for him.

But Jace, being Jace, hadn't bought it. Those narrow, piercing eyes had seen through her pose easily. He was a businessman, accustomed to coping with minds shrewder and more calculating than Amanda's, and with the knowledge of long acquaintance, he could read her as easily as a newspaper.

"I hear you've had to put the house itself on the market," he said frankly. "At the rate your mother's going, before long you'll be selling the clothes off your back to support her."

Her lower lip had threatened to give her away even more, but she'd caught it in her teeth just in time. "I'll manage."

"You don't have to manage, Amanda," he said curtly. There was a curious hesitation in him, a stillness that should have warned her. But it hadn't. "I can make it right for you. Pay the bills, keep the ranch going. I can even support that scatterbrained parent of yours, though the thought disgusts me."

She'd eyed him warily. "In exchange for what, exactly?" she'd asked.

"Come and live with me," he said.

The words had hit her like ice water. Unexpected, faintly embarrassing, their impact had left her white. She was afraid of Jason; terrified of him on any physical level. Perhaps if he'd been gentler that night when he'd surprised her by showing up for her birthday party...but he hadn't, and the thought of what he was asking turned her blood cold. She hadn't even bothered to explain. She'd turned around before he had time to react, rushed into the house, slammed and locked the door behind her, all without a word. And the memory of that day had been between them ever since, like a thorny fence neither cared to climb.

It was a blessing that Jace thought her instinctive response to him was an act. If he'd known the truth, that she quite simply couldn't resist him in any way, it would have been unbearable for her. Jace would love having a weapon like that to use on her. And if he knew what she really felt . . . it didn't bear consideration.

Love. There was no way that she could deny the feeling. What a tragedy that all her defenses had finally deserted her, and bound her over to the enemy. This gossamer, sweet wind of sensation made her want to laugh and sing and cry all at once, to run to Jace with her arms outstretched and offer him anything, everything, to share her life with him, to give him sons. . . .

Tears misted her eyes. Tess would give him those. Perfect sons with perfect minds, always neat, very orderly, made to stand around like little statues. Tess would see to that, and Jace was too busy to bother. He wanted heirs, not love. It wasn't a word he knew.

Why did it have to be Jace? she asked in anguish. Why not Terry, or Duncan, or the half dozen other men she'd dated over the years? Why did it have to be the one man in the world she couldn't have? Her poor heart would wear itself out on Jace's indifference.

It was a good thing that she and Terry were leaving at the end of the week. Now that she knew what her fear of Jace really was, she could stay away from him. She could leave Casa Verde and never see him again. The tears came back, hot and bitter. How terribly that hurt, to think of never seeing him again. But in the long run, it would be less cruel than tormenting herself by being near him.

Resolutely, she dried the tears and exchanged the aqua lounging dress for her jeans and a pink top. She crumpled the dress into her suitcase, vowing silently that she'd never wear it again. As she tucked it away, she caught the faint scent of the tangy cologne Jace wore, clinging to the fabric.

Marguerite was busily addressing dainty deckle edge envelopes in her sitting room on the second floor when Amanda joined her.

"Hello, dear, have enough sun?" the older woman asked pleasantly, pausing with her pen in midair.

"In a sense," she replied. "I came in to lend you a hand but then I ran into Jace and stopped to patch him up."

Marguerite's face changed, drew in. "Is he all right?"

"Yes, it was just a gash in his arm," she replied, easing the fears she could read plainly in the older woman's eyes. "I never did find out how it happened. One of the cows, I guess."

Marguerite's dark eyes hardened. "Those horrible beasts," she exclaimed. "Sometimes I think the

Whitehall men have more compassion for breeding stock than they do for women! Except for Duncan, bless him."

Amen, Amanda thought as she pulled over a dainty wing chair next to Marguerite's writing table and sat down.

"Jace actually let you put a bandage on him?" she asked her young companion. "I'd have thought little Tess would have been standing by just in case."

"Apparently not," she replied, hoping her face didn't show any of what had really happened. What she didn't know was that her mouth was still swollen, despite the cold compress, and there were marks on one delicate cheek which were made by the rasp of a man's slightly burred cheek.

But Marguerite kept her silence, aware of the peculiar tension in her companion. "You're sure you don't mind helping?" she asked, pushing some envelopes and a page of names and addresses toward her.

"Of course not." Amanda took a pen and began to write in her lovely longhand.

"Jace didn't argue about letting you play nurse?" she continued gently.

"He did at first," she murmured.

Marguerite glanced at her, amused. "You're coming to the party, of course," she said. "These are just unforgivably late invitations to a few friends whom I'm sure can make it despite the short notice. The party's going to be held at the Sullevans'. They have a huge ballroom, something we haven't."

Amanda nodded, remembering the enormous Sullevan estate with its graceful curves and gracious hospitality. "I can't come, you know," she said gently.

Marguerite looked across at her with a knowing smile. "I'll get you a dress."

"No!" Amanda burst out, horrified as she remembered Jace's threat.

But Marguerite's attention was already back on the invitations. Amanda started to write, unaware of the faint, amused smile on the older woman's face.

*   *   *

Duncan and Marguerite were the only ones at the breakfast table when Amanda went downstairs after a restless night. Jace, she was told, had long since gone to his office, in a black temper.

"He gets worse every day lately," Duncan remarked, glancing at Amanda with a smile as she took the seat beside him. "You wouldn't know why, Amanda?"

She tried to hide her red face by bending it over her cup of black coffee. "Me? Why?"

"Well, you were both conspicuously absent from the supper table," he observed. "You had a sick headache, and Jace had some urgent business at the office."

Marguerite was just beginning to make connections. One silver eyebrow went up in a gesture reminiscent of her eldest son. "Did you and Jace argue yesterday, Amanda?" she asked gently.

"It's downright dangerous to have them in the same room together lately," Duncan teased. "He flies at her and she flies right back. God help anyone who gets between them."

"Where's Terry, I wonder?" Amanda hedged, helping herself to some scrambled eggs and little fat sausages.

"He and I were up late discussing the campaign," Duncan explained. "He's probably overslept. I've got to fly to New York today on business." He sipped his coffee, set the china cup down gently in its saucer, and stared at Amanda. "Jace agreed to talk with Terry tonight."

"Did he? That's nice," she murmured.

He studied her downbent head, reading accurately the wan, drawn look about her face, the dark circles under her eyes.

Marguerite finished her breakfast and crumpled her napkin beside her plate, lifting her coffee cup with a smile. "How lovely to have one uninterrupted meal," she sighed. "Duncan, breakfast with you is so restful."

"I don't own controlling interest in the properties," he reminded her.

The words reminded Amanda of what Jace had said, and she winced unconsciously.

Marguerite's dark eyes flashed. "I'd like to get rid of it all," she grumbled, "except for a little of the ranch. Maybe we weren't so wealthy in the old days, but at least we could eat a meal without someone being called away on business. And Jace didn't push himself so hard."

"Didn't he?" Duncan asked gently. "He always has. And we both know why."

Marguerite smiled at him wistfully. "And what do you think about the end result?"

"I think there's a distinct possibility of success," he said mysteriously, lifting his coffee cup as if in a toast.

"You people do carry on the strangest conversations," Amanda remarked between mouthfuls.

"Sorry, dear," Marguerite apologized nicely. "Just old suspicions."

"Want to come to New York with me?" Duncan asked Amanda suddenly. "I'm just going for the day. We'll ride the ferry over to Staten Island and make nasty remarks about the traffic."

Her eyes lit up. The prospect of being carefree for one whole day was enchanting, especially when she wanted so desperately to keep out of Jace's way.

"Could I?" she asked, and her whole face changed, grew younger. "Oh, but Terry..." she murmured, her enthusiasm dampening.

"He'll be just fine with me," Marguerite said cheerfully. "I'll take care of him for you, and tonight he and Jace will be busy discussing the accounts. So why not go, dear? You look as if you could use a little gaiety."

"If you don't mind...."

"Go put on a pretty dress," Duncan told her, grinning. "I'll give you a whole half hour."

"Done!" Amanda said excitedly. She excused herself from the table and darted upstairs. It was like being a child again. She'd forgotten the magic of being wealthy enough to take off and go anywhere, any time. The Whitehalls took it for granted, just as Amanda had once, but those days were long past. Now she had to budget everything, especially groceries. Trips and holidays were something she could no longer afford.

She changed into a white sundress with yellow daisies on the bodice and a full eyelet skirt, a delightful little frock she'd found on sale at a small boutique last fall. She scooped up her lightweight tan sweater and slipped on her sandals in a rush, barely stopping long enough to check her makeup and add another pin to the hair she had carefully tucked into a neat chignon. She forgot her purse and had to go back for it. Not that there was more than a few dollars in it, but she felt more secure having it.

She darted downstairs to find that Terry had finally made it to the breakfast table. He looked sleepy and faintly hung over, but he grinned at Amanda pleasantly.

"Hi!" she said. "I'm going to desert you and go to New York, okay?"

"Sure. Have a good time. I'll work on my sales pitch out by the pool," he told her.

"Just don't fall in. He can't swim," she told the others with a laugh.

"We can't all be fish like you in the water," came the teasing reply.

"If you're ready," Duncan said, slipping into his brown suit coat.

"More than," Amanda told him.

He studied her outfit carefully, as his eyes narrowed on the sweater. "Honey, there's a lot of difference between Texas and New York, and we'll be leaving after dark. Are you sure that sweater's going to be enough on your arms?"

Amanda nodded, too proud to admit that the only coat she owned was back in San Antonio, and that it wouldn't have done for anything more than a trip to the neighborhood grocery.

"I'll loan you my spring coat," Marguerite said easily, smiling. "You simply can't pack coats, Duncan, they're too bulky," she added.

Amanda blessed her for that, knowing the older woman had deliberately covered up for her.

Marguerite came back with a lightweight gray coat, very stylish, and very expensive.

"But I can't . . ." Amanda protested.

"Of course you can, dear, I have several more, and we're about the same size. Here, try it on."

She helped Amanda into it, and it was a perfect fit. Her soft brown eyes said it all, and Marguerite only nodded.

"Have fun, now, and don't be too late. Which plane are you taking?"

"The Piper," Duncan called back, as they went out the front door. "Don't keep supper for us, we'll have it there."

The twin-engine plane made good time, and Duncan was a good pilot. Almost as good as Jace, and not quite as daring. Before Amanda knew it, they were landing in New York's sprawling terminal, despite the wait to be sandwiched in between jumbo jets.

Duncan hailed them a taxi with the flair of an experienced traveler and hustled Amanda inside. He gave the driver an address and leaned back with a sigh.

"Now, this is the way to travel," he told her. "No bags, no toothbrush, just leap on a plane and go."

She laughed, catching his exuberant mood. "Sure. Since we've come this far, let's just go on to Martinique."

"Now, there was a fun island," he replied, going back in time. "Remember when you and I flew down there with Uncle Macklin and forgot to tell Mother? I thought the end of the world was coming when they caught up with us. But we had fun, didn't we?"

"We certainly did," she replied, turning her head against the seat to look at him. He was nothing like Jace. She liked his boyish face, his sparkling personality. If only she could have loved him.

"I hate it when you do that," he remarked, grinning.

"Do what?" she asked softly.

"Measure me against Jace. Oh, don't bother to deny it," he said when she started to protest. "I've known you too long. Anyway, I don't really mind. Jace is one of a kind; most men would fall short of him by comparison."

She let her eyes drift to the moving meter. "Sorry. I wasn't trying to be mean."

His hand found hers and squeezed it. "I know that. The joy of being with you, Mandy, is that I can be myself. I'm glad to have you for a friend."

She smiled at him. "Same here."

"Of course, it wasn't always friendship," he said, lifting a corner of his mouth. "I had a crush on you when you were about sixteen. You didn't even notice, you were too busy trying to keep out of Jace's way. I was terribly jealous, you know."

"Did you, really?" she asked. "Duncan, I'm so sorry...!" Maybe that explained the lie he'd told Jace about her reason for inviting him to the long-ago birthday party.

"Just a crush, darling, and I got over it fast. I'm glad I did. It was never there for you, was it?" he asked, more serious than she'd ever seen him.

"No," she said honestly. "It never was."

"If I can help, Mandy, in any way, I will," he said suddenly.

His kindness, coming on the heels of Jace's antagonism, was her undoing. Hot tears swelled up in her eyes and overflowed onto her cheeks in a silent flood.

"Mandy," he said sympathetically, and drew her gently against him, rocking her softly while she cried. "Poor little mite, it's been rough, hasn't it? I should have been keeping in touch. You need looking after."

She shook her head. "I can take care of myself," she mumbled.

"Sure you can, darling," he laughed gently, patting her shoulder.

"It's just...if I could will Mama to somebody with tremendous assets," she laughed.

"Some rich man will come along and save you eventually," he told her. "After all, your mama is still a beautiful woman. Sweet, intelligent..."

"...addlepated and selfish," she finished with a wry grin, drawing back to pull a handkerchief from her purse and dab at her wet eyes with it. "I don't usually give in to self-pity. Sorry. It gets to be a heavy load sometimes, having all the responsibility."

"Which you shouldn't, at your age," he said tautly. "You haven't been able to do anything but support her since it all happened. I know, you don't mind, but the fact is, you're not being allowed a life of your own. All you're doing is working to keep Bea up. There's nothing left for you to enjoy after you pay the bills, and it isn't fair, Amanda."

"Duncan, if I don't do it, who will?" she asked gently. "Mother can't work. She's never had to. What would she do?"

"People could rent her, an hour at a time, to stand in the corner and look beautiful while holding a lamp or something," he suggested.

She burst out laughing at the idea. "You're horrible."

"That's why you like me," he returned. "Amanda, remember the summer we tied bows on Jace's sale bulls just before that auction?"

She whistled softly. "Do I ever! We'd never have outrun him if you hadn't got that brilliant idea to turn out all his brood mares as we went through the barn."

"That made him even madder," he recalled. "I went to spend a week with my aunt that very evening, before Jace got back from the sale. And you, if I remember rightly, went away immediately to boarding school."

"I felt it would be safer living in Switzerland at that point in my life," she grinned. "He was furious!"

He sighed. "They were good days, weren't they, Amanda?"

She nodded. "What a shame that we have to grow up and become dignified."

6
*

They were homeward bound when some unfamiliar sound woke her. She sat straight up in the seat to find Duncan struggling with the controls, his face more somber than she'd seen it in years.

"What's the matter?" she asked with a worried frown.

He was bending slightly forward, one hand on the wheel, the other on the instrument panel. "I think it's the left mag, but I can't tell yet."

"Mag?" she echoed.

"Magneto." He reached for the ignition switch and turned it momentarily left and then right. The plane was literally doing a hula in midair. Duncan gritted his teeth. "I'm going to try different power settings and ease in on the mixture, then I'll know if we can risk going on," he mumbled to himself.

She just stared, the language he was speaking vaguely incomprehensible to her. But whatever he was doing, it didn't seem to help. The vibration in the plane was terrible.

He cursed under his breath. "Well, that's it. We'll have to put down at Seven Bridges and have it fixed. I won't risk going any farther like this."

Duncan nosed the Piper down where the string of runway lights stretched like a double strand of glowing pearls through a low-lying mist.

"God, I hope there's not a cow on the landing strip," he mumbled as he held the vibrating airplane on course.

"You're such a comfort to me, Duncan," she said, biting back her nervousness. "Where did you say we were?"

"Seven Bridges, Tennessee," he grinned. "Hang on, honey, here goes."

"I trust you," she told him. "We'll be okay."

"I sure as hell hope so."

The next few minutes were the most dangerous Amanda could ever remember. The engines felt like they were trying to shake apart, and the landing lights in that fog were a little blurry. If Jace had been at the controls, she'd never have worried at all...she was sorry she had to think of that, knowing that Duncan was doing his best. But Jace had steel nerves, and his younger brother, despite his flight experience in the twin-engine plane, didn't. Once, as he put the plane down, he lost control just for a split second and had to pull up and come around again, an experience that threatened to turn Amanda's hair white.

Her hands gripped the edge of her seat so hard that she could feel the leather give under them, but not a word passed her lips. Nothing she said would help, and it might distract Duncan fatally. She kept quiet and whispered a prayer.

Duncan eased the plane down, his eyes on the controls, the landing strip, the airspeed indicator, the artificial horizon, the altimeter. Now training was taking over, he relaxed visibly, and put the twin-engine plane carefully down the runway with a gentle screeching noise followed by a downgrading of the engine, and sudden, total silence as he cut the power entirely and taxied in.

"In the veritable nick of time," he sighed wearily.

"You done good, as they say," she teased, able to relax now that they were safe. "Now, how do we get home?"

"Hitchhike?" he suggested with a grin.

"Call for reinforcements?" she suggested.

"Reinforcements would be Jace," he reminded her, "and my jaw hasn't healed from the last time I upset him."

She hadn't thought about that. They'd promised to be home by midnight, and it was...she sighed deeply.

"Shall we see if the gentleman has a house for rent with a good view," she asked with a nervous laugh, "and maybe a couple of jobs open?"

"At this point, it might be wise to consider the folly of going home."

They climbed out of the plane in the rear and the fixed base operator approached them out of a lighted hangar wiping his hands on a rag. He was a big, aging man with a shock of white hair and a toothy smile.

"Thought I heard a plane," he grinned. "Got problems?"

"One of my magnetos went out on me," Duncan told him. "I'm going to need a new one, if you've got one you can put on for me."

"What is she? A Piper Navajo by the look," he guessed, and Duncan nodded. "Sure, I can fix it, I think. I run an aviation service, and the wife and I live in that trailer over there." He chuckled. "I couldn't sleep, so I came down here to wrestle with a rewiring job in an old Aeronca Champion I just bought. Well, let's have a look at your problem."

Minutes later, Amanda was comfortably seated in Donald Aiken's trailer with his small, dark-haired wife, Annette, enjoying the best cup of coffee she'd ever tasted while she recuperated from the hair-raising experience.

They were discussing the economy when Duncan and the airport operator walked in.

"Donald can fix it," Duncan said with a tired grin. He needed a shave, and looked it, but at this hour of the morning it didn't really matter.

"Thank goodness," she sighed. "You know, we really do need to call your mother. We can make her promise not to tell Jace...."

"Uh, I'm afraid you won't be calling anybody long-distance," Donald said apologetically. "Or locally either for the time being. Cable got cut, and they're still trying to fix it. I heard it over the radio earlier while I was working. Sure am sorry."

Duncan sighed. "It's fate," he said, nodding. "Out to get me."

"I'll protect you, Duncan," Amanda promised.

"Unless I miss my guess, you're going to need protection as much as I am." He shook his head. "Well, can't be helped."

"It won't take long," Donald said encouragingly, finishing a quick cup of coffee. "We'll have you on your way in no time," he promised.

No time turned out to be two hours, and it was thanks to Donald's skill as a mechanic that they were able to take off at all.

The sun had not yet risen when Duncan set the twin-engine plane down on the Casa Verde landing strip, but the sky was already lightening with the approaching dawn.

Tired and bedraggled, they got out of the plane and stood quickly on the apron looking around at the quiet, pastoral landscape.

"Peaceful, isn't it?" Duncan asked, taking a deep breath of fresh air.

"So far," she agreed with a wan smile. "They'll have heard us land, of course."

"It's never failed yet."

As if in answer to the remark, they heard the loud, angry roar of one of the ranch's pickup trucks.

"Would you care to bet who's driving it?" Duncan asked with cool nonchalance.

"Oh, I think I have some idea," she returned. Her knees felt curiously weak. Circumstance it might have been, but she knew without guessing what Jace's reaction was going to be, and she wanted to run. But there was no place to go. Jace was already out of the truck and striding toward them with homicide in his eyes.

He hadn't slept. That registered in Amanda's tired mind even as his dangerous gaze riveted itself to Duncan as he approached them. He needed a shave badly, and his face was pale and haggard. He was wearing gray suit pants with a half unbuttoned white shirt, and over it was his suede ranch coat. The familiar black Stetson was pulled cockily over one eye, and he looked fierce and uncivilized in the gray half-light.

"Uh, hi, Jace," Duncan said uneasily.

He'd barely got the words out when Jace reached him, hauling back to throw a deadly accurate right fist into his jaw and knock him sprawling backward onto the pavement.

"Do you know what we've been through?" Jace breathed huskily, his temper barely leashed. "We expected you by midnight and it's daylight. You let us sit here without even a phone call...Mother's in tears, damn you!"

"It's a long story," Duncan muttered, holding his jaw as he sat up, his face contrite. "I swear to God, we've had a night ourselves. The right magneto went in one of the engines and I almost crashed the plane getting us down."

She could have sworn Jace paled. His glittering eyes shot to Amanda and ran over her like hands feeling for breaks after a fall. "Are you all right?" he asked curtly.

She nodded, afraid to risk words. She'd never seen him like this.

Duncan picked himself up, feeling his jaw gingerly. "Damn, Jace, I wish you'd yell instead of hit," he mused, geared to his brother's temper after years of conditioning.

"What happened?" came the terse reply.

Duncan explained briefly the events that had mounted up to delay them, adding that the cable had been out and they couldn't even telephone.

Jace's face got, if possible, even harder. "You could still have phoned before you left New York," he reminded his brother.

Duncan smiled sheepishly. "I know. But we were having such a good time that I just didn't think. Then, when we finally got to the airport, I was afraid to waste the time."

"I even tried to call the terminal in New York to find out when you filed your flight plan," Jace continued grimly.

"Guilty on all counts," Duncan agreed. "I don't have a good excuse. I just ... didn't think."

Jace's bloodshot eyes narrowed. "I'm going to let you explain that to Mother."

Duncan waited for Amanda, who'd been quiet, and held out his hand, but Jace got to her first, catching her arm in a grip that was frankly punishing. His eyes went over the expensive coat and narrowed.

"You didn't have a coat with you," he said, his tone challenging.

"No..." she started to explain.

"Didn't I warn you about gifts?" he demanded.

It was too much. The night, the near-crash, the worry about getting home, and then Jace's fury...it was just too much. A sob broke from her throat and she started crying, little noises escaping her tight throat, tears rolling pathetically down her cheeks.

"Oh, for God's sake, Amanda...!" Jace burst out.

"Leave her alone, Jace," Duncan said quietly, and stopped to draw her against him. "I scared her out of her wits. And if the coat bothers you, blame Mother. Amanda didn't have one and Mother loaned it to her."

Jace looked as if he wanted to throw things. But he whirled without another word, his face terrible, and got in behind the wheel of the truck. Duncan eased Amanda into the seat first, watching her shrink away from contact with Jace when he got in on the other side of her and closed the door. Jace started the truck and left rubber behind taking off.

They had to go over the explanations again for Marguerite, who was pale and worn out from crying, hugging the two of them as if they'd come back from the dead. To Amanda's silent relief, Jace disappeared upstairs as soon as they got home. She couldn't cope with him right now.

"I'm so glad you're safe," Marguerite sniffed, sipping black coffee with a sodden handkerchief clutched in one thin hand. "I was so worried."

"I wish we could have let you know," Amanda said gently, wiping her own face, "but there wasn't any way. I'm so sorry we upset you."

"Jace more than me," she said with a damp smile. "He wore ruts in my carpet. I've never seen him so upset.'

"He hit Duncan," Amanda said, faintly resentful.

"Duncan deserved it," the injured party said sheepishly, "and you know it."

Marguerite sighed. "You're lucky that's all he did. He threatened worse things while we waited, and I know he smoked a carton of cigarettes."

"Would anyone mind if I went to bed for what's left of the night?" Amanda asked gently. "I know you two are just as tired as I am, but...."

"You go right ahead, dear," Marguerite said with an affectionate smile. "Duncan and I will be right behind you. Rest well."

"Where's Terry, by the way?" Amanda asked suddenly, remembering him belatedly.

"He went to bed early and we didn't wake him," Marguerite explained. "He's missed all the excitement."

Amanda smiled wanly. "I'll see you both later, and I really am sorry," she added gently, bending to kiss Marguerite's cheek as she passed her.

The fatigue and lack of sleep hit her all at once when she got to her room. She took off the sundress and her sandals, but she couldn't seem to stay awake long enough to get out of her slip and hose before she drifted off in a heap at the foot of her bed.

Through a fog, she felt herself being lifted and placed under something soft and cool. Her heavy eyelids opened slowly, as if in a dream, to find a hard, tanned face looming over her.

"Sleepy?" he asked in a voice too soft to be Jace's.

She nodded. Her vision was blurred, as if she was dreaming. Perhaps she was.

He brought the cover up to her waist, his eyes lingering on the lacy bodice of her slip where it exposed the soft, pale swell of her breasts.

"I'm not dressed," she murmured drowsily.

"I can see that," he replied softly, with an amused smile.

"You're mad at me," she recalled, frowning. "I don't remember...why...but..."

"Don't think. Go to sleep."

Her eyes drifted down to the growth of beard on his tanned face and involuntarily her fingers reached up to touch it. For a dream, he felt warmly real.

"You haven't slept either," she whispered.

"I couldn't, until I knew," he said gruffly.

"Were you worried?" she asked.

"Worried!" He laughed shortly, but his eyes were still turbulent with emotion. "My God, I had visions of the two of you lying mangled in the wreckage of the Navajo. And you were going up and down Broadway!"

She dropped her eyes to his broad chest where his shirt was unbuttoned, and the curling dark hairs on the bronzed skin were damp, like the hair on his head, as if he'd just come from a shower.

"We were having fun," she said inadequately.

"You always had fun with him." There was a world of bitterness in the words.

"And I always ran from you," she murmured gently. Her fingers traced the long, chiseled curve of his warm mouth. "I could never get close to you," she told him, weariness making her vulnerable, loosening her tongue. "The day I invited you to the party, I was scared to death. I wanted you to come so much, and you were like stone."

"Self-defense, Amanda," he replied quietly, his eyes slow and bold on the lacy white slip and the white flesh peeking out of it. "I didn't like the way you made me feel. I didn't like being vulnerable either."

She laughed wistfully. "All I ever managed to do was make you lose your temper."

"Are you sure?" He caught her hand and drew it to his warm, hard chest, pressing its palm against the hard, shuddering beat of his heart. "Feel what you do to me," he murmured, watching the surprise in her sleepy eyes. "I can look at you and my heart damned near beats me to death. It's been that way for years and you've never even noticed."

Her lips fell open, in astonishment. Jace had always been so self-sufficient, so controlled. It was new and exciting to consider the possibility that she could do this to him, that she could make him feel the same shuddering excitement that filled her when he touched her.

"I think...I was afraid to notice," she whispered shakily, "because I wanted it so much...."

His breath was coming hard and fast now, his eyes going down to her softly parted lips. Like a man in a trance, he bent his head, his eyes staring straight into hers.

The tension between them was almost unbearable. She could feel the warm, smoky sigh of his breath on her lips, the slight mingling scents of soap and cologne as he bent over her, the blazing warmth of his body where her cool hands were pressed against his chest.

"Jason..." she whispered apprehensively.

His open mouth brushed against her lips while he watched her. "Hush," he whispered gently. "I only want to touch you, to taste you, to be sure that you're here and safe and not lying in a field somewhere torn to pieces. God, I've never been so afraid!"

"You shouted at me," she reminded him, the words muffled against his mouth as it brushed and caressed in a maddening, tantalizing motion.

"You'd scared me out of my wits, what did you expect?" he growled. He moved, leaning both arms on the sheet on either side of her, his chest arching over hers as he studied her flushed face. "You little fool, can't you get it into your head that I'm not rational when it comes to you? Does it give you some kind of juvenile kick to knock me off-balance, the way you did in the living room?"

She studied his hard mouth quietly, loving the chiseled perfection of it, the sensations it could cause. "I never realized before that I *could*...knock you off-balance."

His eyes dropped to the brief, almost transparent bodice of her slip. "Lying there so soft and sweet," he murmured, "and I'm making small talk when all I want out of life right now is to strip you down to your skin and taste every silky inch of you."

Her heart turned over. "What time is it?" she asked quickly.

"You're afraid, aren't you?" He lifted his hand and touched, very lightly, the soft swell of her breast with his hard fingers, smiling when she caught them and moved them to her shoulder. "You did that once before," he reminded her. "At that party, years ago. I carried the memory around like a faded photograph for years. You were so deliciously innocent." His eyes darkened, his face tautened. "And now you're a woman, not so innocent, so why pretend?"

She chewed on her lower lip, too weary to deny it, to fight with him. "I'm tired, Jason," she whispered meekly.

He took a deep breath. "And I'm not?" he asked. His eyes searched hers. "I've been pacing up and down in my room, trying to get myself back together. I know that if I try to get some sleep, every time I shut my eyes I'll see the look on your face when I jumped on you about the damned coat."

"But Marguerite..." she began.

"Insisted. I know, Duncan told me, remember?" He smoothed the hair away from her face. "I was worried sick, honey," he said quietly. "and hurt."

"I couldn't hurt you," she whispered curiously.

"Couldn't you?" His eyes dropped to her mouth. "You don't know how much you could hurt me," he murmured, bending. He eased her mouth under his, cherishing it, touching it lightly, gentling it in a silence that was only broken by the sound of a breeze outside the open window and the soft sigh of Jace's breath while he kissed her.

She reached up to hold him, but he caught her hands and spread them against his cool, broad chest, tangling her fingers in the mat of curling dark hair.

"Have you ever learned how to touch a man?" he asked against her parted lips.

She caressed him with nervous, unsure hands while the touch of his tormenting mouth drove her slowly mad.

"Kiss me hard," she whispered achingly, her slitted eyes looking up into his.

"In a minute." A faint triumphant smile touched his mouth. "I like it like this, don't you? Slow and easy, I like to hold back as long as I can, it makes everything more intense," he whispered against her lips. "Come on, honey, don't just lie there and let me do it all. Help me."

She almost blurted out that she didn't know how, that her only intimate experience had been with him. With other men she had never gone beyond kissing.

She opened her mouth to his, and reached up to hold him, to draw his heavy, warm body against hers so that he was half-lying across her, the crushing pressure of his weight dragging a moan from her throat.

"Not so hard, baby," he whispered, drawing back a little to look at her. "It's been a long time since I made any effort to go slow with a woman. Let it be gentle with us, this time."

The words awed her, touched her. She reached up and touched his hard mouth with her fingertip, her dark eyes searching his light ones while her heart hammered in her throat. "I don't know much..." she blurted out, the admission not quite what she meant it to be.

"It's all right," he said quietly. He smoothed her lips under his softly, slowly. "Don't you want to touch me?" he whispered, and his fingers drew against her waist, her rib cage, up to the soft, high curve of her breasts. "God knows, I want to touch you," he added huskily, and his hands moved to cup her soft breasts with a light touch that made her tremble all the same and catch at his fingers wildly.

He drew back, studying the apprehension in her eyes watchfully. "I won't hurt you," he said softly.

"I know. I..." she stared up at him helplessly, "I need time," she whispered.

He drew in a hard, heavy breath, leaning his weight on his forearms as he poised just above her. "You've had seven years," he reminded her.

"You've hated me for seven years," she corrected sadly. "Jason, you can't expect me to...to trust you...to give...."

He reached down and kissed her roughly. "To give yourself to me, why can't you say it?" His eyes narrowed. "All right, I'll accept that. You need time to get used to the idea, and I'll give you that. But not much, Amanda. I've waited longer than I ever intended already, and I'm damned near the end of my rope. I've gone a hell of a long time without a woman."

She gasped at him and would have pursued that, but he bent suddenly and she felt the firm, warm pressure of his mouth against the bare curve of her breast where the strap had fallen away. Her body arched instinctively at the unexpected pressure, at the newness of a man's lips on her body, and she gasped.

"Do you like it?" he murmured against her silky skin, and drew the strap down even farther to seek the deep pink peak with his warm mouth in an intimacy that made her grasp his dark hair with both hands to jerk him away. A mistake, she saw that immediately, because his eyes had a brief and total view of the curves his lips had touched, before she was able to jerk the bodice back in place.

He studied her flaming face with interest. "Was it always in the dark before?" he murmured, smiling. "I'm glad you left at least one first for me. What's that saying about the delight to be found in small packages?"

"You beast!" she whispered, flushing more wildly than ever.

He chuckled softly, watching her jerk the sheet over herself. He sat up, as smug as a tiger with one paw on its prey.

"Small but perfect, love," he said gently, and for a moment he seemed like a stranger, his silver eyes almost gentle, his face faintly kind.

Impulsively, she reached out and touched his bare chest, looking up at him with all the unasked questions in her eyes. "I'm sorry you and Marguerite were worried."

He only nodded. "You'd better get some sleep."

"You had, too," she murmured. "You won't be able to work at all."

"I'll have hell keeping my mind on work, all right," he admitted, staring into her puzzled eyes. He leaned down, his mouth poised just over hers. "Hard, this time," he whispered gruffly, "and open your mouth...."

He crushed her lips under his, fostering a hunger like nothing she'd ever felt before. It was a meeting of mouths that was as intimate as the merging of two souls. She arched up against him, her mouth wild, her nails biting into his shoulders, moaning in a surrender as sweeping as death. She loved him so, wanted him so, and for this instant he was hers. She wanted nothing more than to give him everything she had to give, despite all the arguments, all the harsh words.

He drew back, breathing heavily, his eyes blazing with suppressed desire. He caught her wrists and drew her hands gently away from his shoulders, easing her back down on the pillows.

"I'd rather saw off my right arm than leave you," he said in a husky whisper. "Oh, God, I want you so!"

She caught her trembling lower lip in her teeth, staring up at him helplessly, beyond words.

He drew a heavy breath and leaned down, brushing her mouth lightly with his, a tender caress after the storm. "You could still sleep with me," he remarked quietly, searching her misty eyes. "No strings, just sleep. I'd like to hold you against me, see you lying there in my bed."

The flush went all the way down her body, and he watched it with a passing confusion in his glittering eyes.

"What if your mother or Duncan happened to walk in?" she asked unsteadily, trying to make light of it when she wanted nothing more than to do just as he'd suggested.

He searched her eyes. "Then I'd have to marry you, wouldn't I?" he asked with a faint smile. He got up before she could decide whether or not he was joking, and the moment was lost. He glanced back at her from the open door.

"Sweet dreams, honey. Sleep well. God knows, I won't," he added, his eyes sweeping the length of her body under the thin sheet.

"Good night, Jason," she whispered softly, "or should I say good morning?"

He smiled, then turned and went through the door without looking back. Amanda stared after him for a long time before she turned over and closed her eyes with a sigh.

7
*

She opened her eyes to a shaft of midmorning sunlight that streamed across the fluffy blue coverlet, and as her soft brown eyes stared at the ceiling, the memory of Jace's visit sent tingles of excitement all over her. She threw her legs over the edge of the bed and sat up, staring at the door, her face bright, her eyes brimming with excitement. Jace! Had it really happened? She touched her mouth and looked in the mirror, as if looking for evidence of the kisses he'd pressed against it. There was a faint bruise high on one arm, and she remembered with a thrill of pleasure the blaze of ardor she'd shared with him. It hadn't been a dream after all. But had he felt the same pleasure she had? Or had it all been something he already regretted in the cold light of day? Would he be different? Would he smile instead of scowl, would he be less antagonistic? Or would he hate her even more . . . ?

She got into jeans and a scoop-necked powder blue blouse and hurried downstairs, her hair loose and waving around her shoulders, her eyes full of dreams.

It was past ten o'clock, and she hadn't really expected Jace to be at the breakfast table, but she felt a surge of disappointment anyway when she opened the dining room door and found only Marguerite and Terry there, Terry looking faintly irritated.

"There you are," he sighed. "Look, Mandy, you'll have to handle this account from here on in. Jackson called me a few minutes ago and he doesn't like the television spot we worked up—says it's too 'suggestive.'"

"But his son approved it," she protested.

"Without his permission, it seems," Terry grumbled. He gulped down the rest of his coffee and stood up. "Sorry to leave you like this, but if we lose that account we're in big trouble. It's the largest one we have—I don't need to remind you about that.''

"No, of course not. Don't worry," she said with a smile, "I can take over here."

"I never did get to talk to Jace last night," he grinned back at her. "Maybe you'll have better luck." Then he thanked Marguerite for her hospitality, reminded Amanda to call him at the airport when she got into San Antonio after she finished discussing the account, and hurried away to get a cab.

"You don't sound quite as nervous of Jason as you did," Marguerite murmured, eyeing her with a mischievous gleam in her eyes. "I wonder why?"

Amanda flushed in spite of herself and burst out laughing. "I'll never tell," she murmured.

"I thought he'd get around to showing you how upset he'd been," the older woman remarked as she stirred cream into her hot coffee. "I've never seen him like that. By the way," she added, glancing at Amanda, "I have a delightful surprise for you."

"What?" Amanda asked, all eyes.

"It will have to wait a little," came the mysterious reply, with a smile. "Jason's at the office this morning, but I think he may be in for lunch. Oh, and Duncan's at the dentist." She bit back a smile. "Jason loosened two of his caps."

Marguerite left minutes later for an arts council meeting, and Amanda took advantage of her absence to work on the presentation she planned to make to Jace. She hadn't much hope of his acceptance. He might enjoy making love to her, but she suspected he had a chauvinistic attitude toward women in business, and she was afraid he wouldn't even listen to her. It would be just like him.

Her mind kept going back to the things he'd said, to his explanation of the proposition he'd once made her. He'd actually been asking her to marry him all those years before. She sighed, closing her eyes at the thought. To be his wife, to have the right to touch him whenever she wanted, to run to him when he came home at night and throw herself into his arms, to look after him and see that he got enough rest, to plan her life around his, to buy things for him...she might have had all that, if only she'd been mature enough to realize it wasn't a proposition after all. She'd resented it all these years, and now there was nothing to resent; only something to regret with all her heart. Now she loved him, wanted him, needed him as only a woman could, and he was forever out of reach. He enjoyed the feel of her in his arms. But he still doubted her innocence, and he'd made it very clear he didn't have marriage in mind anymore. He simply wanted to sleep with her. Because now he had money, and she didn't. And he'd never be sure if she wanted him or the wealth she'd lost; he wouldn't take a chance by asking her to marry him again. She knew that.

She was so engrossed in her thoughts that she didn't hear the phone ring until the maid came and said it was for her.

She lifted the receiver on the phone by the sofa, wondering if Terry could be calling so soon after he'd left.

"Hello?" she murmured hesitantly.

"Hello, yourself," came Jace's reply in a voice like brown velvet. "What are you doing?"

"W...working on the ad presentation," she faltered.

"You don't sound very confident," he remarked. "If you don't believe in your own abilities, honey, how do you expect me to?"

"I do have confidence in the agency," she returned, her fingers trembling on the cord. "It's just that...I didn't expect you to call."

"Even after this morning?" he asked softly, and laughter rippled into the receiver. "I've got some nasty scratches on my back because of you."

She felt the heat rush into her cheeks as she remembered the way she'd dug her nails into him so hungrily. "It's your own fault," she whispered, smiling. "Don't make me take all the blame."

"Witch," he chuckled. "Come down to the office about eleven-thirty. I'll take you to lunch."

"I'd like that," she said softly.

"I know something I'd like better," he said bluntly.

"You lecherous man," she teased, feeling somewhat disoriented to hear him talking to her like this.

"Only with you, Miss Carson. You have such a delicious body...."

"Jace!"

"Don't worry, it's not a party line," he laughed. "And my office is soundproof."

"Why?" she asked without thinking.

"So the rest of the staff won't hear the screams when I beat my secretary," he said matter-of-factly.

She burst out laughing. "Do you treat all your employees like that?"

"Only when they don't do as they're told," he returned. "Don't be late. I'm sandwiching you in between a board meeting and a civic club luncheon."

"A luncheon?" she asked. "But you shouldn't be having lunch with me..."

"I'll have coffee at the luncheon and tell them I'm on a diet."

"Nobody will believe that," she murmured. "Not as streamlined as you are."

"So you do notice me?"

"You're very attractive," she breathed, feeling her face flush again as she murmured the words.

There was a satisfied sound from the other end of the line. "Eleven-thirty. Don't forget," he said.

"I won't," she promised, and the line went dead.

She'd never been in the building before. It was a skyscraper in downtown Victoria, huge and imposing, with a fountain and greenery outside and huge trees in pots inside. Jace's office was on the fifth floor. She took the elevator up and walked across the large expanse of soft cream-colored carpet to his secretary's massive, littered desk.

"Is Jace...Mr. Whitehall in?" she asked nervously.

The secretary, a tall brunette with soft blue eyes, smiled at her. "Can't you hear the muffled roar?" she whispered conspiratorially, nodding toward the office, from which the rumble of Jace's deep angry voice was just audible. "A big real estate deal just fell through at the last minute and now Jace is trying to straighten out the mess. It's been something or other all morning long. Sorry, I didn't mean to cry all over you. Do you really want to see him?" she finished with wildly arched eyebrows.

"Oh, yes, I'm very brave," Amanda promised with a tiny grin.

"Angela, get me the file on the Bronson Corporation," Jace snapped over the intercom. "And let me know the minute Miss Carson gets here."

Angela looked at Amanda, who nodded, and spoke into the intercom, "She's here; shall I send her in, or does she need something to stand behind?"

"Don't be cute, Miss Regan," he said.

She stepped into his office hesitantly, her heart racing, her eyes unsure as conflicting memories tore at her. He didn't look any different; his face was as hard as usual, his eyes giving nothing away in that narrow gaze that went from the V neck of her amber dress down the full skirt to her long tanned legs and her small feet encased in strappy beige sandals. But last night had seemed to be a turning point for Amanda, and she wondered if Jace really was as untouched by it as he seemed. If last night hadn't affected him, would he revert to the old antagonism and start taunting her as he had before? She clutched her purse nervously as the secretary smiled at her, winked and closed the door on her way out.

Jace was wearing a deep brown suit with a chocolate striped shirt and complementing tie, and his dark hair was just slightly ruffled, as if he'd been running an impatient hand through it. He looked so vibrantly masculine that she wanted to reach out and touch him, and that response frightened her.

"Thinking of running back out?" he asked quietly.

She shrugged her shoulders and smiled hesitantly. "Your secretary thought I might need a shield."

"Anyone else might. Not you." He got up and moved

around the desk, his slow, graceful stride holding her gaze until he was standing just in front of her.

"Hi," she said softly, meeting his eyes with apprehension in her own.

He leaned his hands on either side of her against the door, trapping her, so close that she could feel the warmth of his tall, muscular body, catch the scent of his tangy, expensive cologne.

"Hi," he murmured, and something new was in his eyes, something she could barely define. Attraction, yes, perhaps even sensual hunger, but there was something else in that silvery gaze, too, and she couldn't decide exactly what it was.

He reached down and touched his cool, firm lips lightly to hers, drawing back just a breath to watch her.

"Just once," he murmured, "why don't you kiss me?"

She caught her breath at the idea of it, and the temptation was too great to resist. She clutched her small purse in one hand and held on to his sleeve with the other, going on tiptoe to press her lips softly against his.

He nipped at her lower lip with his teeth, a tantalizing, soft pressure that made her hungry. "You know what I like," he murmured under his breath.

She did, and almost without conscious effort, both arms went up around him while she nuzzled his mouth with hers to part his chiseled lips, letting the tip of her tongue trace, lightly, the long, slow curve of his mouth. Against her softness, she could feel the sudden heavy drum of his heart, hear the roughness of his breath.

"Like this, Jason?" she whispered against his mouth.

"Like this," he murmured, letting his body press her back against the smooth wood of the door, its hard contours fitting themselves expertly to hers. He crushed her soft mouth under his, taking control, the hunger in him almost tangible in the hot, tense silence that followed. A soft, strange sound whispered out of her throat as the madness burned into her mind, her body, and she felt the powerful muscles contract against her, the warmth of his body burning where it touched her in a long aching caress.

He drew back a breath to look down at her flushed face, her passion-glazed eyes. "Now you know," he murmured in a husky deep tone.

"Know what?" she murmured blankly.

"Why the room is soundproof," he chuckled softly.

She flushed, dropping her eyes to his strong brown throat.

"What sweet little noises you make when I make love to you," he whispered against her forehead, easing the crush of his body. "It's good between us, Amanda. You're not a nervous little virgin anymore, you don't cringe away when I touch you. I like that."

If he only knew the truth! she thought with a twinge of pain at the words. She knew only what she'd learned from him.

He glanced at the thin gold watch on his wrist. "We'd better go, if you don't want to be rushed through the first course. I've only got an hour."

"Are you sure you want to..." she began.

He bent and kissed her half-open mouth hard, springing back from the door in the same breath. "I'm sure. Hungry?"

She smiled shyly up at him. "Ravenous," she murmured.

He chuckled, glancing at her soft, slightly swollen mouth. "What an admission," he remarked, and laughed outright at the expression on her face. "Come on, honey, let's go."

"My lipstick!" she whispered as he started to open the door.

He studied her mouth. "You don't need it," he told her. "You're quite lovely enough without all that paint."

"That wasn't what I meant," she replied, staring up at him. "You've got it all over you."

He reached for his handkerchief, handed it to her and stood watching her intently while she wiped it away from his lips and cheek, his firm hands at her waist making her so nervous she fumbled slightly.

"Now," she murmured, handing him back the soiled handkerchief. "Your guilty secret is safe with me."

He chuckled deeply. "You little horror. What makes you think I feel guilty?"

"You didn't want anyone to see the lipstick," she reminded him. "I should have let you walk out there like that. It would have been an inspiration to your secretary."

"She doesn't kiss me," he told her.

She tried not to look too pleased. "She's very pretty," she murmured.

"Her boyfriend has a black belt in karate and he runs a very reputable newspaper," he told her.

She couldn't repress a grin. "Oh."

"Jealous of me, Mandy?" he asked, opening the door for her.

"Murderously," she whispered coquettishly, stepping out into the waiting room before he had time to get even.

He took her to a plush restaurant with burgundy carpeting and white linen tablecloths and horseshoe-shaped chairs upholstered with genuine leather. She ordered a chef's salad, jumping ahead of Jace before he could order for both of them, and he gave her a meaningful glare as he gave his own order of steak and potatoes.

"I'm liberated," she smilingly reminded him when the waitress left.

He glowered at her, leaning back to light a cigarette and blow out a thick cloud of smoke. "So am I. What about it?" he asked.

She laughed at that, her nervous fingers toying with her water glass. "I thought I'd irritated you."

"Honey, I'll admit that I think women look better in skirts than they do wearing pants, but I'll be the first to say that they are every bit as capable in business as men are."

That got her attention. Her lovely brown eyes opened wide. "I didn't realize you thought that way."

"I told you once, Amanda, you've never really known me at all," he remarked quietly.

"So it seems." She gripped the glass tighter. "Would you let me tell you why I think my ad agency could handle that Florida investment of yours and Duncan's?'' she persisted.

He rolled the cigarette between his fingers. "Go ahead."

"All right." She leaned forward on her forearms, watching the lights play on his dark hair. "You're developing a resort in inland Florida. It doesn't border on the ocean or the gulf, it isn't even on a river. It's near a large lake, though, and it's in a very picturesque area of central Florida surrounded by citrus groves and some cattle ranching. Why not let us plan a campaign around the retirement concept? It's in a perfect location," she went on, noticing the interest he was showing. "There's peace and quiet, and no resorts or tourist traps nearby to draw hordes of visitors every year. Since you're incorporating a shopping mall and gardens into the complex, it would be literally a city in itself. People are flocking to Arizona and places farther west than Texas to get sun and year-round peace and quiet along with it. Why not sell them serenity and natural beauty?"

He pursed his chiseled lips. "What kind of advertising did you have in mind?" he asked, and there was no condescension in his tone.

"You're planning to open the complex in six months, aren't you?" she asked, and he nodded. "Then this is the perfect time to do some feature material and work up ads for the more sophisticated magazines, those which appeal to an older, financially independent segment of the reading populace. There are two daily newspapers and three large radio stations, plus a weekly newspaper which all impact on the area where the complex is located. We'll do a multimedia ad campaign targeted to reach all those audiences. Then we'll get the figures on where the largest number of new Florida residents come from and send brochures to prominent real estate offices in those northern cities. We'll develop a theme for the complex, a logo, have a grand opening and get the governor or several politicians to make speeches, send invitations to the press, and—"

"Hold it!" he laughed, watching the excitement brighten her eyes. "Can I afford this saturation?"

She named a figure and both his eyebrows went up. "I hardly expected a figure that reasonable from you," he said bluntly.

Her eyes widened. "Why not?"

He shrugged. "I've already been approached by an ad agency out of New York." His eyes met hers. "The figure they named was several thousand more."

She snapped her fingers with a sigh. "Oh, drat!" she said with mock irritation.

He chuckled at that, but the smile quickly faded. "Who'd be handling the account, Amanda, you or your... partner?"

"Both of us," she replied, "although I have the journalism degree," she added with a smile, "so I do most of the writing. Terry's forte is art and layout and mechanicals."

He blinked. "Mechanicals?"

"For the printer. Press-ready copy."

"And what if you launch this campaign and I don't sell condominiums?" he asked matter-of-factly.

"I throw myself under the wheels of your Mercedes while singing, 'What do I say, dear, after I say I'm sorry.'"

He finished his cigarette and crushed it out with a faint smile playing on his chiseled lips.

"Well?" she asked impatiently.

He looked up and met her eyes just as the waitress came toward them with a heavily laden tray. "I'll think about it and let you know at the party at the Sullevans'. Fair enough?"

She sighed. "Fair enough."

The meal was tantalizing; she hadn't realized until she started eating how hungry she was. She finished her salad, and refused dessert, lingering over thick, rich coffee while Jace attacked an enormous strawberry shortcake overflowing with fresh whipped cream.

"Calories, calories," she sighed, hating the sight of the delicious thing.

He smiled at her over his spoon. "I don't have to watch my waistline. I run it all off."

"I know. You work all the time."

"Not all the time," he reminded her with a pointed glance at her mouth.

She lowered her blushing face to her coffee cup.

Jace pulled into the parking lot behind the Whitehall building and followed Amanda's instructions to pull up short just in front of the small compact car she'd borrowed from Marguerite.

"Thank you for lunch," she said, "and for listening about the account."

"My pleasure, Miss Carson," he replied, his eyes searching her face quietly. "We'll take in a show at the Parisienne tonight. There's a trio there I think you'll enjoy, and we can dance."

Her heart leaped up into her throat. "Me?" she whispered.

He leaned over and brushed his mouth tantalizingly against hers in a kiss just brief enough to leave her feeling empty when he drew away.

"You," he murmured gently. His eyes searched hers. "We're going to talk tonight."

"About what?" she asked dazedly.

"About you and me, honey," he replied curtly, "and where we go from here. After what happened last night, I'm not going to let you run away again."

"But, Jace—"

"I don't have the time right now. Out you get, doe-eyes, I've got work to do. We'll talk about it tonight. Wear something sexy," he added with a wicked grin.

She opened the door and closed it, sticking out her tongue at him. He chuckled, waving as she put her car into gear and roared away.

Her spirits were soaring as she drove back to Casa Verde. What could Jace want to talk about? Marriage, perhaps? She drifted off into a delightful daydream, seeing herself in white satin and Jace in a tuxedo, standing be-

fore a minister in a church with stained-glass windows. If
only! To marry Jace, to share his name, his home, his
bed, his children . . . it would be the culmination of every
dream she'd ever had. Of course, she reminded herself,
he could be about to make a proposition of an altogether different kind. But she didn't think so. Jace's eyes
had been too intent, his kisses too caring, for it to be only
lust that he felt. No, he had something permanent in
mind, he must have. Her eyes lit up like candles in a dark
room. How magical it would be if he loved her, too, if he
felt the same devastating excitement that she felt when
she was with him, touching him, holding him. Please, let
it be, she prayed silently, let it be, let it be!

She pulled up at the entrance of Casa Verde and rushed
up the steps, all the dreams shimmering in her eyes as she
opened the front door.

"Is that you, dear?" Marguerite called. "In the living
room!"

She followed the voice, her mouth open to tell
Marguerite what a lovely lunch she'd had with Jason,
when she saw the second person in the room.

"See? I told you I had a surprise for you!" Marguerite
exclaimed, her dark eyes lighting up merrily.

"Hello, darling," Beatrice Carson greeted her daughter, rising in a cloud of amber chiffon to float across the
room, her blond hair in a high coiffure, her soft brown
eyes full of love and laughter.

Amanda allowed herself to be embraced and fussed
over, numbly, her mind spinning off into limbo as she
realized the problems this was going to create. Things had
been going so beautifully, Jason had been so different.
And now Bea was here, and all the lovely dreams were
shredding. Jason would think she'd sent for her mother,
he'd never believe that Marguerite had done it. He'd be
furious, because he hated Amanda's mother, he always
had.

"Well, don't you want to know why I'm here?" Bea
asked in her lovely soft voice.

"Uh, why are you here, Mother?" Amanda
asked obligingly.

"I'm getting married, darling! You're going to have a father!" Bea gushed.

Amanda sat down. She had to. It was too much, too soon. "Married?"

"Yes, darling," her mother said, sitting down beside her to catch her hands and hold them tightly. Bea's fingers were cold, and Amanda knew she was nervous. "To Reese Bannon. He asked me two days ago, and I said yes. You'll like him. He's a very strong man, very capable, and you can come and stay with us whenever you like."

"But...why have you come to Casa Verde?" Amanda breathed.

"Marguerite kindly offered to help me pick out my trousseau and plan the wedding," Bea replied with a beaming smile. "And I knew you'd want to be included as well. It's going to be a small affair, in Nassau, and we're having a reception afterward at the house. It's lovely, dear, he calls it Sea Jewel and it has its own private beach with lots of sea grape trees and poincianas and the water is such an incredible green and blue and aqua all mixed and sparkling...you'll simply love it!"

"When are you getting married, Mother?" Amanda asked, just beginning to realize that Reese would inherit the responsibility for her mother and her mother's debts.

"Next week!" Bea sighed. "I wanted more time, but Reese was simply adamant, so I gave in. I'm so excited!"

"Yes, so am I," Amanda smiled, pressing her mother's fingers. Bea was such a child, so full of ups and downs, so sparkling bright, like an amber jewel. Amanda couldn't help loving her, even while she blanched at some of her escapades and spending sprees.

"Mother, about the trousseau...we don't have very much in the bank..." Amanda began cautiously.

"Oh, I'm buying the trousseau, it's my wedding gift," Marguerite said with a happy sigh. "I can't wait to get started. Bea, we simply must go to Saks tomorrow morning early. There's so little time...!"

"Yes, indeed," Bea agreed, and launched into the reception plans.

Amanda sat beside her, listening, smiling now and then at her mother's exuberance, and only going upstairs when the afternoon had drifted away to change for supper and worry about Jace's reaction. She had a horrible premonition that he wasn't going to be at all pleased.

She dressed carefully in a becoming gray skirt with an embroidered pink blouse, noting with pleasure the way it molded her slender body. The fit was perfect, and though the clothes were two years old, they didn't show it. Amanda took excellent care of her wardrobe, making innovative alterations to keep it up to date. A scarf here, some jewelry there, the addition of a stylish blouse to an old but classic suit made all the difference. Shoes had been a problem at first, but she quickly learned to buy at the end of the season, when prices were slashed. She never bought anything except during sales. She couldn't afford to.

She was just running a brush through her long hair when there was a slight tap on the door and her mother came in, vividly captivating in a pale pink dress that highlighted her rosy complexion and exquisitely coiffed hair.

"I thought we might go downstairs together," Bea suggested softly. "I...well, I know Jason doesn't like me, and he's much less likely to say something if I'm with you," she added with a nervous smile. "You haven't told him about the bull, have you, darling?"

"No, Mother," Amanda replied soothingly. She put down the brush and hugged her petite mother. "I'm so glad you've found someone. I know how lonely you've been the last few years."

"Not so very lonely, my dear," Bea replied. She touched her daughter's cheek. "I had you, after all."

Amanda smiled. "We had each other."

Bea nodded. She studied her daughter's face intently. "Marguerite said that you and Jason are...softening toward one another. Is that so?"

Amanda blushed fiercely and turned away. "I'm not sure. I don't know if he even likes me."

"Amanda..." Bea bit her lower lip. "Dear, I've often wondered if all that arguing between you wasn't really an indication of something much deeper than dislike. You've shied away from Jason for many years. I'd like to think it wasn't because of my quite ridiculous attitude toward him when you were in your teens. I was a dreadful snob. I only wish I'd realized it at the time, before the damage was done."

"What damage?"

"Between you and Jace." Bea studied the carpet. "Amanda, men like Jason Whitehall are very rare creatures. The man's man isn't popular these days, women much prefer softer men who cry and hurt and make mistakes and apologize on bended knee, and that's all very well, I suppose. It's a new world, a new generation, with new and better ideas of what life should be." Her eyes were wistful for a moment. "But men like Jason are a breed apart. They make their own rules and they don't bend. A woman who's lucky enough to be loved by a man like that is . . . blessed." She drew a long, quiet sigh. "Oh, Mandy, don't run from him if you love him," she burst out. "Don't let the rift I've caused between you blind you to Jason's good qualities. I lost my happiness, but you still have a chance for yours."

"Mother, I don't understand what you're saying," Amanda whispered blankly.

"You're such a good girl, my dear," Bea murmured, her eyes sad and full of vanished dreams. "But it takes so much more than noble intentions with some men...."

"Bea, are you in there?" Marguerite called.

Bea looked faintly irritated. "Yes, dear, we're coming!" She patted Amanda's arm. "I'll try to explain it to you later. I must tell you something, a secret I've kept from you. We'll talk later, all right?"

"Yes, darling," Amanda replied with a puzzled smile. "Let's go down."

They were sitting in the living room, waiting for dinner to be served, when Jason came in from the office. He looked tired and out of sorts, his silver eyes glittering in a face that showed every day of its age.

He caught sight of Bea as soon as he entered the room, and he seemed to explode.

"What the hell are you doing here?" he asked the stunned woman. Her eyes shot to Amanda's white face. "A little premature, wasn't it, calling Mama? I don't remember making any promises."

Amanda started to speak, but Bea was quicker. "I invited myself," she told him, rising like a little blond wraith to face him bravely. "I'm getting married, Jason. I came to invite my daughter to the wedding."

"Oh, you're marrying this one?" he asked cuttingly, his eyes openly hating her. "Will you be as faithful to him as you were to that poor damned fool you married last time?"

"Jason, where are your manners?" Marguerite burst out. "Bea's my friend!"

"Like hell she is," Jason replied coldly, eyeing Beatrice, and Amanda saw her mother's face go sheet-white.

"What are you talking about?" Marguerite persisted.

"Ask your...friend," Jason growled. "She knows, don't you, Mrs. Carson?" He emphasized the "Mrs.," making an insult of it.

"Leave my mother alone," Amanda said, standing. Her eyes fenced with his. "You've no right to insult her like that. You don't know her."

"Honey, I know more about her than you'd believe," he replied with a cold smile. "Remind me to tell you one day, it'll open your eyes."

"You...you...cowboy!" Amanda threw at him, her lower lip trembling, her eyes bright with tears.

"That sounds more like old times," he told Amanda, something like a shadow passing over his face. "I like it better when you drop the pretense. I told you once, and I'll tell you again, you aren't getting your hands on my money." He glanced harshly at Bea. "And you might as well send Mama home. I'm not financing her wedding. And neither are you, Mother," he informed Marguerite coldly. "If you so much as try to buy that well-heeled slut a handkerchief at any department store in town, I'll close down every account you've got." He turned on his heel and walked out the door, his spine rigid with dislike and temper.

Marguerite threw her arms around Bea. "Oh, my dear, I'm so sorry! I don't know what's the matter with him!"

Bea wept like a child, tears running down her cheeks. Amanda put her arms around her, taking her from Marguerite, and held her tight.

"It's all right, Mama," she cooed, as she had so many times. "It's going to be all right."

But even as she said it, she knew better. Her world was upside down, Jace hated her again, and she only wished she knew why. Could he really hold a grudge so long, from childhood, and hate Beatrice for something she'd said to him years ago? Why did he hate her so passionately! And why in the world did he call her a slut? Heaven knew, Bea might be a lot of things, but that wasn't one of them. She was so proper, always socially correct. She would never dream of soiling her reputation with an extramarital affair. Amanda rocked Bea gently, her eyes meeting Marguerite's pained ones over the thin shoulder. Jace could be so cruel. Her eyes closed. How could he say such things after the passion that had burned between them like a wildfire out of control? She'd thought that he might care for her, especially after the New York trip, after the kisses they'd shared. But he hadn't cared. He didn't care. And how was she going to protect her fragile mother from his unreasonable hatred? She felt like crying herself. The day had begun with such promise, only to end in desolation.

The three women sat down to supper without Jace, who came back downstairs an hour later dressed in brown slacks, a tweed jacket and a white roll neck shirt. He walked out of the house without a word, probably on his way to see Tess, Amanda guessed.

"Don't look so tragic, darling," Bea said gently, sensing her daughter's depression. "It will all work out. Things do, you know."

Amanda tried to smile. "Of course they will," she agreed numbly.

"I could just strangle my son," Marguerite said under her breath, stabbing viciously at a piece of steak on her plate. "Of all the colossal gall ... !"

"Don't dear," Bea pleaded, touching her friend's manicured hand lightly. "Jace can't help the way he feels about me, and there is some justification. After all..." she bit her lip jerkily. "After all," she tried again with a pained glance at Amanda, "it was I who ran into his bull, not Amanda. She wasn't even driving."

Marguerite's eyes widened. "You? But Amanda said..."

"She was trying to protect me. No," Bea sighed miserably, "that's not true. I begged her to protect me. Knowing how Jace dislikes me, I was afraid he'd deny me the hospitality of Casa Verde, so I let poor Amanda take the blame for it all...to my shame," she finished weakly. Her lovely dark eyes misted with tears as she looked at her shocked daughter. "I know I've been a trial to you, my dear. I seem to have walked around in a trance since your... since your father's death."

"That doesn't give Jason the right to call you foul names," Marguerite interrupted, her own dark eyes blazing. "I think it's outrageous and as soon as he calms down, I'm going to tell him so."

Amanda couldn't help the brief smile that twitched her lips. Marguerite was no braver than she when it came to facing Jace's fiery temper.

The next day passed in a foggy haze, with Bea and Amanda cautiously keeping close to Marguerite's side and avoiding Jace as much as possible. He managed to find plenty to keep him busy around the ranch and at his office, but the eyes that occasionally glanced Amanda's way were icy gray, cold. It was as if that magical night had never happened, as if he'd never touched her with tenderness. And Bea, for all her usual gaiety, seemed crushed, almost guilty. Reese Bannon had promised to wire her the money for her trousseau, despite Marguerite's protests that she wanted the privilege of buying it. The two older woman spent most of the day shopping, while Amanda kept to her room and mourned for what might have been.

Bea and Marguerite went to visit a mutual friend that evening after supper, and Amanda returned to her room to change into slacks and a blouse. When she went back down, wandering out onto the darkened porch to enjoy the cool peace of evening, a movement caught her eye and made her start. She'd reached the big rocking chair at the side of the porch when a quiet figure detached itself from the swing and stood up.

"Don't run away," Jace said quietly. "I'm not armed."

She hated the bitterness in his deep voice. The very sound of it was like an ache in her soul. She could hardly bear to be near him after the harsh accusations he'd made. But she sat down in the huge, bare wood rocker and leaned back. The woven cane made a soft, creaking sound as she began to rock. The sound, combining with the murmur of crickets and frogs, was a wild lullaby in the sweet-scented darkness.

There was a snap and a grating sound, as Jace lit a cigarette. She could see its orange tip out of the corner of her eye.

"I didn't think you'd be at home," she remarked coolly.

"Obviously, or you'd still be hiding in your room," he said curtly.

She leaned her head back against the rocking chair, gazing out into the darkness. Jace made her feel like a tightly wound rubber band. She felt as remote from him as the moon when he drew into himself like this.

"You sat out here with me once before on a moonless night," he remarked suddenly, his voice deep and quiet in the stillness. "Remember, Amanda?"

"The night your father died," she recalled, feeling again the emptiness of the rooms without Jude Whitehall's domineering presence, the weeping of Marguerite and Bea. . . . "We didn't say two words."

He laughed shortly. "You sat beside me and held my hand. Nothing more than that. No tears or wailing, or promises of comfort. You just sat and held my hand."

"It was all I could think to do," she admitted. "I knew how deeply you cared about him...even more than Duncan did, I think. You aren't an easy man to offer comfort to, Jason. Even then I expected you to freeze me out, or tell me to go away. But you didn't."

"Men don't like being vulnerable, honey, didn't you know?" he asked in a strangely gentle tone, and she remembered another time when he'd made a similar remark. "I wouldn't have let anyone else near me that night, Amanda, not even Mother, do you know that? You've always managed to get close when I'd have slapped anyone else away." He drew on his cigarette. "I'd let you bandage a cut that I wouldn't let a doctor touch."

She felt her heart pounding. Watch out, she reminded herself, this is just a game to him, and he's a master player. Don't let him hurt you.

She stood up with a jerky motion. "I'd better go in. It's getting late."

"Amanda, talk to me!" he growled.

"About what?" she managed tearfully. "About my mother? About myself? We're sluts, you said so, and you know everything, don't you, Jason God Almighty Whitehall!"

She turned and ran for the front door, hearing his harsh, muffled curse behind her.

More restless than ever the next morning, Amanda wandered down to the stable to look at a new snowy white Arabian foal. It brought back memories of the old days on her father's ranch when she'd spent hours watching the newborn foals, never tiring of their amusing antics. This one was a colt, on wobbly little legs that looked far too long for him.

She was so involved in the sight of the colt and his mother that she didn't hear the sound of approaching horses' hooves. She did hear the rapidly nearing footsteps a moment later, though, and turned just in time to see Jace coming down the wide aisle, his booted feet sinking into the fresh, honey-colored woodchips that covered the floor.

He moved with a slow, easy grace that was as much a part of him as that worn black Stetson pulled low on his forehead. She loved the very sight of him, but she turned away from it, hurting all over again at his insults, his rejection.

"All alone?" he asked curtly. "Where's brother Duncan this morning?"

"At the office," she said tightly.

"And the others?" he added, refusing to even speak Bea's name.

"Gone to town shopping." She glared at him. "And not to spend your money."

He ignored that, watching the colt. "Not afraid of me, kitten?"

"Or of twenty like you," she shot back, turning away, too proud to let her very real apprehension show.

She leaned over the stall gate and stared down at the colt, who was suckling his mother. The white mare stood with her ears pricked and alert, watching the humans closely.

Jace moved to the gate beside her, so close that his arm touched hers where it rested on the rough wood, and a sweet, reckless surge of delight filled her.

"Do you still show them?" she asked, hoping to change the subject.

"I don't have the time, honey," he said, and his voice was no longer angry. "The Johnsons' daughter enters one or two a year on the horse show circuit, and I've got a few trophies from bygone days, but most of my stock is at stud. I let Johnson handle the show circuit. All I do is take credit for the trophies."

She feathered a glance at him, amazed at the humorous note in his voice. "Who shows you?" she asked lightly, surprising him.

He raised an eyebrow at her and shoved his hat back over his dark, unruly hair. "Daring, aren't you?"

She shook back her silvery blond hair until it drifted around her shoulders in a cloud. "I like to live dangerously once in a while," she agreed.

He flicked her cheek with a lean finger. "Not on my land," he cautioned. "I wouldn't want to be responsible for your getting hurt." He cut a hard gaze down at her, holding her eyes deliberately in a heady silence.

Her lips parted slightly from the shock of it, and his eyes caught the movement, darting to the soft pink mouth with unnerving quickness.

She fought down the longing to move closer to him, to feel his hard body against hers, to tempt his mouth into violence . . . having experienced the skill of that beautiful mouth, she was unbearably hungry for it. She tore her eyes away from his and struggled to control her quick, unsteady breathing.

"The, uh, the foal is lovely," she said unsteadily.

He moved closer, coming up behind her to make retreat impossible, his muscular arms resting on the gate on either side of her to imprison her there. His body was warm, and she could feel its heat, smell the tangy cologne he used drifting down into her nostrils.

"Do . . . you have any more?" she continued when he didn't answer her.

She felt his breath in her hair. "You smell of wildflowers," he murmured sensuously.

"It's my shampoo," she whispered inanely.

He shifted, bringing her body into slight, maddening contact with his. She could feel his powerful legs touching hers, his broad chest at her shoulder blades.

"How many Arabians do you have now?" she asked in a high, unfamiliar voice.

"Enough," he murmured, bending to nuzzle aside the hair at her neck and press his warm, open mouth to the quivering tender flesh he found under it.

"Jason!" she gasped involuntarily.

His chest rose and fell heavily against her back. His mouth moved up, nibbling at her ear, her temple. "God, your skin is soft," he whispered huskily. "Like velvet. Satin."

Her fingers gripped the gate convulsively while she fought for control and lost. Her throat felt as if there were rocks in it.

Even while she was protesting, her body was melting back against his, yielding instinctively.

His hands moved, gripping her tiny waist painfully.

"Oh, Jason, you mustn't!" she managed in a hoarse plea. "Not after all the things you've said!" she accused, hating him for what he could do to her.

"I don't give a damn what I said," he growled in a haunted tone. "I want you so much, I ache with it!"

She struggled, but he whipped her around and pinned her against the gate with the carefully controlled weight of his body. His eyes burned down into hers, his face taught with longing.

Tears of intense emotion welled in the wide brown eyes that pleaded with him. Her soft hands pressed against the unyielding hardness of his chest.

"Are these games really necessary?" he asked curtly. "I know what I do to you, I can feel it. Do you have to pretend? I don't mind if you're experienced, damn it, it doesn't matter!"

She shoved against him furiously, only to find herself helpless in those hurting, powerful hands. "Let me go, Jason Whitehall!" she blurted out. "I'm not experienced, I'm not easy, and I'm not pretending!"

His nostrils flared as he held her rigid body. "Do you expect me to believe that? My God, you were wild in my arms, as hungry for it as I was."

"I don't sleep around!" she exclaimed.

"Your mother does," he returned fiercely.

She glared at him. "More of your unfounded slander, cowboy?"

His eyes glittered dangerously. "I found her in my father's bedroom," he fired back, contempt in every hard line of his face. "A month before he died. She was still married to that poor, cold fish of a father of yours."

Her face went stone white. It was unthinkable, that Bea would have behaved like that with Jude Whitehall! He was lying, he had to be! But there wasn't any trace of deception in his expression. He meant it!

"My mother?" she breathed incredulously.

"Your mother," he returned coldly. "The only consolation was that no one knew—not Duncan, especially not my mother. But I did," he added gruffly. "And every time I saw her, I wanted to wring her soft neck!"

She licked her lips, feeling their dryness with a sense of unreality. "It wasn't because she snubbed you," she whispered, knowing the truth now.

"No. It was because she was carrying on an affair with my father, and I couldn't stop it. All I could do was try to protect my mother. I did that, but your mother took years off his life. She robbed us all."

She lowered her eyelids wearily. It was the last straw. And she had never even suspected!

"And you think I'm like her," she whispered. "That was why you assumed I was sleeping with Terry."

"Something like that." He laughed shortly. "You don't think it was because I was jealous?"

She shook her head with a bitter little smile. "That would never occur to me." She drew in a deep, ragged breath. "I'll pack and leave today."

His hands tightened, hurting. "Not yet. What about your precious account? Your *partner* won't be pleased if you let it slip through your fingers."

Her eyes flew open, tormented and hurting. "Why don't you just shoot me?" she asked, tears in her eyes. "You've made life hell for me for so long…and Mother and her spending sprees . . . now you tell me . . . she was cheating on my father . . . oh, God, I wish I was dead!"

Panic striken, mad with wounded pride and betrayal, she broke away from him with a surge of maniacal strength, and ran outside. Catching sight of Jace's horse tethered by the door, she vaulted into the saddle before he could stop her. Ignoring his curt command to rein in, she leaned forward, over the silky mane, and gave the spirited horse its head, blindly hanging on as they plunged into the nearby forest and kept going.

The animal reacted to its rider's emotional upheaval by putting on a frantic burst of speed and going too close under a low-hanging limb. Amanda, with some inner warning, looked up through tear-blinding eyes, but she was too late to save herself. The limb came straight at her, and she felt the rough scrape of wood, the jar of impact, just before a numbness sent her plummeting down into a strange darkness.

8

*

Duncan was sitting beside her when she opened her eyes to blazing sunlight, medical apparatus, and a wicked headache.

"I won't ask the obvious question," she said weakly and tried to smile. "But I would like to know who clubbed me."

Duncan smiled back, pressing the slender hand lying on top of the crisp white hospital sheet. "A pecan limb, actually," he said. "You didn't duck."

"I didn't have time." She felt her forehead and touched her throbbing brow, aware of painful bruising all over her body. "Have I been here long?"

"Overnight," he replied. "Jace's been pacing the halls like a madman, muttering and smoking, and being generally abusive to every member of the hospital staff who came within snarling distance."

Jace! It all came back. The argument, the accusation he'd made, her own shock at finding out, finally, the reason he hated her and Bea so much. Her dark eyes closed.

Duncan watched her closely, frowning slightly. "What did he say to you, Mandy?" he asked quietly.

"Nothing," she lied.

"Don't lie to me," he said without malice. "You've never done it before. He hurt you, didn't he?"

"What happened was between Jace and me," she told him. Her wan, drawn face made a smile for him. "I could just as easily have fallen off. I ran into a limb, that's all."

"He acts guilty as hell," he said, studying her. "Like a hunted man. He's been in and out of here six times already, just looking at you."

"I'm not telling you anything, Duncan, you might as well give up."

He sighed angrily. "Your mother will be by later," he said finally, giving in, but with reluctance. "She was here earlier."

"When can I go home?"

He shrugged. "They want to do some more tests."

"I don't need any more tests," she said stiffly, already crumpling under visions of a mountainous hospital bill that her meager insurance wouldn't pay.

Duncan read her worried expression accurately. "Don't start worrying about money," he told her. "The bill is our responsibility."

"The devil it is!" she burst out, sitting up so fast she almost fell off the bed. She pushed back her straggly hair, and her dark eyes burned. "Oh, no, Duncan, I'm not having Jason Whitehall throw another debt up to me."

He caught onto that immediately. "What debt has he been throwing up to you?" he asked sharply.

She flushed, and averted her gaze to the venetian blinds letting slitted beams of sunlight into the cheery yellow room.

"How nice of you to come and visit me, Duncan," she said sweetly. "When can I go home?" she asked again.

He sighed with exasperation. "I'll ask the doctor, all right?"

"Tell him I said I'm leaving in the morning, and he can take his tests and . . ." she began.

"Now, now," he said soothingly. He reached over and pushed the hair away from her forehead. "God, you're going to have a bruise there!" he murmured.

"Purple, I hope," she said lightly. "I've got a gorgeous cotton frock with purple flowers, it'll be a perfect match."

"You," he grinned, "are incorrigible."

"Oh, being slammed in the head by trees does wonders for me," she agreed saucily, smiling up at him from her pillow.

He stuck his hands in the pockets of his beige trousers, shaking his dark head. "I wouldn't recommend trying it too often," he said. "You could have too much of a good thing."

She lifted a hand to her forehead and winced. "You can say that again. How's Jace's horse, by the way?"

"Fine," he replied. "Thanks to you. He didn't hit his head."

She started to answer him, but the door swung open and Jace walked in. He was still in a nasty temper, it showed in the hard lines of his face, his blazing darkened silver eyes. But he looked haggard, too, as if he hadn't slept. His dark brown roll neck sweater and cream-colored slacks looked rumpled as well. And his hair was tousled, as if his hands had worried it.

Amanda stiffened involuntarily, looking vaguely like a small wild creature in a trap. Jace's sharp gaze didn't miss the expression that flitted across her pale features, and it tightened his jaw.

"How are you?" he asked curtly.

"Just dandy, thanks," she said with bravado. She even smiled, although her eyes were like dead wood.

"The doctor said you had a close call," he added quietly, ignoring Duncan. "If you'd been sitting a fraction of an inch higher in the saddle, you'd have broken your damned neck."

"Sorry to disappoint you," she said in a ghostly voice, her lower lip trembling with the hurt she felt as she met his cold, unfeeling gaze.

He turned away, glaring at Duncan. "I thought you had a meeting with Donavan on that Garrison contract."

Duncan bristled, one of the few times Amanda had ever seen him stand up to Jace. "The contract can damned well wait. Maybe you can turn off your emotions, but I can't. I was worried about Amanda."

"She looks spry enough to me," he bit off.

"Easy words for the man who put her in the hospital!" Duncan threw at him.

Jace's eyes exploded. He moved toward Duncan, checking himself immediately with that iron control that was part of him. His eyes shifted to Amanda, blaming, accusing, but she only lifted her chin and stared back at him.

"I put myself here, Duncan," she said with quiet dignity. "Don't blame your brother for that."

"Since when did I ask you to defend me?" Jace demanded hotly.

She dropped her eyes to the green hospital gown with its rounded neckline showing above the sheet that was drawn up to her waistline. She only had two gowns with her on this trip, neither of which was suitable to be seen in. She was glad no one had bothered to bring one for her to wear.

"God forbid that I should stand up for you," she said in a husky whisper, feeling the whip of the words even through the daze of drugs and the headache.

"Why don't you go back to the ranch and fuss over your damned horse?" Duncan asked shortly. "He's part of the blood stock, remember, worth far more than a mere woman!"

"How would you like to step outside with me?" Jace asked in a goaded tone.

"Please!" Amanda pleaded, holding her head as the pain swept a wave of nausea over her. "Please don't fight. Both of you, just go away and let me groan in peace."

"Can I bring you anything?" Duncan said tightly.

She shook her head, refusing to open her eyes and look at either one of them. "I'll be fine. Just tell them I'm checking out in the morning, if you don't mind, Duncan."

"You'll check out when the doctor says so, and not one minute before," Jace told her curtly.

"I will check out when I decide to," she replied, opening her eyes and sitting up straight in the bed to glare across the room at him. "I am not a woman of means anymore, as you so frequently remind me. I am one of the nation's deprived, and that goes for insurance as well as wardrobe. I cannot afford," she said deliberately, "to enjoy the hospitality of this lovely white hotel longer than

one full day or I will be paying off the bill in my dotage.
I am leaving tomorrow. Period.''

"Like hell," Jace shot back. His face went rigid. "I'll
take care of the bill."

"No!" she burst out, eyes blazing. "I will gladly starve
to death before I'll let you buy me a soda cracker! I hate
you!"

A shadow passed across his face, but not a trace of expression showed on it. He turned without another word
and went out the door.

"Whew," Duncan breathed softly. "Talk about having the last word...."

"Are you going to argue with me, too?" she grumbled.

"Not me, darling," he laughed. "I'm not up to your
weight."

She nodded. "I'm glad you noticed," she smiled.

"I only wish I knew what was going on between you
and my brother," he added narrowly.

She avoided his eyes. She couldn't tell him about the
terrible accusation Jace had made. She couldn't do that
to Duncan, who'd stood by her for so long, against such
odds. Her weary eyes closed. Jace could hate her and it
didn't matter, not anymore. She was tired of writhing
under his contempt, tired of aching for him. At least
when he was hating her he wouldn't look close enough to
see how desperately she loved him.

Less than an hour later, Bea came in, her face terribly
pale, her eyes troubled. She hugged Amanda gently, tears
rolling down her cheeks, her normally faultless coiffure
looking unkempt. She sank down into a deep, padded
chair by the bed and held Amanda's hand tightly.

"I've been so worried," she confessed. "I feel responsible."

Amanda stared at her. "Mother! Why should you feel
guilty? It was my fault."

"Duncan says you argued with Jason," Bea said
doggedly. "And I'll bet it was about me. It was
wasn't it, darling?"

Amanda dropped her eyes to the small, thin-skinned hand clasping her own. "Yes," she sighed wearily, too weak to pretend anymore.

"About me . . . and his father," Bea suggested hesitatingly.

Amanda nodded without raising her eyes.

Bea sighed, worrying her lower lip with her teeth. "I'd hoped you'd never have to be told," she whispered. "I was sure that Jason knew, but I hoped . . . ." Her dark eyes met her daughter's, and they were bright with pain. "I loved him, Amanda," she whispered tearfully. "He was everything Jason is, and more. A man who could carry the world on his shoulders and never strain. I hated what I was doing, even then, but I was helpless. I'd have gone to him on my deathbed if he'd called me." She brushed away a stray tear. "I loved your father, Amanda, I did. But there was no comparison between that love and what I felt for Jude. I hurt your father, and Marguerite, very much, and I'll always be sorry for that. But as long as I live, I'll remember the way it was when Jude held me; I'll cherish those crumbs of memory like a miser with a treasure until I die, and I can't apologize. He was the air I breathe."

Amanda stared at her blankly, her lips trembling, trying to form words. When Jace had made his accusation, it had been so easy to deny it. But now she had to face the truth. Bea was revealing a love as powerful as that Amanda felt for Jace. She studied her mother's delicate features, and saw for the first time the deep sadness lurking in her eyes. How would it be if Jace were married? Would she feel any less deeply about him? And if he wanted her, would she be able to deny him, loving him? It was so easy to pass moral judgment . . . until you found yourself in the shoes of the judged.

"You feel that way about Jace, don't you?" Bea asked gently, her gaze intent.

Amanda nodded, smiling bitterly. "For all the good it will ever do me. He only wants me, Mother, he doesn't love me."

"With Jude, it was one and the same thing," Bea said quietly. "I imagine his son is no different. But you have an advantage that I didn't, my darling. Jace isn't married."

"He hates me," came the sad reply. "It hasn't stopped him from wanting me, but he hates what he feels."

Bea's small fingers contracted. "Perhaps you'll have to take the first step toward him," she said gently, with a tiny smile. "Amanda, nothing is as important as love. Nothing. Those few weeks I had when Jude was the sun in my sky are as precious as diamonds to me. Nothing can ever take away the memory of them. I keep him here, now," she whispered, touching the soft fabric over her breast, "with me always, wherever I go. I care for Reese Bannon, in the same fond way that I cared for your father. I can be happy with him. But Jude was the love of my life, as Jace is the love of yours. I had no chance at all, Amanda. My happiness was built on the crumbling dreams of another woman. But you have the chance. Don't throw it away for pride, my darling. Life is so very short."

Amanda pressed the small hand holding hers, and tears welled in her eyes. She hadn't realized that her mother was a woman, with all a woman's hopes and needs. Perhaps all Bea's mad sprees were her way of rebelling against a life too confining, dreams unrealized. She was childlike in a sense, but such a sad, lonely child. Remembering Jude Whitehall, how closely his son resembled him, Amanda could even understand Bea's passion for him. She could understand it very well.

"I love you," she whispered to her mother.

Bea sniffed through her tears. "I'm a weak person," she whispered brokenly, with a tiny smile.

Amanda shook her head. "Just a loving woman. If Jace loved me back, it wouldn't matter if he had ten wives, I wouldn't be able to stop my feet from taking me to him. I do love him so!"

Bea moved onto the bed and gathered her daughter into her frail arms. "Hush, baby," she whispered, as she had when Amanda had been small and hurt. "Mama's here. It's going to be all right."

Amanda closed her eyes and let the tears come. She'd never felt so close to Bea, not since her childhood.

She got up the next morning, dressed while holding on to the bed for support, and ran a brush through her hair. Marguerite came in to find her sitting quietly on the edge of the big reclining chair in the corner, looking pale and fragile and terribly vulnerable. The only clothes she had to put on were those she'd been wearing when she had the accident—the same jeans and white top. They were dirty and stained, but at least she was out of the shapeless hospital gown and wearing what belonged to her.

"My dear, you aren't really going to try and go back to the ranch so soon, are you?" Marguerite asked gently.

"I'm going home," she said in a small voice. She barely looked able to sit up. "All the way home. I've got the bus fare. I know Mother wants me to stay and help her plan the wedding, but I just can't. She'll understand."

The older woman sighed. "I was afraid you'd say that, so I took the necessary precautions. I do hope you'll forgive me someday."

Amanda blinked. She felt faintly nauseated, and her head was swimming. Marguerite's words didn't register at first, until the door opened and Jace walked in, very elegant in gray slacks and a patterned gray and tan sports jacket over an open-necked white shirt.

"She wants to take a bus home," Marguerite said with compassionate amusement, turning her dark eyes on her son. "Just as I expected."

Jace moved forward, and Amanda jerked backward as he reached for her. Something—a faint movement in his face almost registered in her whirling mind, but she stared up at him resentfully.

"Where's Duncan?" she asked apprehensively.

"At work," Jace said harshly. "Where I should be."

"Jace!" Marguerite exclaimed.

"I didn't ask you to come," she said through numb lips, glaring up at him. "I can get home all by myself."

His nostrils flared, his eyes glittered. "Brave words," he said curtly.

Her eyes dropped to his brown throat, and she felt all the fight go out of her in a long, weary sigh. Her body wasn't up to it. She slumped in the chair. "Yes," she whispered, "very brave. I hurt so," she moaned, dropping her aching head into her hands as hot tears stung her eyes.

Jace reached down and lifted her in his hard arms, holding her clear of the floor.

"Don't," she whimpered. "They have wheel-chairs. . . ."

"And I don't have all day to wait for them to bring one," he growled. "Let's go, Mother."

Marguerite followed them out into the hall, muttering at Jace's broad back.

"I've already signed you out," Jace said quietly. "And if you say one word about the bill," he added, glaring into her eyes from a distance of bare inches, "I'll give you hell, Amanda."

Her eyes closed, making the wild sensations she felt in his warm, hard arms even more sensuous. "When have you ever given me anything else?" she whispered.

"When have you let me?"

The question was soft and deep, and it shocked her into opening her eyes and looking straight up into his. The impact of it went right through her body. She couldn't drag her gaze away from his. It stimulated her pulse, stifled her breath in her body. Her sharp nails involuntarily dug into his shoulder.

They were outside now, in the parking lot, and Marguerite had gone around the Mercedes to unlock the passenger side.

Jace's eyes dropped to Amanda's soft, parted mouth. "Sharp little claws," he whispered, and Marguerite was too far away to hear. "And I know just how much damage they can do."

She gasped, shaken by his reference to those moments of intimacy they had shared. His arms drew her imperceptibly closer before he walked around the car with her. "Shocked, Amanda?" he asked quietly.

She grasped at sanity. "Scarlet women don't get shocked," she reminded him shakily.

"I'm beginning to wonder if my first impression wasn't more accurate than my second," he replied in a low tone. His eyes sought hers. "Was it, Amanda?"

"I don't know what your first impression was," she reminded him.

"Pretty devastating, little one," he said under his breath. He slid her in onto the back seat of the small car while Marguerite held the door open for him and then turned to get into the passenger seat.

Amanda met Jace's narrow eyes from a distance of scant inches as he put her down, so close that she could smell the after-shave he'd used clinging to his darkly tanned face.

He drew away in a matter of seconds, although it seemed as if time had stopped while they stared at one another, and her eyes involuntarily clung to his tall figure while he went around the car and got behind the wheel.

"Dear, are you sure you're up to going home with us?" Marguerite asked worriedly. She half-turned with one elegant clad arm over the back of the seat to study the younger woman. "You look so pale."

"I'm fine," Amanda assured her in a voice that didn't sound like her own. She avoided Jace's gaze in the rear-view mirror.

How could she tell Marguerite—sweet, gentle Marguerite—that all this anguish was the result of Bea's love for a married man...for her best friend's husband? Amanda might be able to understand her mother, but Jace never would. He'd never loved. He couldn't know how it was to want someone so much that nothing else, no one else, mattered.

*   *   *

The next morning, amid a storm of protest from Marguerite and Amanda, Bea left for Nassau. She and Reese would wait until Amanda was well enough to attend the ceremony, she promised, pushing the date up a month. Reese wouldn't mind, she assured her daughter.

"He's a dear man," she told Amanda. "I think you'll appreciate him even more when you get to know him. You must come and stay with us."

Amanda smiled at the mother she'd only just begun to know. "I may need to," she agreed with a secretive smile.

Bea hugged her tightly. "Are you sure you'll be all right?"

"I'll be fine, now. Really, I will."

Bea kissed the pale cheek and went out without looking back—a habit she'd formed early in life—and allowed Marguerite to take her to the airport. Amanda wished silently that she might have been well enough to go with her mother and run away.

But as she found out later, lying in the lovely blue room, staring at the ceiling with a horribly throbbing head, she wasn't in any condition for travel.

The one bright spot in the day was the arrival of a florist with a huge bouquet of carnations, roses, baby's breath and heather, sandwiched in with lily of the valley, irises, mums, daisies—a profusion of color and scent.

"For me?" she choked.

The florist grinned, setting the arrangement on her bedside table. "If your name is Amanda Carson."

"If it wasn't, I'd change it right now," she vowed.

"Hope you enjoy them," he said from the door as he closed it.

She struggled into a sitting position, her narrow strapped green gown sliding off one honey-colored shoulder while she leaned over to put her nose to a small yellow rosebud. Whoever had ordered the flowers knew her taste perfectly; knew how much she loved yellow roses and daisies, because they were dominant in the bouquet.

The door opened again and Duncan strolled in, grinning. Amanda caught him around the neck the minute he

came within range and hugged him wildly, through a mist
of tears, barely noticing that Jace had followed him and
was standing just inside the doorway, scowling.

"Oh, Duncan, you angel, what a wonderful thing to
do," she cried, sobbing and laughing all at once as she
kissed his lean cheek, oblivious to the puzzled look on his
face and the fury in Jace's.

"Huh?" Duncan blinked.

"The flowers, silly," she laughed, and her eyes danced
as they had when she was still a girl, lighting up her sad,
wan face like a torch so that she was exquisitely beautiful with her silver blond hair cascading around her, and
the thin green gown emphasizing her peaches and cream
complexion and dark eyes. "They're so beautiful. No
one ever sent me flowers before, did you know? And
I...what is it?" she asked as he continued to stare va-
cantly at her.

"I'm glad you like them, but I didn't do it, darling,"
he admitted sheepishly.

"Then, who...?"

Jace turned and left the room before she could continue, and Amanda frowned after him. It couldn't
be...could it?

Her fingers trembled as she reached for the card and
fumbled the envelope open.

"Must have been Terry...no, it couldn't have been,"
Duncan corrected, frowning, "because we thought it
would save explanations if we didn't bother him. And if
Mother had done it, she'd have said something..."

Amanda was reading the card, tears welling suddenly
in the eyes she closed on a pain that shuddered all
through her body. The card fell lightly to the blue
coverlet, like a frail white leaf loosened from its stem by
a faint, cold breeze.

There was no message on the white card. Only a black,
bold scrawl that was as familiar as her own, and a single
four-letter name. "Jace."

9

*

Jace didn't go near her for the rest of the day, and she knew that she'd hurt him. Despite his scorn for Beatrice Carson, it was clear that he was still vulnerable to her daughter. Had the flowers been a peace offering?

Duncan sat and played gin rummy with her all evening, winning hand after hand until she finally refused to play with him anymore out of sheer exasperation.

"Spoilsport," he goaded. "It's early yet. You're going to force me to go out in search of other entertainment."

"Don't call me names, you cheating cardsharp," she said in her best Western drawl. "I ought to call you out and plug you, stranger."

"The marshal don't like gunplay in this here town," he replied narrow-eyed.

She tossed her hair. "A likely story. You, sir, are simply cowardly."

"Yes, miss, I shore am!" he grinned.

She laid back against the pillows with a weary smile. "Thanks for keeping me company, Duncan. I do feel better now. In fact, I may even be able to get up in the morning."

"Don't push it."

"I have to." She studied her clasped hands. "I have to leave just as soon as I can," she ground out. "I can't take being around Jace much longer."

"He won't bite," he promised her.

She smiled wanly. "Care to bet?"

He drew a deep breath. "Exactly what is going on, can't you tell me?"

She shook her head. "Private, I'm afraid."

"That sounds ominous, like guns at ten paces or something," he teased, and his brown eyes danced at her.

"I almost wish it was, but he'd have me outgunned on the first draw," she admitted. "I can't fight Jace and win. I don't think anyone can."

"I'm not so sure about that."

"I am."

"Getting sleepy?"

She shook her head. "Just worn out. I didn't even manage to finish my supper, I was so tired."

"You'll be up raiding the kitchen before dawn, mark my words," he scolded.

She laughed. "Maybe."

Duncan's prediction came true shortly after midnight, when she found that she couldn't ignore her growling stomach an instant longer.

She slipped on her old robe and slippers and opened the door into the hall. She tiptoed past Jace's darkened room, her heart shaking her briefly with its beat, and down the dimly lit stairs. Her feet made no noise at all on the carpet, and she found the kitchen without a slip and turned on the light.

Marguerite's kitchen was absolutely spotless—mosaic tile floors, done in the same blue and white motif as the bathrooms, looked recently polished, and the huge stove that Mrs. Brown used for baking was a blazing white. The big counters and huge oak cabinets were a cook's dream. So was the long solid oak table used to prepare food on. There were two or three chairs scattered around, and frilly blue curtains at the darkened windows. Amanda thought idly that it would be a pleasure to work in.

The clean pots and pans cried to be used, so she opened the double-doored refrigerator, knowing her hostess wouldn't mind if she made herself a snack. She pulled out eggs and a big ham, and took down some spices from the cabinet, proceeding quietly to make herself a huge, mouth-watering omelet. She was in the middle of cooking it when the back door suddenly swung open and Jace walked in.

She froze at the sight of him, and he didn't look any less stunned to see her standing at the stove in her robe, her blond hair in a lovely tangle around her shoulders, hanging down to her waist in back.

He was wearing a suede jacket and his familiar black Stetson, jeans that were layered in dust, and old boots with scuffed toes. He didn't look like a corporate executive. He looked the way Jason Whitehall used to look when she was a girl—like a cowboy struggling to carve an empire out of a few hundred head of cattle, a lot of sweat, and a generous amount of business sense.

"What are you doing out of bed?" he asked quietly, closing the door behind him.

"I was hungry," she replied softly.

He glanced toward the pan she was holding on the burner.

"That smells like an omelet," he said.

"It is." She checked it to make sure it wasn't burning. "Ham and egg."

"It smells delicious."

She glanced at him. He looked hungry, too. And cold and tired. There were gray hairs at his temples that she'd barely noticed before, and new lines in his hard face. "Want some?" she asked gently.

"Got enough?" he countered.

She nodded. "I'll make some coffee...."

"I'll make it. Women never get it strong enough." He shrugged out of his jacket to disclose a faded blue-patterned cotton shirt, and threw it onto an empty chair with his hat. He found the coffeepot and proceeded to fill it with apparent expertise while Amanda took up the omelet and put bread into the toaster.

"Butter," she murmured, turning back toward the refrigerator.

"I'll get it," he said.

She took out the toast and laid it on one plate while she went to the cabinet to get a second one for him.

Jace leaned on the counter and lit a cigarette, but his silvery eyes followed her all around the kitchen, quiet and strange, tracing the slender lines of her body in the old blue terry cloth robe.

She barely glanced at him as she came back with the plate and set it down on the counter. Her heart was doing acrobatics in her chest, but she tried to look calm, working with deft, efficient hands to divide the omelet, and giving him the lion's share of it.

"Hold it," he said, laying a quick hand on her wrist, "that's more than half."

His touch was warm and light, but she looked down at the lean, darkly tanned fingers with a sense of impending disaster, her face flushing at the emotions playing havoc inside her.

"I ... wasn't really that hungry," she admitted. She glanced up at him shyly, and away again. "You ... you don't look like you even had supper."

He traced a rough pattern on the soft flesh of her wrist. "I didn't."

She moved away from him to put the pan in the sink, wondering at the strange mood he was in.

"Is something wrong?" she asked.

"Only with me," he said on a rough sigh. "I couldn't sleep."

She stared down at the soapy water in the frying pan. "I'm sorry about the flowers," she whispered. "I didn't realize ... that you'd sent them." Her eyes closed. "You've been so cruel."

"Because I told you the truth about your mother?" he demanded. "Why not? You're old enough."

She turned, staring across into his blazing eyes. "Did you have to be so brutal about it?" she asked.

"There's no other way with you," he said quietly. "At least it gets your attention."

Her lips parted. "I don't understand."

He laughed mirthlessly. "Of course not."

Her eyes pleaded with him. "Jace, can't you find it in your heart to forgive her?"

"Forgive her? She's nothing but a slut!" he ground out. "Like her daughter," he added coldly.

She drew in a harsh, hurt breath. "You think you know everything there is to know about me, don't you?"

"All I need to know," he agreed, finishing the cigarette and stubbing it out in an ashtray on the sideboard.

"How wonderful to never make a mistake, to never be wrong!" she cast at him.

He turned and caught her blazing eyes with his own. "I make mistakes," he corrected quietly. "I made my biggest one with you."

"How, by not shooting me instead of the bull?" she choked.

"By not taking you into my bed when you were sixteen," he said quietly, and there was no mockery, no teasing light in his eyes now.

Her face went blood red. "As if I'd have gone!" she cried.

"I could have had you the other night," he reminded her, his eyes narrowing. "You were a great deal more vulnerable than that when you were sixteen, and you wanted me even more than you do now."

"That's a lie!" she gasped, outraged.

"The only difference," he continued coldly, "is that it wasn't permissible back then, when the Whitehalls were still just middle class. Now that the shoe's on the other foot, it's perfectly all right for you to want me. Even to give in to me. And why not, it wouldn't be the first time."

Her fingers clenched on the handle of the pan in the sink, and she felt pain as she gripped it.

"I'd rather take poison," she breathed.

One corner of his chiseled mouth went up. "Really?" His eyes swept down over her slender body. "So would I. You can arouse me when you try, but then, so could anything in skirts. One body's the same as another to a hungry man."

"Go to hell!" she burst out.

"I've been there," he told her. "I don't recommend it. Come and eat your omelet, Amanda, before it gets cold.

These coy little performances are beginning to wear on my temper.''

He took the plates to the table. Amanda let go of the pan and started blindly toward the dining room, her face stark white, her heart shaking her with its anguished beat. All she wanted from life at that moment was to escape from him.

But he wasn't about to let her escape that easily. He reached out and caught her wrist in a steely grasp, halting her in place.

"You're not going anywhere," he said in a dangerous undertone. "I said sit down."

She licked her dry lips nervously and sat down at the table in the seat he indicated. But she only stared at the omelet through her tears, feeling so sick she was afraid to take a bite of it.

Jace laid down his fork and moved his chair close to hers.

"Amanda?"

There was a foreign softness to his deep voice. It was the final undoing. A sob broke from her throat and let the dam of tears overflow down her cheeks until her slender body was shaking helplessly with them.

"For God's sake, don't!" he growled.

"Please . . . let me go to bed," she pleaded brokenly. "Please . . . !"

"Oh, hell." He pulled a clean handkerchief from his pocket and mopped up her tears, and all the anger and spite seemed to go out of him at once. "Here, eat your omelet," he said gently, as if he was speaking to a small child. "Come on. Let me see you taste yours first."

"Why?" she sniffled, looking up at him through tear-spiked lashes.

"I hear that you've been threatening to make me a bowl of buttered toadstools," he mused, and a faint smile eased the rigid lines of his face. "I'd hate to think you laced this omelet with them."

She smiled involuntarily, and her face lit up. He watched the change in her, fascinated.

"I wouldn't poison you," she whispered.

"Wouldn't you, honey?" he asked gently. His fingers reached out to touch, very lightly, the tracks of tears on her flushed cheeks. "Not even with all the provocation I've given you?"

She studied his darkly tanned face solemnly. "I'm sorry," she said.

"For what?"

Her eyes fell to the deep yellow omelet with its cubes of pink ham on her plate. "About what ... my mother did."

He drew in a sharp breath. "Eat your omelet."

She stared across at his impassive face as he turned his attention to his own plate.

"Not bad," he murmured after a taste. "When did you learn to cook?"

"When we moved to San Antonio," she said, picking up her fork to spear a chunk of omelet. "I didn't have much choice. Mother couldn't cook at all, and we couldn't afford to eat out." She smiled as she chewed and swallowed the fluffy mouthful. "The first time I tried to fry squash I cut it up raw into the pan and didn't put a drop of oil in it. You could smell it all over the building."

He glanced at her, and one corner of his mouth went up. "You didn't eat that night, I gather."

"Not much," she laughed. "I forgot to salt the macaroni, and burned the meat...." Her voice sighed in memory. "I'm still not a good cook, but I'm better than I was." She studied his rough, arrogant profile. "You learned to cook in the service, didn't you?"

That seemed to surprise him. He stared at her searchingly before he turned his attention to his coffee. "One of my specialties was fried snake," he said drily.

"Green Berets, wasn't it?" she recalled with a tiny smile as she toyed with her toast. "I remember how striking you used to look in uniform...."

"You were just a baby then," he teased.

"I'm glad," she said suddenly, as a blinding thought floored her. How would it have been all those years ago to have been a woman, and in love with Jace as she was now—to watch the afternoon newscasts about Vietnam knowing his unit was over there. . . .

"What's the matter?" he asked quietly.

She shook her head. "Nothing."

He swallowed down his coffee and leaned back in his chair to light a cigarette. He looped his finger over an ashtray and dragged it in front of him. "Where do you live in San Antonio?" he asked conversationally.

She glanced at him and away. It was as if Bea had never come. They were talking now as they had that day at the restaurant—freely, openly, like two people who understood and respected one another.

"In a one bedroom efficiency apartment," she replied. "Right downtown. I can walk to work, and it's convenient to the corner grocery store, too."

"You don't own a car?"

"Can't afford one," she said sheepishly. Her soft brown eyes teased his. "They break down."

He drew a long, slow breath. His lean hand went up to unfasten the top buttons on his shirt, as if the warmth of the kitchen was uncomfortable for him. Her eyes involuntarily followed the movement and he smiled sensuously at her.

"Want me to take it off?" he asked in a lazy, teasing drawl.

She caught her breath, remembering without wanting to the feel of that mat of thick, curling hair on his chest under her fingers.

She averted her eyes, wrapping both hands around her coffee cup.

He chuckled softly, but he didn't stop until he'd opened the shirt all the way down, baring his bronzed chest in the sudden tense stillness of the room. His hand rubbed over it roughly and he drew in a long, heavy yawn.

"God, I'm so tired," he said heavily. He raised the cigarette to his chiseled lips.

"Why did you send the flowers?" she asked. An instant later she could have bitten her tongue for the impulsive question.

His silver eyes searched hers. "You might have died," he said bluntly, "and I'd have been responsible. The flowers were by way of apology," he added gruffly, looking away. "I never meant you to be hurt like that."

She stared at his sharp profile, knowing how it shook that towering pride of his to admit he was sorry about anything. And suddenly she realized how much it must have hurt him to know that his father was unfaithful to Marguerite. Knowing it, trying to protect his mother.... All of her own pain fell away as she studied him, just beginning to understand his point of view.

"Would you listen, if I explained something to you?" she asked gently.

His silver eyes cut at her. "Not if it's about your mother," he said bluntly.

She drew in a sharp breath, her cold hands clenching around the coffee cup. "Jason, have you ever been in love?" she asked harshly. "So deeply in love that nothing and no one else mattered? I don't pretend to know how your father felt, but Mother loved him beyond anything on earth. There was never anyone but Jude for her, not even my own father. It was a once-in-a-lifetime kind of love, and she had the bad luck to feel it for a married man. I'm not condoning what she did, but I can at least understand why she did it. She loved him, Jace."

His eyes dropped to his cigarette. He stared at the growing ash on it and suddenly stabbed it out in the ashtray. "When is the wedding?" he asked curtly.

"In a month. I'll be joining Mother and Reese in the Bahamas for the ceremony."

He studied her downbent head. "And in the meantime?"

"I'm going back to San Antonio as soon as I'm well enough to travel," she said honestly, tears in her voice. "You can let Terry know your decision about the account," she added in a whisper.

He drew in a weary breath. "As far as I'm concerned, it's yours. You can iron out the details with Duncan." He stood up. "If you want to leave here that badly, go ahead."

Her lovely eyes filled with tears as she looked up at him. He wasn't going to bend an inch. He could let her walk away, out of his life, and not feel a thing. But she loved him too much to let go.

"Is that what you want?" she asked bravely, her face pale in the soft light of the kitchen.

His jaw tautened, his silver eyes narrowed. "You know what I want."

Yes, she knew all too well. Perhaps Bea was right. Love was the most important thing. A few hours in Jace's arms might not be proper, but it would be a soft memory to wrap around herself in the long, empty years ahead. She loved him so much. Would it be so wrong to spend just one night with him?

"All right," she said softly, her tone weak but unfaltering.

He scowled down at her. "All right, what?" he asked.

She lifted her face proudly. "I'll sleep with you."

His nostrils flared with a sharp indrawn breath. "In return for what, exactly?" he asked harshly.

"Does everything have to have a price tag?" she murmured miserably, standing up. "I want nothing from you!"

"Amanda!"

She stopped at the doorway, her back to him. "Yes?"

There was a brief, poignant silence. "If you want me, come back here and prove it."

She almost ran. It would have been in character, and it was what she would have done a few months earlier. But now she knew there was more to Jason's ardor than an angry kiss in the moonlight. She knew how exquisitely tender he could be, how patient. And her need of him was too great to ignore. There was no limit to the demands he could make on her now that she knew how desperately she loved him.

She turned and went back to him, pausing at the table, her eyes faintly apprehensive as they looked up into his. He hadn't moved at all, and his gaze was calculating as it met hers.

"Well?" he asked.

She moved closer, searching her mind for a few clues as to what would be expected of her. She'd never tried to seduce a man before. A couple of old movies came to mind, but one called for her to crawl into his sleeping bag and the other would only work if she could already be undressed and in his bed when he came out of the shower.

Experimentally, she linked her hands around his neck and reached up on tiptoe to brush her lips against his jutting chin. He wouldn't bend an inch to help her, and his chin was as far as she could reach.

"You might help me a little," she pointed out, puzzled by the faint amusement in his silver eyes.

"What do you want me to do?" he asked obligingly.

"If you'd bend your head just an inch or so...."

He bent down, watching her as she looked up at him hesitantly. Nervous, inhibited, it was all she could do to make that first movement toward him, to put her mouth against his and yield her body to the strength of his.

She closed her eyes and pressed herself against his tall frame, her mouth suddenly hungry as the love she felt melted into her veins like a drug. But it wasn't enough. It was like kissing stone, and even when she increased the pressure of her lips, he didn't seem to feel the need to respond.

She drew away and looked up at him, her eyes soft with hunger, her breath unsteady. "Oh, Jace, teach me how..." she whispered brokenly.

His eyes widened, only to narrow and glitter down at her, something passing across his face like a faint shadow as his hands touched her waist and untied the robe with a lazy, deft twist.

She caught his hands as he eased the robe down her arms, leaving her standing before him in only the pale mint gown that was all but transparent, its low neckline giving more than a glimpse of her small, perfect breasts.

"You offered yourself to me," he reminded her, something calculating in his gaze. "Cold feet, Amanda?"

She swallowed nervously. "No," she lied. She let him dispose of the robe, looping it over the chair she'd vacated. His fingers went to the thin spaghetti straps that held the bodice of the gown in place, toying with the bow ties.

"Jason, it's getting late!" she whispered, feeling a sense of panic, the age-old fear of a woman with her first man.

"Easy, honey," he murmured, his hands suddenly soothing on her back, his lips gentle as they touched her flushed face. "Just relax, Amanda, I know what I'm doing. Relax, honey, I'm not going to rush you, all right? That's better," he mused, feeling some of the tension ease out of her with the leisure of his movements, his tone. "Are you afraid of making love with me?" he whispered.

She swallowed down her fear. "Of course not," she managed in a voice straight from the tomb.

"Show me."

She drew back and looked up at him helplessly; it was like being told to play an instrument when she'd never learned to read music. Her look pleaded with him.

His eyes narrowed, but not in anger. Some strange, quiet glow made them darken. He looked down at her with a kind of triumph as one deft hand flicked open the bow on her shoulder. He repeated the gesture with the other bow and held her eyes while the gauzy fabric slid unimpeded to her waist and she felt the soft breeze from the open window on her sudden bareness.

She blushed like a schoolgirl, hating her own inexperience, hating the expertise behind his action, frightened at the intimacy between them even though she'd initiated it.

His eyes dropped to the high, soft curves he'd uncovered, studying them in the tense silence that followed.

"My God, you're lovely," he said quietly. "As sweet as a prayer...."

She caught her breath. "What... an incredible way to put it," she whispered.

He drew his eyes back to hers. "What did you expect, Amanda, some vulgar remark? What's happening between us isn't cheap, and you're not a woman I picked up on the street. You belong to me, every soft inch of you, and there's nothing shameful about my looking at you. You're exquisite.''

Her eyes held his, reading the tenderness in them. "I...like looking at you, too," she said breathlessly, her fingers lightly touching the powerful contours of his chest, tangling gently in the wiry, curling dark hair over the warm bronzed muscles.

"Mandy..." he breathed, drawing her very gently to him until her softness melted into his hardness, until she could feel the hair-roughened muscles pressing against her own taut breasts, and he heard her gasp.

"Now kiss me," he whispered huskily, bending his head, "and let me show you how much we can say to each other without words."

He took her mouth with a controlled ferocity that made her breath catch in her throat, tasting it, savoring it, in a silence wild with the newness of discovery. She lifted her arms around his neck, holding him, her body trembling where its bareness was crushed warmly to his until she felt such a part of him that nothing short of death could separate them. She loved him so! To be in his arms, to feel the raw hunger of his mouth cherishing hers, penetrating it, devouring it, was as close to paradise as she'd ever been. Tears welled in her eyes at the intensity of what she was feeling with him, at the depth of the love she couldn't deny even when she cursed it for making her weak.

His arms contracted at her back and ground her body into his for an instant before he lifted his head and looked down into her soft, yielding eyes.

"I want one word from you," he said in a gruff, unsteady voice, and the arms that held her had a fine tremor. "I ache like a boy with his first woman, and I can't take much more of this."

She knew exactly what he meant, and there was only one way she could answer him after the way she'd responded. She loved him more than her own life, and even though she'd probably hate both of them in daylight, the soft darkness and the sweet pleasure of his body against hers would be a memory she could hold for the long, empty years ahead without him.

She opened her mouth to speak, to tell him, when the beautiful dream they were sharing was shattered by the sudden, loud roar of a car's engine coming up the driveway.

Jace said something violent under his breath and held Amanda close in his arms, burying his face in her throat in a silence bitter with denial until the tremor went out of his arms, until his shuddering heartbeat calmed.

Her fingers soothed him, brushing softly at the cool strands of hair at his temples. "I'm sorry," she whispered tenderly. "I'm sorry."

His lips brushed her silky skin just below her ear and moved up to touch her earlobe. "Are you really?" he whispered. "Or is it like a reprieve?"

"I don't understand," she murmured.

He drew back, his eyes missing nothing as they probed hers. "You're a virgin, aren't you, Amanda?" he said quietly.

She flushed, her face giving her away, and he nodded, dropping his eyes to the soft curves pressed so closely against him. "I should have known," he mused, and a corner of his mouth went up as he carefully eased her bodice back in place and lifted her hand to hold it there while he retied the spaghetti straps with a sophisticated carelessness that had her gaping at him.

"I...I tried to tell you before," she faltered, "but you wouldn't listen."

"I was jealous as hell, and hurting," he said bluntly. "Jealous of Black and jealous of my own brother. I thought you came because of Duncan and I wanted to strangle you both."

"You're the only one I wanted," she breathed, her eyes telling all her secrets to him in the soft, sweet silence that followed.

He caught her narrow hips and drew them against the taut, powerful lines of his legs, watching the faint tremor that shook her.

"I like to watch your face when I hold you like this," he said tightly. "Your eyes turn gold when you're aroused."

Her eyes closed on a wave of pure hunger. "Jace," she whispered achingly, clinging to him.

"I want you, too," he whispered back, but for all the wild, fervent hunger she could sense in him, the lips he pressed against her forehead were breathlessly gentle. "Damn Duncan...!" he ground out as the sound of the car door slamming burst into the silence.

Jace let her go with a rough sigh, his eyes caressing as they swept down her slender body. "You'd better go on up. I'm not in the mood for any of Duncan's witty remarks, and I'd hate to end the day by knocking out any more of his teeth."

She smiled at him, the radiance of her face giving her a soft beauty that made him catch his breath. "Poor Duncan," she murmured.

"Poor Duncan, hell!" He grabbed up her robe and helped her into it, jerking the ties together to pull her body against him. He bent and kissed her roughly, his lips hard, faintly hurting. "You're mine, honey," he told her, his breath warming her mouth. "And I'm not sharing you. Once I take you into my bed, I'll kill another man for touching you."

"Jace!" she whispered, stunned at the cool violence of the words.

"I've waited seven years for you," he said harshly. "I'm through waiting. By the time this weekend is over, you'll belong to me completely."

She stared up at him helplessly, understanding him with a painful clarity. "I...I was going back to San Antonio after the party tomorrow night."

"Was is right," he said, his eyes hard. "You're staying now. I want the whole damned world to know you're mine. There'll be no hushed up weekends at your apartment, no climbing the back stairs to your bedroom. It's all going to be open and above board, so you'd better start making plans." He released her and turned her around with a slight push in the direction of the door. "Go to bed. We'll talk about it tomorrow night."

She looked over her shoulder at him when she reached the door. "Does . . . everyone have to know?" she asked, feeling the shame wash over her like the night air.

"Why in hell not?" he wanted to know.

It was different for men. Why should he care? She turned and walked toward the door.

"Amanda!" He studied her face as she turned. "The light's gone out of you. What is it? Something I said?"

"I'm just tired," she assured him with a wan smile. "Just tired, Jason. Good night."

10

*

Amanda wore a white and yellow eyelet sundress downstairs the next morning, her eyes dark-shadowed from lack of sleep, her heart tumbling around wildly in her chest as she approached the dining room. All night she'd agonized over it, and she was no closer to a solution. How did Jace expect her to survive the contempt in his mother's eyes, in Duncan's eyes, when he calmly announced that Amanda was his new mistress? But she loved him so much that the thought of going away, of living without him, was worse than the certainty of death. She cared too much to go, now. It would be like leaving half of her soul behind, and she was too weak to bear the separation.

She moved into the carpeted room hesitantly, her eyes colliding instantly with Jace's across the length of the table with the impact of steel against rock. He studied her quietly, one corner of his mouth lifting, his expression impossible to read.

"Good morning, dear," Marguerite said with a smile, "I'm glad you're up early, we've got so much to do to get ready for the party tonight. Now, about your dress...."

"Leave that to me," Jace said with a smile. "I'll take care of it."

Marguerite raised an eyebrow and looked from his smug face to Amanda's flushed one, and smiled. "Anything you say, dear," she murmured, lowering her eyes to her filled plate.

Duncan came in yawning, oblivious to the undercurrents around him. "Good morning." He plopped down in a chair and glanced from Jace to Amanda and grinned. "Everybody sleep well?" he asked.

Amanda's face went redder, and Jace leaned on his forearms with a smoking cigarette in his hard fingers, one eye dangerously narrowed as he glared at his brother. He didn't say a word, but he didn't have to. The look had always been adequate.

Duncan grimaced, reaching for cream and sugar to put into his coffee. "Talk about looks that kill . . . ! Have a heart, Jace, I didn't mean a thing."

Marguerite frowned. "Did I miss something?"

"I think we both did," Duncan muttered, irrepressible. "Jace was in the kitchen alone when I got in at two o'clock this morning, looking like a wounded bear."

"Jason always looks like a wounded bear at two o'clock in the morning," his mother reminded him.

"His lip was swollen," Duncan added with a sly glance at Amanda, who swallowed her coffee too fast and choked.

"That doesn't prove anything," Jace said with a half-amused expression as he lifted the cigarette to his lips.

Amanda, remembering the feel of his lower lip as she nibbled at it, glanced at him and felt the floor reeling out from under her at the shared memory reflected in his silvery eyes.

"Do behave," Marguerite cautioned Duncan. "And where were you until two in the morning, by the way?"

"Following my big brother's sterling example," he replied with a grin at Jace.

"You were at the office working?" Marguerite blinked.

Duncan sighed. "Jace doesn't work all the time."

Marguerite finished her breakfast and drew up her linen napkin with a flourish to dab at her lips. "Duncan, you're in a very strange mood this morning. Perhaps you need a vacation?"

"That's just what I need," Duncan agreed quickly. "How about Hawaii? You could come with me, Mother, the sea air would do you good."

"The sea air gives me infected sinuses," she reminded him, "besides, how could you pick up girls with your mother along? Be sensible."

Duncan laughed. "Oh, Mother, I wouldn't trade you for all Jace's cattle."

Marguerite beamed. "Well, I'd better get busy. Jace..." she studied him a little apprehensively. "You will be kind to Amanda?"

He lowered his eyes to his coffee cup. "I'll make an effort," he assured her.

"Good. Duncan, would you drive me? My car's acting up, I'm going to have the garage take it in for inspection," she fired at her youngest son, as she started out the door.

"But, I'm still eating..." Duncan protested, a forkful of egg halfway to his mouth.

"Finish it when we get back," she returned implacably.

Duncan stared at the egg and put it down. "I'll buy myself a stale doughnut or something," he murmured wistfully. "Bye, all," he called over his shoulder, winking at Amanda.

Once they were out of the room, Jace looked up, his eyes catching Amanda's, holding them.

"Hello," he said softly.

Wild thrills ran through her at the lazy tone, the smile. "Hello," she whispered back, her eyes lighting up like soft brown lights, her face radiant.

"I like you in white and yellow," he remarked, studying her. "You remind me of a daisy."

"Daisies don't tell," she remarked, clutching her coffee cup to still the trembling of her hands.

He smiled, drawing her eyes to the chiseled mouth her own had clung to so hungrily the night before. His lower lip was just slightly swollen.

"Duncan doesn't miss a trick," he remarked with a deep chuckle.

She flushed delightedly. "I'm sorry," she said gently.

"Why? I like those sharp little teeth," he murmured sensuously. "I could feel them nibbling at my mouth long after I showered and went to bed."

She didn't even feel the heat of the cup in her hand. "I thought I'd never sleep...."

"That makes two of us," he agreed. His face was expressionless, suddenly, his eyes blazing the length of the table at her. "Come here."

She put the cup down and went to him, dazed at the newness of being able to look at him without fear of discovery, without having to explain it. He caught her around the waist and pulled her down onto his lap, letting her head fall back against his shoulder so that he could look down at her. He smelled of expensive cologne, and his soft brown silk shirt was smooth against her cheek, his tanned throat visible at the open neck.

"I almost came for you last night," he said quietly, his eyes dark and faintly smiling. "That damned bed was so big and empty, and I wanted you almost beyond bearing."

"I didn't sleep, either," she admitted. Her fingers reached up to trace his mouth. She noted that he was clean-shaven now, the smoothness of his skin a contrast to the faint raspiness which had been there last night.

He tipped her mouth up and bent to kiss her. His lips were slow, tender, easing hers apart to deepen the kiss, his breath coming quicker as he grasped the nape of her neck and suddenly crushed her mouth under his in a hungry, deep passion. The kiss seemed to go on forever, slow and hard and faintly bruising in the soft silence of the dining room. His arms brought her up closer, cradling her, the sounds of silk rustling against cotton invading her ears along with her own faint moan as she returned the kiss with her whole heart.

Her fingers went to the buttons on his shirt and she unbuttoned it slowly, only half aware of what she was doing, consumed with the need to touch him, to savor the sensuous maleness of his hair-roughened flesh.

He caught her hand as it tangled in the curling hair, drawing back a little, his eyes narrow, his heart pounding heavily in his chest. "If you touch me, I'm going to touch you," he said gruffly. "And we don't have time for what it would lead to."

She licked her dry lips, aware of the warm pressure of his lean fingers where they pressed hers to his body. "Would it lead to that?" she whispered.

"The way I feel right now, yes," he replied. His mouth brushed her closed eyelids. "Oh, God, I love for you to touch me," he whispered huskily.

She smiled, leaning her flushed cheek against his chest. "It's so strange...."

"What is?" he murmured against her forehead.

"Not fighting you."

He drew a long, slow breath. "I've given you hell for a long time."

"Maybe you had reason to." She sighed softly. "Jace, I'm sorry about Mother...."

He touched his forefinger against her lips, looking down at her with a strange, brooding expression. "I'm not over it, yet," he said quietly. "But I think I'm beginning to understand. Emotions aren't always so easy to control. God knows, I lose my head every time I touch you."

She smiled lazily. "Is that so bad?"

"For me it is." He reached over to crush out the cigarette smoldering in his ashtray. "I've never been demonstrative. I've had women, but always on my terms, and never one I couldn't walk away from." He looked down at her, scowling. "You make me feel sensations I didn't know I could experience. They wash over my body like fire when I hold you, when I touch you . . . you pleasure me, Amanda. That's an old-fashioned phrase, but I can't think of anything more descriptive."

She drew her hand against his hard cheek. "I think we pleasure each other," she said quietly. "Do I really belong to you?"

"Do you want to?"

She nodded, unashamed, her eyes worshiping every line of his face.

He drew his hand across her waist, trailing it up over the fabric across her firm, high breasts, pausing to cup one of them warmly, his eyes darting to catch the stunned expression on her face.

"You'll get used to being touched like this," he said softly.

"Will I?" she managed breathlessly.

His eyes searched hers. "I hadn't thought about it until now, but you've never let a man look at you the way I did last night, have you? I'd always thought you were experienced until I saw that wild blush on your face. And when I held you like that....." He smiled gently. "I'll remember it the rest of my life. More than anything, I wanted to be the one to teach you about love. I thought you'd given that privilege to some other man, and I hated you for it."

"I never wanted anyone but you," she said simply, her eyes sad as she thought how little of him she'd really have when it was all over. He'd tire of her innocence eventually, he'd tire of being with her. They had so much in common, but all he wanted was her body, not her mind or her heart.

"What's wrong?" he asked softly.

She shrugged. "Nothing. What did you mean about a dress?"

"Curious?" He chuckled, putting her back on her feet. "Come on, and I'll show you."

He led her into the exclusive department store, straight to the women's department, to the couture section. She pulled back, but he wouldn't let go of her hand. He turned her over to the sleek saleslady with a description of the kind of dress he wanted her to try on for him.

"Yes, sir, Mr. Whitehall," the poised, middle-aged woman said with a smile. "I have just the thing . . . !"

"But, I don't want you to buy me a dress," Amanda protested as the saleslady sailed away toward the back.

Jace only smiled, his eyes hooded, mysterious. "Why not? Did you plan to go to the party in slacks?"

That hurt. It hadn't mattered so much, being without, until he made such a point of it. And to have the people in this exclusive store know that he was buying her clothes—what were they going to think? She might as well be some man's bought woman. Her eyes misted.

Well, it was the truth, wasn't it? She'd already promised herself to him.

Her eyes lowered, her face paper white.

"What is it?" he asked gently, lifting her face to his puzzled eyes. "Honey, what did I say?"

She tried to smile and shook her head, but she was choking to death on her pride.

"Here it is," the saleslady cooed, reappearing with a fantasy of hand-painted organza which she was holding up carefully by the hanger. It was sheer and off-white with a delicate pattern of tiny green leaves. The bodice was held in place by swaths of the same silky fabric. Amanda, even when she'd had money to burn, had never seen anything so lovely.

"Just perfect," the saleslady promised, and named the house it had been designed by. Before Amanda could protest, she was shuttled off to a fitting room, where she was eased into the dream of luxury by deft, cool hands.

She stared at herself in the mirror. It had been so long since she'd worn such an expensive dress, felt the richness of organza against her slender body. The pale green highlighted her deep brown eyes, lent a hint of mystery to the shadows of her face. The color was good for her honey tan skin, too, giving it a rich gold color that went well with her long, wispy curls of silvery blond hair.

"Are you going to spend the day in there?" a deep, impatient voice grumbled from just outside the curtain.

She shifted her shoulders and walked out gracefully, her eyes apprehensive as his lightning gaze whipped over her while the saleslady stood smugly to one side.

"Isn't it just perfect?" the older woman said with a smile.

"Perfect," Jace said quietly, but he was looking at Amanda's flushed face, not at the dress, and the look in his silver eyes made her knees go weak. "I'll take it."

Amanda took the dress off and waited for it to be boxed, her eyes on Jace's expressionless face.

"I haven't asked the price," she said softly, "but it's going to be an arm and a leg, Jace. I'd really rather get something . . . less costly."

"I'm not poor," he reminded her with a wry glance. "Remember?"

Her eyes lowered. She felt faintly sick inside. Was that what he thought of her, that she'd finally given in for mercenary reasons, that she was allowing herself to be bought for a few pretty clothes and an unlimited allowance? She stood with her head bowed while Jace got out his credit card and took care of the details. He handed her the box with the exclusive store name on it, watching quietly as she stared down at it blankly.

He sighed heavily, turning away. "Let's go," he said tightly.

He unlocked the door of his silver Mercedes and, taking the box from her, tossed it carelessly into the back seat before he went around and got in behind the wheel. There was a carefully controlled violence in the way he started the car and pulled it out into traffic.

"Light me a cigarette," he said, tossing the package of menthol cigarettes into her lap.

She obeyed him without even thinking, using the car lighter, and handed it back to him without a word.

"Well, don't you like the damned dress?" he asked shortly.

"It's very nice. Thank you."

"Will you please, damn it, tell me what's upset you?" he asked, slanting an irritated glance at her.

"Nothing," she said softly. Her eyes were staring straight ahead, her heart breaking.

"Nothing." He took a draw from the cigarette. "This isn't the best way to begin a relationship, doe-eyes."

"I know." She drew in a steadying breath. "I love the dress, Jason. I just . . . I wish you hadn't spent so much on me."

"Don't you think you're worth it, honey? I do." He reached across the console and took her hand in his, locking his hard, cool fingers into hers with a slow, sensuous pressure that made her breath catch.

She stared down at his brown fingers, so dark against her soft tan. His hand squeezed warmly, swallowing hers, his thumb caressing. "You're so dark," she murmured.

"And you're so fair," he replied. He glanced at her briefly before he turned his attention back to traffic. "I'm sorry I have to go to the office. I'd rather spend the day with you."

She sighed wistfully, looking down again. "I'd have liked that," she murmured absently.

"So would I." He drew his hand away to make a turn, and there was a comfortable silence between them until they pulled up in front of the house. "I won't be here until the last minute, but wait for me," he told her. "You're going to the Sullevans' with me, not with Duncan."

"Yes, Jason," she said gently.

He leaned across her to open the door, his face barely an inch away, and she could smell the expensive tang of his cologne, the smoky warmth of his breath. Her eyes lingered on the hard lines of his dark face and involuntarily fell to his mouth. Impulsively she moved her head a fraction of an inch and brushed her lips against his.

He caught his breath, his eyes suddenly fiery, burning with emotion.

"Sorry," she whispered, shaken by the violence in the look.

"For what?" he asked tautly. "Do you have to ask permission to kiss me, to touch me?"

"I . . . I'm not used to it."

"I told you this morning," he said gruffly, "I love the feel of your hands on me. My God, you could climb into bed with me if you felt like it, and I'd hold my arms open for you, don't you know that?"

She reached up and tentatively brushed a strand of hair away from his broad forehead, her eyes warm on his face. "It's so new," she whispered.

"Yes." He bent and took her mouth gently under his, probing her soft lips, his breath whispering against her cheek as his hand held her throat, holding her face up. "Oh, God, your mouth is so soft," he whispered tenderly, "I could spend the rest of my life kissing you."

She reached up and slid her arms around his neck. "I like kissing you, too," she murmured. She kissed him back, hard, her arms possessive.

"Don't go to work," she whispered.

"If I stay here, I'll make love to you," he murmured against her eager mouth, his hands cupping her face while he tasted every sweet curve of her lips. "And I don't want to do that yet."

"I think that's a terrible thing to say," she murmured back.

His lips smiled against hers. "I want it to be just right with you," he whispered.

She felt a tingle of excitement run the length of her body as the words made pictures in her mind. Jace's body against hers on cool, crisp sheets, the darkness all around them, his mouth on her soft skin. . . .

"You trembled," he whispered softly. "Thinking about how it would be with me?"

"Yes," she admitted breathlessly.

"God . . . !" He half lifted her across the seat, crushing her against his hard chest, his mouth suddenly rough, demanding, as it opened on hers. She went under in a maze of surging emotion, moaning softly at the hunger he was arousing.

All at once he let her go, easing her away from him breath by breath, his eyes stormy, hungry. "Get out of here before I wrestle you down on the floorboard," he murmured half-humorously.

"Pagan," she breathed, easing her long legs out the door.

"Puritan," he countered. "I'll see you tonight. And don't put your hair up. Leave it like that."

She got her box out and stared at him through the open door. "It won't look elegant enough," she argued.

"I don't want you elegant," he returned, his eyes sliding over her. "I want you just the way you are, no changes. Remember, wait for me."

"All right."

He closed the door and drove off without looking back.

*   *   *

That evening she stood in her bedroom, dressed in the exquisite gown Jace had bought for her. It fit like a caressing glove. She stared in the mirror as if she'd never seen her own reflection, marveling at the soft lines that emphasized all her best features. The frothy skirt drew attention to her long, slender legs with its curling mass of layered ruffles. The bodice clung to her small, high breasts, draping across them with just a hint of sensuality. And the cut emphasized just how tiny her waist really was. The green and white pattern was the perfect foil for her blond fairness, lending her a sophistication far beyond her years. With her hair long and soft down her back, she looked more like a model than an advertising executive.

She was nervous when she went downstairs an hour later, to join Jace and Duncan and Marguerite in the living room where they were enjoying a last-minute drink.

They were deep in a discussion, but Jace turned in time to watch her entrance, and something flashed like silver candles in his eyes as they traveled slowly over her. Something strangely new lingered there...pride... possession....

Her own eyes were drawn to the figure he cut in his elegant evening clothes. The darkness of the suit, added to the frothy whiteness of his silk shirt, gave him a suave masculinity that made her want to touch him. He was devastating, like something out of a men's fashion magazine, and was completely unaware of his own attraction as a cat of its mysterious eyes.

Two other heads turned abruptly, their attention caught by the utter silence, and Duncan let loose with a long, leering whistle.

"Wow!" he burst out, moving forward to walk around her like a prospective buyer around a sleek new car. "If you aren't a dream and a half. Where did you get that dress?"

"The tooth fairy brought it," she said lightly, avoiding Jace's possessive eyes.

Marguerite laughed. "You're a vision, Amanda. What a lovely dress!"

"Thank you," she murmured demurely.

Duncan started to take her arm, only to find Jace there ahead of him. "My turn, I think," he said with a level look that started Duncan backstepping.

"Who am I to argue?" Duncan teased. He turned to Marguerite. "Mother?"

Marguerite moved forward, very elegant in her pale blue satin gown and fox stole. "Oh, Amanda, I forgot...your arms will chill in the night air!"

"No, they won't!" Amanda argued quickly, already dreading that chill, but too proud to accept charity.

"Nonsense! I have a lovely shawl. Just a minute." And she walked to the hall closet, coming instantly back with a black mantilla-style shawl which she draped around the young girl's shoulders. "Now! Just the thing, too. It makes you look mysterious."

"I feel rather mysterious," Amanda said with a smile, and caught her breath as Jace came up beside her to guide her out the door with a lean, warm hand at her waist.

Amanda had never been as aware of Jace as she was on the way to the Sullevans' house. Her eyes were involuntarily drawn to his hard profile, his mouth, and she felt swirls of excitement running over her smooth skin at the memory of his kisses. He glanced sideways once and met her searching eyes as they stopped for a red light, and the force of his gaze knocked the breath out of her. She let her eyes fall to his lean, strong hands on the steering wheel, and it was all she could do not to lean across and run her fingers over them. If only things had been different. She was Jace's woman now, but not the way she wanted to be. He thought she was only interested in his money, when all she truly wanted was to be allowed to love him. Her eyes stared blankly out the window. She wondered miserably how he was going to arrange it all. Would she have an apartment in town? Or would he buy her a house? She flushed, thinking of Marguerite's face when Jace told her. No back alleys, he'd said, but then he wasn't considering how much it was going to hurt Amanda. Why should he, she thought bitterly, he was a man. Men considered their own pleasure, nothing else, and it wouldn't hurt his reputation.

The big house was ablaze with light when they got there, and Amanda felt dwarfed by Jace even in her spiked heels as they walked into the foyer to be met by Mr. Sullevan, Marguerite's co-host. The elegant entranceway was graced by a huge Waterford crystal chandelier, cloud-soft eggshell white carpet under their feet and priceless objets d'art on dainty tables lining the walls.

"What a showplace!" Duncan murmured, walking into the crowded ballroom with Jace and Amanda while his mother remained behind to help greet the other guests.

"Old money," Jace replied coolly. "This spread was part of a Spanish land grant."

"Well, it's something. And speaking of things that are easy on the eyes," Duncan added with a mock leer at Amanda, "that's an enticing little number you're wearing tonight. You never did tell me where you got it."

Jace's eyes glittered a warning at his brother, and his hand found Amanda's at the same time, linking his fingers with hers in a possessive grasp.

"I bought it for her," he told Duncan, his voice soft and dangerous.

That note in Jace's deep tones was enough for Duncan. He'd heard it too many times not to recognize it.

"Excuse me," he murmured with a wry smile at Amanda, "I think I'll go scout the territory for single beauties. See you later."

Amanda's face was a wild rose. She couldn't even look at Jace. "Was that necessary?" she said in an embarrassed, strangled tone.

"You're mine," he replied curtly. "The sooner he knows it, the safer he's going to be."

She looked up at him. "You made me sound cheap, Jason," she said in a voice that trembled with hurt.

His eyes narrowed, his face hardened at the remark, as if he couldn't believe what she'd said. "What the hell are you talking about? I don't understand you, Amanda. I've offered you everything I can. Take it or leave it!"

With a small cry, she tore away from him and ran through the crowd to where Duncan was sipping punch at the buffet table beside the crystal punch bowl.

He took one look at her white face and handed her a small crystal cup of punch, his eyes glancing across the room to Jace's rigid back in a semicircle of local cattlemen.

"You're safe," he told Amanda. "He'll do nothing but talk cattle futures for the next half hour or so. What happened this time?"

Her lower lip trembled. "He said...oh, never mind, Duncan," she sighed wearily, "what's the use? As far as Jason's concerned, the only asset he's got is a fat wallet." She laughed mirthlessly. "I think I'll become a professional gold digger."

"You haven't got the look," Duncan said blandly. "Have a sandwich."

She took it. "Do I look hungry?" she asked.

"As if you'd like to bite something," he mused, winking. "Don't let him get to you, Mandy, he just doesn't know what's hit him, that's all."

"I wish it were that simple," she sighed with a smile.

"It's not?"

If you only knew, she thought humorously. She stared at the cup of punch and realized she was feeling light-headed. "What's in this?" she asked.

"Half the liquor cabinet," Duncan replied with a grin. "Go slow."

"Maybe I feel reckless," she replied, throwing down the rest of the punch. She handed him her empty cup. "Pour me another round, masked stranger."

"I don't think this is a wise idea," he reminded her, but he filled the small crystal cup again.

"I don't think so either," she agreed. "It's better not to think, it gets you in trouble."

He watched her quietly. "Know something?" he asked gently.

She peeked up at him over the rim of the cup. "What?"

He smiled. "I'm going to like having you for a sister-in-law."

The tears came unbidden and started rolling down her cheeks. It was the last straw. Duncan, dear Duncan, didn't understand. Jason didn't want a wife, he wanted a mistress, someone to satisfy his passions but not to share his life. And if he ever did marry, it wouldn't be Amanda.

"Mandy!" Duncan burst out, aghast at her reaction.

"What relation will you be to his mistress, Duncan?" she whispered brokenly. "Because that's all he wants me for!"

She turned and ran out onto the dark patio, leaning over the balustrade while she wept like a child.

Duncan stared after her, only dimly aware that someone was standing beside him.

"What the hell did you say to her?" Jace demanded, his eyes blazing.

Duncan blinked at him. "Too much, I'm afraid," he said quietly. His eyes searched his brother's. "I told her I was going to enjoy being her brother-in-law. I guess I jumped the gun, but the way you two have been looking at each other lately, it was a natural assumption."

The older man's face hardened. "You've got a big mouth," he said curtly.

"Amen," Duncan said miserably. He frowned. "Are you serious about her being your mistress?" he asked suddenly, his gaze hard.

Jace's eyes flashed wildly. "Mistress?" he burst out.

"That's what she thinks you want," was the cool reply. "She said you think she's a gold digger."

Jace's eyes closed on a harsh sigh. "Oh, my God."

"What is it?" Duncan asked curiously.

"History repeating itself," Jace ground out. But he wasn't looking at Duncan, his eyes were on the patio through the open doors. He started toward it without another word.

Amanda brushed at the hot tears, her heart weighing her down. She wanted nothing more than to get on a plane

and fly away from Casa Verde forever. She needed her
head examined for having agreed to stay until tonight. If
only she had been well enough to leave with Bea! Then at
least she would have been out of Jace's way, out of reach
of his sarcasm, his contempt. She never should have offered herself to him. The gift of love she'd thought to
make him had only lessened his opinion of her. The tears
rushed down her cheeks once more. She'd have to stop
this. She'd have to stop crying. Somehow, she was going
to walk back into that party and smile and pretend she
was the belle of the ball, and then she was going to get
Duncan to take her to the airport. . . .

"It's quiet out here."

She stiffened at the slow, deep voice behind her. Her
hands gripped the stone balustrade, but she didn't turn.

"Yes," she murmured coldly.

She felt rather than heard him move behind her. She
could feel the warmth of his body against her back, feel
his breath in her hair.

His fingers lightly touched the wispy curls over her
shoulders and she tensed involuntarily.

"Amanda . . ." he began heavily.

"I'm going home," she said without preamble,
brushing away the rest of the tears with the back of her
hands. "And you can have the dress back, I don't want
it. Give it to one of your other women," she added curtly.

"There hasn't been another woman," he replied, his
voice clipped, measured. "Not since you were sixteen
years old and I felt your mouth under mine for the first
time."

She froze against the cold stone. Had she heard him
right? Surely her ears were playing tricks on her! She
turned around slowly, and looked up into his shadowed
eyes. Their silver glitter was just faintly visible in the light
from the noisy ballroom.

He rammed his hands into his pockets and glared down
at her, his legs apart, his body tall and faintly arrogant in
the stance. "Shocked?" he asked shortly. "Are you too
innocent to realize that the reason I was so hungry for
you was that I hadn't had a woman in years?"

"Not...for lack of opportunity, surely," she managed unsteadily.

"I've had that," he agreed, nodding. "I'm rich. Women, most of them, would do anything for money."

"Some of them must have wanted just you," she said quietly.

He half smiled. "Desire on one side isn't enough. I don't want anyone but you."

Her eyes searched his in the sudden stillness. Inside, the band was playing a love song, soft and sweet and achingly haunting.

He moved closer, still not touching her, but close enough that she had to look up to see his face.

"Damn it, do I have to say the words?" he ground out.

Her lips fell open. She hung there, trembling, her eyes like a startled fawn's, wide and unblinking.

"I love you, Amanda," he said in a voice like dark velvet, his gaze holding hers, his face taut with barely leashed emotion.

Tears burned her eyes again just before they overflowed and trailed down her cheeks, silver in the dim light.

She lifted her arms, trembling, her lips trying to form words and failing miserably.

He didn't seem to need them. He reached out and caught her up against his taut body, his arms crushing her to him as his mouth found hers blindly and took it in a wild, passionate silence that seemed to blaze up like a forest fire between them.

Her fingers tangled in the cool strands of hair at his nape, her nails lightly scraping against the tense muscles there, her mouth moaning under his, parting, inviting a penetration that caused her slender, aching body to arch recklessly toward his in blatant sensuality.

"Say it," he ground out against her mouth, his voice rasping in the darkness.

"I love you, too," she whispered breathlessly. "Hopelessly, deathlessly..." The rest became a muffled gasp as he kissed her again, his mouth rough and then gentle, tender, as it asked questions and received sweet answers all without a word being spoken.

His mouth slid against her soft, tear-stained cheek to come to rest at her ear, his arms contracting warmly at her back, his breath coming as hard and erratic as her own.

"Let's get something straight right now," he whispered gruffly. "When I said you were mine, I meant for life, and I'm going to put two rings on your finger to prove it. Oh, God, Amanda, I want so much more than the pleasure we're going to give each other in the darkness. I want to share my life with you, and have you share yours with me. I want to hold you when you hurt and dry the tears when you cry. I want to watch you laughing when we play, and see the light in your eyes when we love each other. I want to give you children and watch them grow up on Casa Verde." He drew back and looked down at her with a light in his eyes that she'd waited for, prayed for. "I love you almost beyond bearing, did you know that? I've hurt you because I was hurting. Wanting you, needing you, and I could never get close enough to tell you, because you were forever running away. Don't you think it's time you stopped?" His arms drew her up closer. "Marry me. Live with me. You're the air in my lungs, Amanda. Without you, I'd stop breathing."

She smiled at him through her tears. "It's that way with me, too," she managed brokenly. "I want everything with you. I want to give you everything I have."

"All I want is your heart, love," he said softly, bending. "I'll gladly trade you mine for it."

Her lips trembled as they welcomed his, and the stars went out while she kissed him back as if she were dying, as if they were parting forever and this was the last kiss they would ever share.

She could feel his body taut with longing, feel his heartbeat like muffled thunder against her softness as his hands moved lazily, tenderly on her body and made it tremble with sweet hungers. Her fingers tangled in his black hair and clung, holding his mouth even closer over hers, feeling the smooth fabric of his evening jacket against her bare arms as he shifted her and brought her even closer.

"Are you sure my heart's all you want?" she whispered unsteadily against his devouring mouth, bursting with the joy of loving and being loved, the newness of possession.

He chuckled softly, his face changed, his eyes soft with what he was feeling. "Not quite," he admitted. "The only thing that's saving you right now is that I can't make love to you here."

Her teeth nipped lovingly at his sensuous lower lip. "You could take me home and love me."

"Oh, I intend to," he murmured with a wicked smile. "But not," he added, "until I can get Duncan and Mother out of the way for a few days. And that won't happen until after the wedding, Miss Carson, if I know my mother."

Her dark eyes laughed up at him, loving him. "Back seats are very popular," she pointed out.

"Not with me," he informed her.

"There are motels...."

He looked down his arrogant nose at her and lifted an eyebrow. "Trying to seduce me, Amanda?"

She flushed lightly. "As a matter of fact, I am."

He studied her soft, slightly swollen mouth, and his arms wrapped around her in warm affection. "You came pretty close to it last night," he reminded her, letting his darkening eyes drop to the bodice of her gown. "I'll carry that memory around in my head like the dog-eared picture of you I've carried around in my wallet for the past seven years."

Her eyes widened. "You have a picture of me?"

He nodded. "One Duncan snapped of you, running, with your hair in a glorious tangle and your skirts flying...smiling with the sun shining out of you. I'd like to have you painted like that. My God, it was so beautiful I stole it right out of his room, and felt guilty for a week."

She managed an incredulous smile. "But why didn't you just ask him for it?"

"He'd have known why I wanted it." He brushed his lips gently against her forehead. "Doe-eyes, I've loved you so long," he whispered. "Even when I told myself I hated you, when I snapped at you and deliberately hurt you, it was only because I was hurting. Every time you ran, it hurt me more. And then you made that crack about Duncan, the day I got hurt. I'd have done anything to get the truth out of you, I couldn't live with the thought that he'd touched you the way I wanted to."

"You kissed me," she recalled with a lazy smile, reliving that delicious interlude.

"It was like flying," he said gently, his eyes searching, loving. "Holding you, touching you...I'd waited years, and it was worth every one of them, until I let the doubts seep in again and scared you off. I've never trusted women very much, Amanda; it's been hell learning to trust you." His hands caressed her back gently.

"I'll never betray you," she said firmly. "You're all I'll ever want, Jason, despite my mother...."

He silenced her with a quick, rough kiss. "We'll go to the wedding, would you like that?" he asked curtly. "Amanda, if you were already married, I'd like to think I could keep my hands off you, but I don't know. I'm not sure I could. Maybe it was like that with your mother." He shrugged his broad shoulders. "I never dreamed I'd love you like this," he said, his eyes narrow. "I never realized how much I did until that night you and Duncan flew back late from New York. I prayed like I'd never prayed, and when you were back and safe all I could do was yell."

"But you came to me," she whispered, flushing with the memory.

"And we loved each other," he whispered back, bending to brush his mouth against hers tantalizingly. "The sweetest, slowest, softest loving I've ever known with a woman. The first time between us is going to be like that," he murmured, holding her eyes, watching the shy embarrassment flush her high cheekbones. "I'm going to take all night with you."

"Jason!" She hid her hot face against his chest, hearing the hard, heavy beat of his heart under her ear.

"I'll make it beautiful for you," he whispered, cradling her against him.

"Every time you touch me, it *is* beautiful," she said breathlessly, her eyes closing. "I do love you so, Jason!"

"Just don't ever stop," he murmured. His arms tightened. "Don't ever stop."

"*Now* can I tell her how glad I'll be to have her for a sister-in-law?" came a humorous voice from behind them.

Jace laughed, letting Amanda turn in his possessive arms to face Duncan. "I'll even let you be best man," Jace promised.

"On a temporary basis, of course," Duncan amended with a wry grin. "Mother's already planning the wedding. She, uh, happened to pass by the window a couple of minutes ago."

"You dragged her there, you mean," Amanda laughed.

"Not dragged, exactly," the younger man protested. "More like . . . led. Anyway, when are you going to make it official?"

"In about five minutes," Jace said, feeling Amanda tense. "Before she changes her mind."

"That will be never," she promised over her shoulder, melting at the look in the silver eyes that met hers.

Duncan laughed softly. "I was just remembering back a few years," he explained, noticing the puzzled looks. "When Amanda was calling you 'cowboy' and you were calling her 'Lady.' Ironic."

"She is quite a lady," Jace murmured, smiling at her, and it was no insult this time.

"And as cowboys go," Amanda returned, "he'd be my choice to ride the range with."

"Well, if you two will excuse me, I think I'll go and have a toast with that cute little Sullevan girl. Uh, you might stay away from that window, by the way," Duncan grinned as he turned away. "I think Mother's standing there."

"Duncan," Amanda called.

He turned, "Hmm?"

"Why did you really ask me down here with Terry? Why did you offer us the account?"

Duncan grinned from ear to ear. "Because when you left here six months ago, I just happened to notice that Jace walked around in a perpetual temper and swore every time your name was mentioned. I figured he had it so bad that a little helping hand might improve his disposition. So I gave your very helpful partner a call." He looked from one of them to the other. "And they say Cupid carries a bow. Ridiculous. He carries a telephone, of course, so that he can get people together. See you later, big brother," he added with a wink at Jace.

Jace returned it, with a smile, and Amanda saw, not for the first time, the very real affection that existed between the two brothers.

"Feel like breaking the news now?" Jace asked at her ear. "I want to tell them all that you belong to me."

She turned. "I always have, you know," she whispered.

He caught her up against him and kissed her again, his mouth warm and slow and achingly thorough. At the window, inside the ballroom, a silver-haired lady was smiling happily, already working out the arrangements for the first christening in her mind.

PASSION FLOWER

To Victoria, Texas, with love

1

---
*

Jennifer King eyed the closed hotel room door nervously. She hadn't wanted this assignment, but she hadn't had much choice, either. Her recent illness had left her savings account bare, and this job was all she had to hold on to. It was a long way from the brilliant career in interior decorating she'd left behind in New York. But it was a living.

She pushed back a loose strand of blond hair and hoped she looked sedate enough for the cattleman behind the door. The kind of clothes she'd favored in New York were too expensive for her budget in Atlanta.

She knocked at the door and waited. It seemed to take forever for the man inside to get there. Finally, without warning, the door swung open.

"Miss King?" he asked, smiling pleasantly.

She smiled back. He was much younger than she'd expected him to be. Tall and fair and pleasant. "Yes," she said. "You rang for a temporary secretary?"

"Just need a few letters done, actually," he said, taking the heavy portable typewriter from her hand. "I'm buying some cattle for my brother."

"Yes, Miss James at the agency told me it had to do with cattle." She sat down quickly. She was pale and wan, still feeling the after-effects of a terrible bout with pneumonia.

"Say, are you all right?" he asked, frowning.

"Fine, thank you, Mr. Culhane," she said, remembering his name from Miss James's description of the job. "I'm just getting over pneumonia, and I'm a little weak."

He sat down across from her on the sofa, lean and rangy, and smiled. "I guess it does take the whip out of you. I've never had it myself, but Everett nearly died on us one year. He smokes too much," he confided.

"Your brother?" she asked with polite interest as she got her steno pad and pen from her large purse.

"My brother. The senior partner. Everett runs the show." He sounded just a little jealous. She glanced up. Jennifer was twenty-three, and he couldn't have been much older. She felt a kinship with him. Until their deaths three years back, her parents had pretty much nudged her into the job they thought she wanted. By the sound of it, Everett Culhane had done the same with this young man.

She dug out her pad and pen and crossed her thin legs. All of her was thin. Back in New York, before the frantic pace threatened her health, she'd been slender and poised and pretty enough to draw any man's eye. But now she was only a pale wraith, a ghost of the woman she'd been. Her blond hair was brittle and lusterless, her pale green eyes were dull, without their old sparkle. She looked bad, and that fact registered in the young man's eyes.

"Are you sure you feel up to this?" he asked gently. "You don't look well."

"I'm a little frail, that's all," she replied proudly. "I'm only just out of the hospital, you see."

"I guess that's why," he muttered. He got up, pacing the room, and found some notes scribbled on lined white paper. "Well, this first letter goes to Everett Culhane, Circle C Ranch, Big Spur, Texas."

"Texas?" Her pale eyes lit up. "Really?"

His eyebrows lifted, and he grinned. "Really. The town is named after a king-sized ranch nearby—the Big Spur. It's owned by Cole Everett and his wife Heather, and their three sons. Our ranch isn't a patch on that one, but big brother has high hopes."

"I've always wanted to see a real cattle ranch," she confided. "My grandfather went cowboying out to Texas as a boy. He used to talk about it all the time, and about the places he'd seen, and the history..." She sat up straight, poising her pen over the pad. "Sorry. I didn't mean to get off the track."

"That's all right. Funny, you don't look like a girl who'd care for the outdoors," he commented as he sat back down with the sheaf of papers in his hand.

"I love it," she said quietly. "I lived in a small town until I was ten and my parents moved to Atlanta. I missed it terribly. I still do."

"Can't you go back?" he asked.

She shook her head sadly. "It's too late. I have no family left. My parents are dead. There are a few scattered relatives, but none close enough to visit."

"That's rough. Kind of like me and Everett," he added. "We got raised by our aunt and uncle. At least, I did. Everett wasn't so lucky. Our dad was still alive while he was a boy." His face clouded, as if with an unpleasant memory. He cleared his throat. "Well, anyway, back to the letter..."

He began to dictate, and she kept up with him easily. He thought out the sentences before he gave them to her, so there were few mistakes or changes. She wondered why he didn't just call his brother, but she didn't ask the question. She took down several pages of description about bulls and pedigrees and bloodlines. There was a second letter, to a bank executive in Big Spur, detailing the method the Culhane brothers had devised to pay back a sizeable loan. The third letter was to a breeder in Carrollton, outlining transport for a bull the man had evidently purchased from the Culhanes.

"Confused?" he murmured dryly when he stopped.

"It's not my business..." she began gently.

"We're selling off one of our best bulls," he said, "to give us enough down payment on another top breeding bull. Everett is trying for a purebred Hereford herd. But we don't have the cash, so I've come down here to do some fancy trading. I sold the bull we had. Now I'm trying to get a potential seller to come down on his price."

"Wouldn't a phone call to your brother be quicker?" she asked.

"Sure. And Everett would skin my head. I came out here on a bus, for God's sake, instead of a plane. We're just about mortgaged to the hilt, you see. Everett says we can't afford not to pinch pennies." His eyes twinkled. "We've got Highland Scots in our ancestry, you see."

She smiled. "Yes, I suppose so. I can see his point. Phone calls are expensive."

"Especially the kind it would take to relay this much information," he agreed, nodding toward what he'd dictated. "If I get it off today, he'll have it in a day or two. Then, if he thinks it's worth giving what the man wants, he can call me and just say a word or two. In the meantime, I've got other business to attend to."

"Shrewd idea," she murmured.

"'Just a couple more," he continued. He leaned back and studied a magazine. "Okay, this one goes to..." He gave her a name and address in north Georgia, and dictated a letter asking if the breeder could give him a call at the hotel on Friday at 1 p.m. Then he dictated a second letter to a breeder in south Georgia, making the same request for 2 p.m. He grinned at her faint smile.

"Saving money," he assured her. "Although why Everett wants to do it the hard way is beyond me. There's a geologist who swears we've got one hell of a lot of oil on our western boundary, but Everett dug in his heels and refused to sell off the drilling rights. Even for a percentage. Can you beat that? We could be millionaires, and here I sit writing letters asking people to call me, just to save money."

"Why won't he sell?" she asked, curious.

"Because he's a purist," he grumbled. "He doesn't want to spoil the land. He'd rather struggle to make the cattle pay. Fat chance. The way things have been going, we're going to wind up eating those damned purebreds, papers and all."

She laughed helplessly at his phrasing and hid her face in her hand. "Sorry," she mumbled. "I didn't mean to laugh."

"It is kind of funny," he confessed. "But not when you're cutting corners like we are."

She got up and started to lift the typewriter onto the desk by the window, struggling with it.

"Here, let me do that," he said, and put it onto the flat surface for her. "You're pretty weak, little lady."

"I'm getting back on my feet," she assured him. "Just a little wobbly, that's all."

"Well, I'll leave you to it. I'm going down to get a sandwich. Can I bring you something?"

She'd have loved a sandwich, but she wasn't going to put any further drain on his resources. "No, thank you," she said, politely and with a smile. "I just had lunch before I came over here."

"Okay, then. See you in a half hour or so."

He jammed a straw cowboy hat on his head and went out the door, closing it softly behind him.

Jennifer typed the letters quickly and efficiently, even down to the cattle's pedigrees. It was a good thing she'd taken that typing course when she was going through the school of interior design in New York, she thought. It had come in handy when the pressure of competition laid her out. She wasn't ready to handle that competitive rat race again yet. She needed to rest, and by comparison typing letters for out-of-town businessmen was a piece of cake.

She felt oddly sorry for this businessman, and faintly sympathetic with his brother, who'd rather go spare than sell out on his principles. She wondered if he looked like his younger brother.

Her eyes fell on the name she was typing at the bottom of the letter, Robert G. Culhane. That must be the man who'd dictated them. He seemed to know cattle, from his meticulous description of them. Her eyes wandered over what looked like a production record for a herd sire, and she sighed. Texas and cattle. She wondered what the Circle C Ranch was like, and while she finished up the letters, lost herself in dreams of riding horseback over flat plains. Pipe dreams, she thought, smiling as she stacked the neat letters with their accompanying envelopes. She'd never see Texas.

Just as she rose from the typewriter, the door opened
and Robert Culhane was back. He smiled at her.

"Taking a break?" he asked as he swept off his hat and
whirled it onto a table.

"No, I'm finished," she said, astounding him.

"Already?" He grabbed up the letters and bent over
the desk, proofreading them one by one and shaking his
head. "Damn, you're fast."

"I do around a hundred words a minute," she replied. "It's one of my few talents."

"You'd be a godsend at the ranch," he sighed. "It
takes Everett an hour to type one letter. He cusses a blue
streak when he has to write anything on that infernal old
machine. And there are all the production records we
have to keep, and the tax records, and the payroll..." His
head lifted and he frowned. "I don't suppose you'd like
a job?"

She caught her breath. "In Texas?"

"You make it sound like a religious experience," he
murmured on a laugh.

"You can't imagine how much I hate the city," she replied, brushing back a strand of dull hair. "I still cough
all the time because of the pollution, and the apartment
where I live has no space at all. I'd almost work for free
just to be out in the country."

He cocked his head at her and pursed his boyish lips.
"It wouldn't be easy, working for Everett," he said.
"And you'd have to manage your own fare to Big Spur.
You see, I'll need a little time to convince him. You'd
barely get minimum wage. And knowing Everett, you'd
wind up doing a lot of things besides typing. We don't
have a housekeeper..."

Her face lit up. "I can make curtains and cook."

"Do you have a telephone?"

She sighed. "No."

"Kind of in the same boat we are in, aren't you?" he
said with a sympathetic smile. "I'm Robert Culhane, by
the way."

"Jennifer King," she said for the second time that day,
and extended her hand.

"Nice to meet you, Jenny. How can I reach you?"

"The agency will take a message for me," she said.

"Fine. I'll be in town for several more days. I'll be in touch with you before I go back to Texas. Okay?"

She beamed. "You're really serious?"

"I'm really serious. And this is great work," he added, gesturing toward the letters. "Jenny, it won't be an easy life on the Circle C. It's nothing like those fancy ranches you see on television."

"I'm not expecting it to be," she said honestly, and was picturing a ramshackle house that needed paint and curtains and overhauling, and two lonely men living in it. She smiled. "I'm just expecting to be needed."

"You'll be that," he sighed, staring at her critically. "But are you up to hard work?"

"I'll manage," she promised. "Being out in the open, in fresh air, will make me strong. Besides, it'll be dry air out there, and it's summer."

"You'll burn up in the heat," he promised.

"I burn up in the heat here," she said. "Atlanta is a southern city. We get hundred-degree temperatures here."

"Just like home," he murmured with a smile.

"I'd like to come," she said as she got her purse and closed up the typewriter. "But I don't want to get you into any trouble with your brother."

"Everett and I hardly ever have anything except trouble," he said easily. "Don't worry about me. You'd be doing us a big favor. I'll talk Everett into it."

"Should I write you another letter?" She hesitated.

He shook his head. "I'll have it out with him when I get home," he said. "No sweat. Thanks for doing my letters. I'll send the agency a check, you tell them."

"I will. And thank you!"

She hardly felt the weight of the typewriter on her way back to the agency. She was floating on a cloud.

Miss James gave her a hard look when she came back in. "You're late," she said. "We had to refuse a call."

"I'm sorry. There were several letters . . ." she began.

"You've another assignment. Here's the address. A politician. Wants several copies of a speech he's giving, to hand out to the press. You're to type the speech and get it photostatted for him.''

She took the outstretched address and sighed. ''The typewriter...?''

''He has his own, an electric one. Leave that one here, if you please.'' Miss James buried her silver head in paperwork. ''You may go home when you finish. I'll see you in the morning. Good night.''

''Good night,'' Jennifer said quietly, sighing as she went out onto the street. It would be well after quitting time when she finished, and Miss James knew it. But perhaps the politician would be generous enough to tip her. If only the Texas job worked out! Jennifer was a scrapper when she was at her peak, but she was weary and sick and dragged out. It wasn't a good time to get into an argument with the only employer she'd been able to find. All the other agencies were overstaffed with out-of-work people begging for any kind of job.

The politician was a city councilman, in a good mood and very generous. Jennifer treated herself to three hamburgers and two cups of coffee on the way back to her small apartment. It was in a private home, and dirt cheap. The landlady wasn't overly friendly, but it was a roof over her head and the price was right.

She slept fitfully, dreaming about the life she'd left behind in New York. It all seemed like something out of a fantasy. The competition for the plum jobs, the cocktail parties to make contacts, the deadlines, the endless fighting to land the best accounts, the agonizing perfecting of color schemes and coordinating pieces to fit fussy tastes... Her nerves had given out, and then her body.

It hadn't been her choice to go to New York. She'd have been happy in Atlanta. But the best schools were up north, and her parents had insisted. They wanted her to have the finest training available, so she let herself be gently pushed. Two years after she graduated, they were dead. She'd never truly gotten over their deaths in the plane crash. They'd been on their way to a party on Christmas Eve. The plane went down in the dark, in a lake, and it had been hours before they were missed.

In the two years since her graduation, Jennifer had landed a job at one of the top interior-decoration businesses in the city. She'd pushed herself over the limit to get clients, going to impossible lengths to please them. The outcome had been inevitable. Pneumonia landed her in the hospital for several days in March, and she was too drained to go back to work immediately after. An up-and-coming young designer had stepped neatly into her place, and she had found herself suddenly without work.

Everything had to go, of course. The luxury apartment, the furs, the designer clothes. She'd sold them all and headed south. Only to find that the job market was overloaded and she couldn't find a job that wouldn't finish killing her. Except at a temporary agency, where she could put her typing skills to work. She started working for Miss James, and trying to recover. But so far she'd failed miserably. And now the only bright spot in her future was Texas.

She prayed as she never had before, struggling from one assignment to the next and hoping beyond hope that the phone call would come. Late one Friday afternoon, it did. And she happened to be in the office when it came.

"Miss King?" Robert Culhane asked on a laugh. "Still want to go to Texas?"

"Oh, yes!" she said fervently, holding tightly to the telephone cord.

"Then pack a bag and be at the ranch bright and early a week from Monday morning. Got a pencil? Okay, here's how to get there."

She was so excited she could barely scribble. She got down the directions. "I can't believe it, it's like a dream!" she said enthusiastically. "I'll do a good job, really I will. I won't be any trouble, and the pay doesn't matter!"

"I'll tell Everett," he chuckled. "Don't forget. You needn't call. Just come on out to the ranch. I'll be there to smooth things over with old Everett, okay?"

"Okay. Thank you!"

"Thank *you*, Miss King," he said. "See you a week from Monday."

"Yes, sir!" She hung up, her face bright with hope. She was actually going to Texas!

"Miss King?" Miss James asked suspiciously.

"Oh! I won't be back in after today, Miss James," she said politely. "Thank you for letting me work with you. I've enjoyed it very much."

Miss James looked angry. "You can't just walk out like this," she said.

"But I can," Jennifer said, with some of her old spirit. She picked up her purse. "I didn't sign a contract, Miss James. And if you were to push the point, I'd tell you that I worked a great deal of overtime for which I wasn't paid," she added with a pointed stare. "How would you explain that to the people down at the state labor department?"

Miss James stiffened. "You're ungrateful."

"No, I'm not. I'm very grateful. But I'm leaving, all the same. Good day." She nodded politely just before she went out, and closed the door firmly behind her.

2

*

It was blazing hot for a spring day in Texas. Jennifer stopped in the middle of the ranch road to rest for a minute and to set her burdens down on the dusty, graveled ground. She wished for the tenth time in as many minutes that she'd let the cab driver take her all the way to the Culhanes' front door. But she'd wanted to walk. It hadn't seemed a long way from the main road. And it was so beautiful, with the wildflowers strewn across the endless meadows toward the flat horizon. Bluebonnets, which she'd only read about until then, and Mexican hat and Indian paintbrush. Even the names of the flowers were poetic. But her enthusiasm had outweighed her common sense. And her strength.

She'd tried to call the ranch from town—apparently Everett and Robert Culhane did have the luxury of a telephone. But it rang and rang with no answer. Well, it was Monday, and she'd been promised a job. She hefted her portable typewriter and her suitcase and started out again.

Her pale eyes lifted to the house in the distance. It was a two-story white frame building, with badly peeling paint and a long front porch. Towering live oaks protected it from the sun, trees bigger than anything Jennifer had seen in Georgia. And the feathery green trees with the crooked trunks had to be mesquite. She'd never seen it, but she'd done her share of reading about it.

On either side of the long, graveled driveway were fences, gray with weathering and strung with rusting barbed wire. Red-coated cattle grazed behind the fences, and her eyes lingered on the wide horizon. She'd always thought Georgia was big—until now. Texas was just un-

real. In a separate pasture, a mare and her colt frolicked
in the hot sun.

Jennifer pushed back a strand of dull blond hair that
had escaped from her bun. In a white shirtwaist dress and
high heels, she was a strange sight to be walking up the
driveway of a cattle ranch. But she'd wanted to make a
good impression.

Her eyes glanced down ruefully at the red dust on the
hem of her dress, and the scuff marks on her last good
pair of white sling pumps. She could have cried. One of
her stockings had run, and she was sweating. She could
barely have looked worse if she'd planned it.

She couldn't help being a little nervous about the older
brother. She had Everett Culhane pictured as a staid old
rancher with a mean temper. She'd met businessmen like
him before, and dealt with them. She wasn't afraid of
him. But she hoped that he'd be glad of her help. It would
make things easier all around.

Her footsteps echoed along the porch as she walked up
the worn steps. She would have looked around more
carefully weeks ago, but now she was tired and run down
and just too exhausted to care what her new surroundings looked like.

She paused at the screen door, and her slender fingers
brushed the dust from her dress. She put the suitcase and
the typewriter down, took a steadying breath, and
knocked.

There was no sound from inside the house. The
wooden door was standing open, and she thought she
heard the whir of a fan. She knocked again. Maybe it
would be the nice young man she'd met in Atlanta who
would answer the door. She only hoped she was welcome.

The sound of quick, hard footsteps made her heart
quicken. Someone was home, at least. Maybe she could
sit down. She was feeling a little faint.

"Who the hell are you?" came a harsh masculine voice
from behind the screen door, and Jennifer looked up into
the hardest face and the coldest dark eyes she'd ever seen.

She couldn't even find her voice. Her immediate reaction was to turn around and run for it. But she'd come
too far, and she was too tired.

"I'm Jennifer King," she said as professionally as she
could. "Is Robert Culhane home, please?"

She was aware of the sudden tautening of his big body,
a harsh intake of breath, before she looked up and saw
the fury in his dark eyes.

"What the hell kind of game are you playing, lady?"
he demanded.

She stared at him. It had been a long walk, and now it
looked as if she might have made a mistake and come to
the wrong ranch. Her usual confidence faltered. "Is this
the Circle C ranch?" she asked.

"Yes, it is."

He wasn't forthcoming, and she wondered if he might
be one of the hired hands. "Is this where Robert Culhane
lives?" she persisted, trying to peek past him—there was
a lot of him, all hard muscle and blue denim.

"Bobby was killed in a bus wreck a week ago," he said
harshly.

Jennifer was aware of a numb feeling in her legs. The
long trip of the bus, the heavy suitcase, the effects of her
recent illness—all of it added up to exhaustion. And
those cold words were the final blow. With a pitiful little
sound, she sank down on the porch, her head whirling,
nausea running up into her throat like warm water.

The screen door flew open and a pair of hard, impatient arms reached down to lift her. She felt herself effortlessly carried, like a sack of flour, into the cool house.
She was unceremoniously dumped down onto a worn
brocade sofa and left there while booted feet stomped off
into another room. There were muttered words that she
was glad she couldn't understand, and clinking sounds.
Then, a minute later, a glass of dark amber liquid was
held to her numb lips and a hard hand raised her head.

She sipped at the cold, sweet iced tea like a runner on
the desert when confronted with wet salvation. She
struggled to catch her breath and sat up, gently nudging
the dark, lean hand holding the glass to one side. She

breathed in deeply, trying to get her whirling mind to slow down. She was still trying to take it all in. She'd been promised a job, she'd come hundreds of miles at her own expense to work for minimum wage, and now the man who'd offered it to her was dead. That was the worst part, imagining such a nice young man dead.

"You look like a bleached handkerchief," the deep, harsh voice observed.

She sighed. "You ought to write for television. You sure do have a gift for prose."

His dark eyes narrowed. "Walking in this heat without a hat. My God, how many stupid city women are there in the world? And what landed you on my doorstep?"

She lifted her eyes then, to look at him properly. He was darkly tanned, and there were deep lines in his face, from the hatchet nose down to the wide, chiseled mouth. His eyes were deep-set, unblinking under heavy dark brows and a wide forehead. His hair was jet-black, straight and thick and a little shaggy. He was wearing what had to be work clothes: faded denim jeans that emphasized long, powerfully muscled legs, and a matching shirt whose open neck revealed a brown chest thick with short, curling hair. He had the look of a man who was all business, all the time. All at once she realized that this man wasn't the hired hand she'd mistaken him for.

"You're Everett Culhane," she said hesitantly.

His face didn't move. Not a muscle in it changed position, but she had the distinct feeling that the sound of his name on her lips had shocked him.

She took another long sip of the tea and sighed at the pleasure of the icy liquid going down her parched throat.

"How far did you walk?" he asked.

"Just from the end of your driveway," she admitted, looking down at her ruined shoes. "Distance is deceptive out here."

"Haven't you ever heard of sunstroke?"

She nodded. "It just didn't occur to me."

She put the glass down on the napkin he'd brought with it. Well, this was Texas. How sad that she wouldn't see anything more of it.

"I'm very sorry about your brother, Mr. Culhane," she said with dignity. "I didn't know him very well, but he seemed like a nice man." She got up with an odd kind of grace despite the unsteadiness of her legs. "I won't take up any more of your time."

"Why did you come, Miss King?"

She shook her head. "It doesn't matter now in the least." She turned and went out the screen door, lifting her suitcase and typewriter from where they'd fallen when she fainted. It was going to be a long walk back to town, but she'd just have to manage it. She had bus fare back home and a little more. A cab was a luxury now, with no job at the end of her long ride.

"Where do you think you're going?" Everett Culhane asked from behind her, his tone like a whiplash.

"Back to town," she said without turning. "Goodbye, Mr. Culhane."

"Walking?" he mused. "In this heat, without a hat?"

"Got here, didn't I?" she drawled as she walked down the steps.

"You'll never make it back. Wait a minute. I'll drive you."

"No, thanks," she said proudly. "I get around all right by myself, Mr. Culhane. I don't need any handouts."

"You'll need a doctor if you try that walk," he said, and turned back into the house.

She thought the matter was settled, until a battered red pickup truck roared up beside her and stopped. The passenger door flew open.

"Get in," he said curtly, in a tone that made it clear he expected instant obedience.

"I said . . ." she began irritatedly.

His dark eyes narrowed. "I don't mind lifting you in and holding you down until we get to town," he said quietly.

With a grimace, she climbed in, putting the typewriter and suitcase on the floorboard.

There was a marked lack of conversation. Everett smoked his cigarette with sharp glances in her direction when she began coughing. Her lungs were still sensitive, and he seemed to be smoking shucks or something equally potent. Eventually he crushed out the cigarette and cracked a window.

"You don't sound well," he said suddenly.

"I'm getting over pneumonia," she said, staring lovingly at the horizon. "Texas sure is big."

"It sure is." He glanced at her. "Which part of it do you call home?"

"I don't."

The truck lurched as he slammed on the brakes. "What did you say?"

"I'm not a Texan," she confessed. "I'm from Atlanta."

"Georgia?"

"Is there another one?"

He let out a heavy breath. "What the hell did you mean, coming this distance just to see a man you hardly knew?" he burst out. "Surely to God, it wasn't love at first sight?"

"Love?" She blinked. "Heavens, no. I only did some typing for your brother."

He cut off the engine. "Start over. Start at the beginning. You're giving me one hell of a headache. How did you wind up out here?"

"Your brother offered me a job," she said quietly. "Typing. Of course, he said there'd be other duties as well. Cooking, cleaning, things like that. And a very small salary," she added with a tiny smile.

"He was honest with you, at least," he growled. "But then why did you come? Didn't you believe him?"

"Yes, of course," she said hesitantly. "Why wouldn't I want to come?"

He started to light another cigarette, stared hard at her, and put the pack back in his shirt pocket. "Keep talking."

He was an odd man, she thought. "Well, I'd lost my old job, because once I got over the pneumonia I was too weak to keep up the pace. I got a job in Atlanta with one of the temporary talent agencies doing typing. My speed is quite good, and it was something that didn't wring me out, you see. Mr. Culhane wanted some letters typed. We started talking,'' she smiled, remembering how kind he'd been, "and when I found out he was from Texas, from a real ranch, I guess I just went crazy. I've spent my whole life listening to my grandfather relive his youth in Texas, Mr. Culhane. I've read everything Zane Grey and Louis Lamour ever wrote, and it was the dream of my life to come out here. The end of the rainbow. I figured that a low salary on open land would be worth a lot more than a big salary in the city, where I was choking to death on smog and civilization. He offered me the job and I said yes on the spot.'' She glanced at him ruefully. "I'm not usually so slow. But I was feeling so bad, and it sounded so wonderful . . . I didn't even think about checking with you first. Mr. Culhane said he'd have it all worked out, and that I was just to get on a bus and come on out today.'' Her eyes clouded. "I'm so sorry about him. Losing the job isn't nearly as bad as hearing that he . . . was killed. I liked him.''

Everett's fingers were tapping an angry pattern on the steering wheel. "A job.'' He laughed mirthlessly, then sighed. "Well, maybe he had a point. I'm so behind on my production records and tax records, it isn't funny. I'm choking to death on my own cooking, the house hasn't been swept in a month . . .'' He glanced at her narrowly. "You aren't pregnant?''

Her pale eyes flashed at him. "That, sir, would make medical history.''

One dark eyebrow lifted and he glanced at her studiously before he smiled. "Little Southern lady, are you really that innocent?''

"Call me Scarlett and, unemployment or no unemployment, I'll paste you one, cowboy,'' she returned with a glimmer of her old spirit. It was too bad that the outburst triggered a coughing spree.

"Damn,'' he muttered, passing her his handkerchief. "All right, I'll stop baiting you. Do you want the job, or don't you? Robert was right about the wages. You'll get bed and board free, but it's going to be a frugal existence. Interested?''

"If it means getting to stay in Texas, yes, I am."

He smiled. "How old are you, schoolgirl?"

"I haven't been a schoolgirl for years, Mr. Culhane," she told him. "I'm twenty-three, in fact." She glared at him. "How old are you?"

"Make a guess," he invited.

Her eyes went from his thick hair down the hawklike features to his massive chest, which tapered to narrow hips, long powerful legs, and large, booted feet. "Thirty," she said.

He chuckled softly. It was the first time she'd heard the deep, pleasant sound, and it surprised her to find that he was capable of laughter. He didn't seem like the kind of man who laughed very often.

His eyes wandered over her thin body with amused indifference, and she regretted for a minute that she was such a shadow of her former self. "Try again, honey," he said.

She noticed then the deep lines in his darkly tanned face, the sprinkling of gray hair at his temples. In the open neck of his shirt, she could see threads of silver among the curling dark hair. No, he wasn't as young as she'd first thought.

"Thirty-four," she guessed.

"Add a year and you've got it."

She smiled. "Poor old man," she said with gentle humor.

He chuckled again. "That's no way to talk to your new boss," he cautioned.

"I won't forget again, honestly." She stared at him. "Do you have other people working for you?"

"Just Eddie and Bib," he said. "They're married." He nodded as he watched her eyes become wide and apprehensive. "That's right. We'll be alone. I'm a bachelor and there's no staff in the house."

"Well . . ."

"There'll be a lock on your door," he said after a minute. "When you know me better, you'll see that I'm pretty conventional in my outlook. It's a big house. We'll rattle around like two peas in a pod. It's only on rare occasions that I'm in before bedtime." His dark eyes held hers. "And for the record, my taste doesn't run to city girls."

That sounded as if there was a good reason for his taste in women, but she didn't pry. "I'll work hard, Mr. Culhane."

"My name is Everett," he said, watching her. "Or Rett, if you prefer. You can cook meals and do the laundry and housekeeping. And when you have time, you can work in what passes for my office. Wages won't be much. I can pay the bills, and that's about it."

"I don't care about getting rich." Meanwhile she was thinking fast, sorely tempted to accept the offer, but afraid of the big, angry man at her side. There were worse things than being alone and without money, and she didn't really know him at all.

He saw the thoughts in her mind. "Jenny Wren," he said softly, "do I look like a mad rapist?"

Hearing her name that way on his lips sent a surge of warmth through her. No one had called her by a pet name since the death of her parents.

"No," she said quietly. "Of course you don't. I'll work for you, Mr. Culhane."

He didn't answer her. He only scanned her face and nodded. Then he started the truck, turned it around, and headed back to the Circle C Ranch.

3

---
*

Two hours later, Jennifer was well and truly in residence, to the evident amusement of Everett's two ranch-hands. They apparently knew better than to make any snide comments about her presence, but they did seem to find something fascinating about having a young woman around the place.

Jennifer had her own room, with peeling wallpaper, worn blue gingham curtains at the windows, and a faded quilt on the bed. Most of the house was like that. Even the rugs on the floor were faded and worn from use. She'd have given anything to be robust and healthy and have a free hand to redecorate the place. It had such wonderful potential with its long history and simple, un-cluttered architecture.

The next morning she slept late, rising to bright sun-light and a strange sense that she belonged there. She hadn't felt that way since her childhood, and couldn't help wondering why. Everett had been polite, but not much more. He wasn't really a welcoming kind of man. But, then, he'd just lost his brother. That must account for his taciturn aloofness.

He was long gone when she went downstairs. She fixed herself a cup of coffee and two pieces of toast and then went to the small room that doubled as his office. As he'd promised the day before, he'd laid out a stack of pro-duction records and budget information that needed typing. He'd even put her electric typewriter on a table and plugged it in. There was a stack of white paper be-side it, and a note.

"Don't feel obliged to work yourself into a coma the first day," it read. And his bold signature was slashed under the terse sentence. She smiled at the flowing hand-

writing and the perfect spelling. He was a literate man, at
least.

She sat down in her cool blue shirtwaist dress and got
to work. Two hours later, she'd made great inroads into
the paperwork and was starting a new sheet when
Everett's heavy footsteps resounded throughout the
house. The door swung open and his dark eyebrows shot
straight up.

"Aren't you going to eat lunch?" he asked.

More to the point, wasn't she going to feed him, she
thought, and grinned.

"Something funny, Miss King?" he asked.

"Oh, no, boss," she said, leaving the typewriter behind. He was expecting that she'd forgotten his noon
meal, but she had a surprise in store for him.

She led him into the kitchen, where two places were set.
He stood there staring at the table, scowling, while she
put out bread, mayonnaise, some thick ham she'd found
in the refrigerator, and a small salad she'd made with a
bottled dressing.

"Coffee?" she asked, poised with the pot in her hand.

He nodded, sliding into the place at the head of the
table.

She poured it into his thick white mug and then filled
her own.

"How did you know I wanted coffee instead of tea?"
he asked with a narrow gaze as she seated herself beside
him.

"Because the coffee canister was half empty and the
tea had hardly been touched," she replied with a smile.

He chuckled softly as he sipped the black liquid. "Not
bad," he murmured, glancing at her.

"I'm sorry about breakfast," she said. "I usually wake
up around six, but this morning I was kind of tired."

"No problem," he told her, reaching for bread. "I'm
used to getting my own breakfast."

"What do you have?"

"Coffee."

She gaped at him. "Coffee?"

He shrugged. "Eggs bounce, bacon's half raw, and the toast hides under some black stuff. Coffee's better."

Her eyes danced as she put some salad on her plate. "I guess so. I'll try to wake up on time tomorrow."

"Don't rush it," he said, glancing at her with a slight frown. "You look puny to me."

"Most people would look puny compared to you," she replied.

"Have you always been that thin?" he persisted.

"No. Not until I got pneumonia," she said. "I just went straight downhill. I suppose I just kept pushing too hard. It caught up with me."

"How's the paperwork coming along?"

"Oh, I'm doing fine," she said. "Your handwriting is very clear. I've had some correspondence to type for doctors that required translation."

"Who did you get to translate?"

She grinned. "The nearest pharmacist. They have experience, you see."

He smiled at her briefly before he bit into his sandwich. He made a second one, but she noticed that he ignored the salad.

"Don't you want some of this?" she asked, indicating the salad bowl.

"I'm not a rabbit," he informed her.

"It's very good for you."

"So is liver, I'm told, but I won't eat that either." He finished his sandwich and got up to pour himself another cup of coffee.

"Then why do you keep lettuce and tomatoes?"

He glanced at her. "I like it on sandwiches."

This was a great time to tell her, after she'd used it all up in the salad. Just like a man...

"You could have dug it out of here," she said weakly.

He cocked an eyebrow. "With salad dressing all over it?"

"You could scrape it off..."

"I don't like broccoli or cauliflower, and never fix creamed beef," he added. "I'm more or less a meat and potatoes man."

"I'll sure remember that from now on, Mr. Culhane," she promised. "I'll be careful to use potatoes instead of apples in the pie I'm fixing for supper."

He glared at her. "Funny girl. Why don't you go on the stage?"

"Because you'd starve to death and weigh heavily on my conscience," she promised. "Some man named Brickmayer called and asked did you have a farrier's hammer he could borrow." She glanced up. "What's a farrier?"

He burst out laughing. "A farrier is a man who shoes horses."

"I'd like a horse," she sighed. "I'd put him in saddle oxfords."

"Go back to work. But slowly," he added from the doorway. "I don't want you knocking yourself into a sickbed on my account."

"You can count on me, sir," she promised, with a wry glance. "I'm much too afraid of your cooking to ever be at the mercy of it."

He started to say something, turned, and went out the door.

Jennifer spent the rest of the day finishing up the typing. Then she swept and dusted and made supper—a ham-and-egg casserole, biscuits, and cabbage. Supper sat on the table, however, and began to congeal. Eventually, she warmed up a little of it for herself, ate it, put the rest in the refrigerator, and went to bed. She had a feeling it was a omen for the future. He'd mentioned something that first day about rarely being home before bedtime. But couldn't he have warned her at lunch?

She woke up on time her second morning at the ranch. By 6:15 she was moving gracefully around the spacious kitchen in jeans and a green T-shirt. Apparently, Everett didn't mind what she wore, so she might as well be comfortable. She cooked a huge breakfast of fresh sausage, eggs, and biscuits, and made a pot of coffee.

Everything was piping hot and on the table when Everett came into the kitchen in nothing but his undershorts. Barefooted and bare-chested, he was enough to hold any woman's eyes. Jennifer, who'd seen her share of almost-bare men on the beaches, stood against the counter and stared like a star-struck girl. There wasn't an ounce of fat anywhere on that big body, and he was covered with thick black hair—all over his chest, his flat stomach, his broad thighs. He was as sensuously male as any leading man on television, and she couldn't drag her fascinated eyes away.

He cocked an eyebrow at her, his eyes faintly amused at what he recognized as shocked fascination. "I thought I heard something moving around down here. It's just as well I took time to climb into my shorts." And he turned away to leave her standing there, gaping after him.

A minute later he was back, whipping a belt around the faded blue denims he'd stepped into. He was still barefooted and bare-chested as he sat down at the table across from her.

"I thought I told you to stay in bed," he said as he reached for a biscuit.

"I was afraid you'd keel over out on the plains and your horse wouldn't be able to toss you onto his back and bring you home." She grinned at his puzzled expression. "Well, that's what Texas horses do in western movies."

He chuckled. "Not my horse. He's barely smart enough to find the barn when he's hungry." He buttered the biscuit. "My aunt used to cook like this," he remarked. "Biscuits as light as air."

"Sometimes they bounce," she warned him. "I got lucky."

He gave her a wary glance. "If these biscuits are any indication, so did I," he murmured.

"I saw a henhouse out back. Do I gather the eggs every day?"

"Yes, but watch where you put your hand," he cautioned. "Snakes have been known to get in there."

She shuddered delicately, nodding.

They ate in silence for several minutes before he spoke again. "You're a good cook, Jenny."

She grinned. "My mother taught me. She was terrific."

"Are your parents still alive?"

She shook her head, feeling a twinge of nostalgia. "No. They died several months ago, in a plane crash."

"I'm sorry. Were you close?"

"Very." She glanced at him. "Are your parents dead?"

His face closed up. "Yes," he said curtly, and in a tone that didn't encourage further questions.

She looked up again, her eyes involuntarily lingering on his bare chest. She felt his gaze, and abruptly averted her own eyes back to her empty plate.

He got up after a minute and went back to his bedroom. When he came out, he was tucking in a buttoned khaki shirt, and wearing boots as well. "Thanks for breakfast," he said. "Now, how about taking it easy for the rest of the day? I want to be sure you're up to housework before you pitch in with both hands."

"I won't do anything I'm not able to do," she promised.

"I've got some rope in the barn," he said with soft menace, while his eyes measured her for it.

She stared at him thoughtfully. "I'll be sure to carry a pair of scissors on me."

He was trying not to grin. "My God, you're stubborn."

"Look who's talking."

"I've had lots of practice working cattle," he replied. He picked up his coffee cup and drained it. "From now on, I'll come to the table dressed. Even at six o'clock in the morning."

She looked up, smiling. "You're a nice man, Mr. Culhane," she said. "I'm not a prude, honestly I'm not. It's just that I'm not accustomed to sitting down to breakfast with men. Dressed or undressed."

His dark eyes studied her. "Not liberated, Miss King?" he asked.

She sensed a deeper intent behind that question, but she took it at face value. "I was never unliberated. I'm just old-fashioned."

"So am I, honey. You stick to your guns." He reached for his hat and walked off, whistling.

She was never sure quite how to take what he said. As the days went by, he puzzled her more and more. She noticed him watching her occasionally, when he was in the house and not working with his cattle. But it wasn't a leering kind of look. It was faintly curious and a little protective. She had the odd feeling that he didn't think of her as a woman at all. Not that she found the thought surprising. Her mirror gave her inescapable proof that she had little to attract a man's eye these days. She was still frail and washed out.

Eddie was the elder of the ranchhands, and Jenny liked him on sight. He was a lot like the boss. He hardly ever smiled, he worked like two men, and he almost never sat down. But Jenny coaxed him into the kitchen with a cold glass of tea at the end of the week, when he brought her the eggs before she could go looking for them.

"Thank you, ma'am. I can sure use this." He sighed, and drained almost the whole glass in a few swallows. "Boss had me fixing fence. Nothing I hate worse than fixing fence," he added with a hard stare.

She tried not to grin. With his jutting chin and short graying whiskers and half-bald head, he did look fierce.

"I appreciate your bringing the eggs for me," she replied. "I got busy mending curtains and forgot about them."

He shrugged. "It wasn't much," he murmured. He narrowed one eye as he studied her. "You ain't the kind I'd expect the boss to hire."

Her eyebrows arched and she did grin this time. "What would you expect?"

He cleared his throat. "Well, the boss being the way he is . . . an older lady with a mean temper." He moved restlessly in the chair he was straddling. "Well, it takes a mean temper to deal with him. I know, I been doin' it for nigh on twenty years."

"Has he owned the Circle C for that long?" she asked.

"He ain't old enough," he reminded her. "I mean, I knowed him that long. He used to hang around here with his Uncle Ben when he was just a tadpole. His parents never had much use for him. His mama ran off with some man when he was ten and his daddy drank hisself to death.''

It was like having the pins knocked out from under her. She could imagine Everett at ten, with no mother and an alcoholic father. Her eyes mirrored the horror she felt. ''His brother must have been just a baby,'' she burst out.

''He was. Old Ben and Miss Emma took him in. But Everett weren't so lucky. He had to stay with his daddy.''

She studied him quietly, and filled the tea glass again. ''Why doesn't he like city women?''

''He got mixed up with some social-climbing lady from Houston,'' he said curtly. ''Anybody could have seen she wouldn't fit in here, except Everett. He'd just inherited the place and had these big dreams of making a fortune in cattle. The fool woman listened to the dreams and came harking out here with him one summer.'' He laughed bitterly. ''Took her all of five minutes to give Everett back his ring and tell him what she thought of his plans. Everett got drunk that night, first time I ever knew him to take a drink of anything stronger than beer. And that was the last time he brought a woman here. Until you come along, at least.''

She sat back down, all too aware of the faded yellow shirt and casual jeans she was wearing. The shirt was Everett's. She'd borrowed it while she washed her own in the ancient chugging washing machine. ''Don't look at me like a contender,'' she laughed, tossing back her long blond hair. ''I'm just a hanger-on myself, not a chic city woman.''

''For a hanger-on,'' he observed, indicating the scrubbed floors and clean, pressed curtains at the windows and the food cooking on the stove, ''you do get through a power of work.''

''I like housework,'' she told him. She sipped her own tea. ''I used to fix up houses for a living, until it got too much for me. I got frail during the winter and I haven't quite picked back up yet.''

''That accent of yours throws me,'' he muttered. ''Sounds like a lot of Southern mixed up with Yankee.''

She laughed again. "I'm from Georgia. Smart man, aren't you?"

"Not so smart, lady, or I'd be rich, too," he said with a rare grin. He got up. "Well, I better get back to work. The boss don't hold with us lollygagging on his time, and Bib's waiting for me to help him move cattle."

"Thanks again for bringing my eggs," she said.

He nodded. "No trouble."

She watched him go, sipping her own tea. There were a lot of things about Everett Culhane that were beginning to make sense. She felt that she understood him a lot better now, right down to the black moods that made him walk around brooding sometimes in the evening.

It was just after dark when Everett came in, and Jenny put the cornbread in the oven to warm the minute she heard the old pickup coming up the driveway. She'd learned that Everett Culhane didn't work banker's hours. He went out at dawn and might not come home until bedtime. But he had yet to find himself without a meal. Jenny prided herself in keeping not only his office, but his home, in order.

He tugged off his hat as he came in the back door. He looked even more weary than usual, covered in dust, his eyes dark-shadowed, his face needing a shave.

She glanced up from the pot of chili she was just taking off the stove and smiled, "Hi, Boss. How about some chili and Mexican cornbread?"

"I'm hungry enough to even eat one of those damned salads," he said, glancing toward the stove. He was still wearing his chaps and the leather had a fine layer of dust over it. So did his arms and his dark face.

"If you'll sit down, I'll feed you."

"I need a bath first, honey," he remarked.

"You could rinse off your face and hands in the sink," she suggested, gesturing toward it. "There's a hand towel there, and some soap. You look like you might go to sleep in the shower."

He lifted an eyebrow. "I can just see you pulling me out."

She turned away. "I'd call Eddie or Bib."

"And if you couldn't find them?" he persisted, shedding the chaps on the floor.

"In that case," she said dryly, "I reckon you'd drown, tall man."

"Sassy lady," he accused. He moved behind her and suddenly caught her by the waist with his lean, dark hands. He held her in front of him while he bent over her shoulder to smell the chili. She tried to breathe normally and failed. He was warm and strong at her back, and he smelled of the whole outdoors. She wanted to reach up and kiss that hard, masculine face, and her heart leaped at the uncharacteristic longing.

"What did you put in there?" he asked.

"One armadillo, two rattlers, a quart of beans, some tomatoes, and a hatful of jalapeno peppers."

His hands contracted, making her jump. "A hatful of jalapeno peppers would take the rust off my truck."

"Probably the tires, too," she commented, trying to keep her voice steady. "But Bib told me you Texans like your chili hot."

He turned her around to face him. He searched her eyes for a long, taut moment, and she felt her feet melting into the floor as she looked back. Something seemed to link them for that tiny space of time, joining them soul to soul for one explosive second. She heard him catch his breath and then she was free, all too soon.

"Would . . . would you like a glass of milk with this?" she asked after she'd served the chili into bowls and put it on the table, along with the sliced cornbread and some canned fruit.

"Didn't you make coffee?" he asked, glancing up.

"Sure. I just thought . . ."

"I don't need anything to put out the fire," he told her with a wicked smile. "I'm not a tenderfoot from *Jawja*."

She moved to the coffeepot and poured two cups. She set his in front of him and sat down. "For your information, suh," she drawled, "we Georgians have been known to eat rattlesnakes while they were still wiggling. And an aunt of mine makes a barbecued sparerib dish that makes Texas chili taste like oatmeal by comparison.''

"Is that so? Let's see." He dipped into his chili, savored it, put the spoon down, and glared at her. "You call this hot?" he asked.

She tasted hers and went into coughing spasms. While she was fanning her mouth wildly, he got up with a weary sigh, went to the cupboard, got a glass, and filled it with cold milk.

He handed it to her and sat back down, with a bottle of Tabasco sauce in his free hand. While she gulped milk, he poured half the contents of the bottle into his chili and then tasted it again.

"Just right." He grinned. "But next time, honey, it wouldn't hurt to add another handful of those peppers."

She made a sound between a moan and a gasp and drained the milk glass.

"Now, what were you saying about barbecued spareribs making chili taste like oatmeal?" he asked politely. "I especially liked the part about the rattlers . . .''

"Would you pass the cornbread, please?" she asked proudly.

"Don't you want the rest of your chili?" he returned.

"I'll eat it later," she said. "I made an apple pie for dessert."

He stifled a smile as he dug into his own chili. It got bigger when she shifted her chair so that she didn't have to watch him eat it.

4

---
*

It had been a long time since Jennifer had been on a horse, but once Everett decided that she was going riding with him one morning, it was useless to argue.

"I'll fall off," she grumbled as she stared up at the palomino gelding he'd chosen for her. "Besides, I've got work to do."

"You've ironed every curtain in the house, washed everything that isn't tied down, scrubbed all the floors, and finished my paperwork. What's left?" he asked, hands low on his hips, his eyes mocking.

"I haven't started supper," she said victoriously.

"So we'll eat late," he replied. "Now, get on."

With a hard glare, she let him put her into the saddle. She was still weak, but her hair had begun to regain its earlier luster and her spirit was returning with a vengeance.

"Were you always so domineering, or did you take lessons?" she asked.

"It sort of comes naturally out here, honey," he told her with a hard laugh. "You either get tough or you go broke."

His eyes ran over her, from her short-sleeved button-up blue print blouse down the legs of her worn jeans, and he frowned. "You could use some more clothes," he observed.

"I used to have a closetful," she sighed. "But in recent months my clothing budget has been pretty small. Anyway, I don't need to dress up around here, do I?"

"You could use a pair of new jeans, at least," he said. His lean hand slid along her thigh gently, where the material was almost see-through, and the touch quickened her pulse.

"Yours aren't much better," she protested, glancing down from his denim shirt to the jeans that outlined his powerful legs.

"I wear mine out fast," he reminded her. "Ranching is tough on clothes."

She knew that, having had to get four layers of mud off his several times. "Well, I don't put mine to the same use. I don't fix fence and pull calves and vet cattle."

He lifted an eyebrow. His hand was still resting absently on her thin leg. "You work hard enough. If I didn't already know it, I'd be told twice a day by Eddie or Bib."

"I like your men," she said.

"They like you. So do I," he added on a smile. "You brighten up the place."

But not as a woman, she thought, watching him. He was completely unaware of her sexually. Even when his eyes did wander over her, it was in an indifferent way. It disturbed her, oddly enough, that he didn't see her as a woman. Because she sure did see him as a man. That sensuous physique was playing on her nerves even now as she glanced down at it with helpless appreciation.

"All we need is a violin," she murmured, grinning.

He stared up at her, but he didn't smile. "Your hair seems lighter," he remarked.

The oddest kind of pleasure swept through her. He'd noticed. She'd just washed it, and the dullness was leaving it. It shimmered with silvery lights where it peeked out from under her hat.

"I just washed it," she remarked.

He shook his head. "It never looked that way before."

"I wasn't healthy before," she returned. "I feel so much better out here," she remarked, sighing as she looked around, with happiness shining out of her like a beacon. "Oh, what a marvelous view! Poor city people."

He turned away and mounted his buckskin gelding. "Come on. I'll show you the bottoms. That's where I've got my new stock."

"Does it flood when it rains?" she asked. It was hard getting into the rhythm of the horse, but somehow she managed it.

"Yes, ma'am, it does," he assured her in a grim tone. "Uncle Ben lost thirty head in a flood when I was a boy. I watched them wash away. Incredible, the force of water when it's unleashed."

"It used to flood back home sometimes," she observed.

"Yes, but not like it does out here," he commented. "Wait until you've seen a Texas rainstorm, and you'll know what I mean."

"I grew up reading Zane Grey," she informed him. "I know all about dry washes and flash floods and stampeding."

"Zane Grey?" he asked, staring at her. "Well, I'll be."

"I told you I loved Texas," she said with a quick smile. She closed her eyes, letting the horse pick its own way beside his. "Just breathe that air," she said lazily. "Rett, I'll bet if you bottled it, you could get rich overnight!"

"I could get rich overnight by selling off oil leases if I wanted to," he said curtly. He lit a cigarette, without looking at her.

She felt as if she'd offended him. "Sorry," she murmured. "Did I hit a nerve?"

"A raw one," he agreed, glancing at her. "Bobby was forever after me about those leases."

"He never won," she said, grinning. "Did he?"

His broad shoulders shifted. "I thought about it once or twice, when times got hard. But it's like a cop-out. I want to make this place pay with cattle, not oil. I don't want my land tied up in oil rigs and pumps cluttering up my landscape." He gestured toward the horizon. "Not too far out there, Apaches used to camp. Santa Ana's troops cut through part of this property on their way to the Alamo. After that, the local cattlemen pooled their cattle here to start them up the Chisolm Trail. During the Civil War, Confederates passed through on their way to Mexico. There's one hell of a lot of history here, and I don't want to spoil it."

She was watching him while he spoke, and her eyes involuntarily lingered on his strong jaw, his sensuous mouth. "Yes," she said softly, "I can understand that."

He glanced at her over his cigarette and smiled. "Where did you grow up?" he asked curiously.

"In a small town in south Georgia," she recalled. "Edison, by name. It wasn't a big place, but it had a big heart. Open fields and lots of pines and a flat horizon like this out beyond it. It's mostly agricultural land there, with huge farms. My grandfather's was very small. Back in his day, it was cotton. Now it's peanuts and soybeans."

"How long did you live there?"

"Until I was around ten," she recalled. "Dad got a job in Atlanta, and we moved there. We lived better, but I never liked it as much as home."

"What did your father do?"

"He was an architect," she said, smiling. "A very good one, too. He added a lot to the city's skyline in his day." She glanced at him. "Your father..."

"I don't discuss him," he said matter-of-factly, with a level stare.

"Why?"

He drew in an impatient breath and reined in his horse to light another cigarette. He was chain smoking, something he rarely did. "I said, I don't discuss him."

"Sorry, boss," she replied, pulling her hat down over her eyes in an excellent imitation of tall, lean Bib as she mimicked his drawl. "I shore didn't mean to rile you."

His lips tugged up. He blew out a cloud of smoke and flexed his broad shoulders, rippling the fabric that covered them. "My father was an alcoholic, Jenny."

She knew that already, but she wasn't about to give Eddie away. Everett wouldn't like being gossiped about by his employees. "It must have been a rough childhood for you and Robert," she said innocently.

"Bobby was raised by Uncle Ben and Aunt Emma," he said. "Bobby and I inherited this place from them. They were fine people. Ben spent his life fighting to hold this property. It was a struggle for him to pay taxes. I helped him get into breeding Herefords when I moved in with them. I was just a green kid," he recalled, "all big ears and feet and gigantic ideas. Fifteen, and I had all the answers." He sighed, blowing out another cloud of smoke. "Now I'm almost thirty-five, and every day I come up short of new answers."

"Don't we all?" Jennifer said with a smile. "I was lucky, I suppose. My parents loved each other, and me, and we were well-off. I didn't appreciate it at the time. When I lost them, it was a staggering blow." She leaned forward in the saddle to gaze at the horizon. "How about your mother?"

"A desperate woman, completely undomesticated," he said quietly. "She ran off with the first man who offered her an alternative to starvation. An insurance salesman," he scoffed. "Bobby was just a baby. She walked out the door and never looked back."

"I can't imagine a woman that callous," she said, glancing at him. "Do you ever hear from her now? Is she still alive?"

"I don't know. I don't care." He lifted the cigarette to his chiseled lips. His eyes cut around to meet hers, and they were cold with memory and pain. "I don't much like women."

She felt the impact of the statement to her toes. She knew why he didn't like women, that was the problem, but was too intelligent to think that she could pry that far, to mention the city woman who'd dumped him because he was poor.

"It would have left scars, I imagine," she agreed.

"Let's ride." He stuck the cigarette between his lips and urged his mount into a gallop.

Riding beside him without difficulty now, Jennifer felt alive and vital. He was such a devastating man, she thought, glancing at him, so sensuous even in faded jeans and shirt. He was powerfully built, like an athlete, and she didn't imagine many men could compete with him.

"Have you ever ridden in rodeo competition?" she asked suddenly without meaning to.

He glanced at her and slowed his mount. "Have I what?"

"Ridden in rodeos?"

He chuckled. "What brought that on?"

"You're so big . . ."

He stopped his horse and stared at her, his wrists crossed over the pommel of his saddle. "Too big," he returned. "The best riders are lean and wiry."

"Oh."

"But in my younger days, I did some steer wrestling and bulldogging. It was fun until I broke my arm in two places."

"I'll bet that slowed you down," she murmured dryly.

"It's about the only thing that ever did." He glanced at her rapt face. Live oaks and feathery mesquite trees and prickly pear cactus and wildflowers filled the long space to the horizon and Jennifer was staring at the landscape as if she'd landed in heaven. There were fences everywhere, enclosing pastures where Everett's white-faced Herefords grazed. The fences were old, graying and knotty and more like posts than neatly cut wood, with barbed wire stretched between them.

"Like what you see?" Everett mused.

"Oh, yes," she sighed. "I can almost see it the way it would have been a hundred and more years ago,, when settlers and drovers and cattlemen and gunfighters came through here." She glanced at him. "Did you know that Dr. John Henry Holliday, better known as Doc, hailed from Valdosta, Georgia?" she added. "Or that he went west because the doctors said he'd die of tuberculosis if he didn't find a drier climate quick? Or that he and his cousin were supposed to be married, and when they found out about the TB, he went west and she joined a nunnery in Atlanta? And that he once backed down a gang of cowboys in Dodge City and saved Wyatt Earp's life?"

He burst out laughing. "My God, you do know your history, don't you?"

"There was this fantastic biography of Holliday by John Myers Myers," she told him. "It was the most exciting book I ever read. I wish I had a copy. I tried to get one once, but it was out of print.''

"Isn't Holliday buried out West somewhere?'' he asked.

"In Glenwood Springs, Colorado,'' she volunteered. "He had a standing bet that a bullet would get him before the TB did, but he lost. He died in a sanitarium out there. He always said he had the edge in gunfights, because he didn't care if he died—and most men did.'' She smiled. "He was a frail little man, not at all the way he's portrayed in films most of the time. He was blond and blue-eyed and most likely had a slow Southern drawl. Gunfighter, gambler, and heavy drinker he might have been, but he had some fine qualities, too, like loyalty and courage.''

"We have a few brave men in Texas, too,'' he said, smoking his cigarette with a grin. "Some of them fought a little battle with a few thousand Mexicans in a Spanish mission in San Antonio.''

"Yes, in the Alamo,'' she said, grinning. "In 1836, and some of those men were from Georgia.''

He burst out laughing. "I can't catch you out on anything, can I?''

"I'm proud of my state,'' she told him. "Even though Texas does feel like home, too. If my grandfather hadn't come back, I might have been born here.''

"Why did he go back?'' he asked, curious.

"I never knew,'' she said. "But I expect he got into trouble. He was something of a hell-raiser even when I knew him.'' She recalled the little old man sitting astride a chair in her mother's kitchen, relating hair-raising escapes from the Germans during World War I while he smoked his pipe. He'd died when she was fourteen, and she still remembered going to Edison for the funeral, to a cemetery near Fort Gaines where Spanish moss fell from the trees. It had been a quiet place, a fitting place for the old gentleman to be laid to rest. In his home country. Under spreading oak trees.

"You miss him,'' Everett said quietly.

"Yes.''

"My Uncle Ben was something like that," he murmured, lifting his eyes to the horizon. "He had a big heart and a black temper. Sometimes it was hard to see the one for the other," he added with a short laugh. "I idolized him. He had nothing, but bowed to no man. He'd have approved of what I'm doing with this place. He'd have fought the quick money, too. He liked a challenge."

And so, she would have bet, did his nephew. She couldn't picture Everett Culhane liking anything that came too easily. He would have loved living in the nineteenth century, when a man could build an empire.

"You'd have been right at home here in the middle eighteen hundreds," she remarked, putting the thought into words. "Like John Chisum, you'd have built an empire of your own."

"Think so?" he mused. He glanced at her. "What do you think I'm trying to do now?"

"The same thing," she murmured. "And I'd bet you'll succeed."

He looked her over. "Would you?" His eyes caught hers and held them for a long moment before he tossed his cigarette onto the ground and stepped down out of the saddle to grind it under his boot.

A sudden sizzling sound nearby shocked Jennifer, but it did something far worse to the horse she was riding. The gelding suddenly reared up, and when it came back down again it was running wild.

She pulled back feverishly on the reins, but the horse wouldn't break its speed at all. "Whoa!" she yelled into its ear. "Whoa, you stupid animal!"

Finally, she leaned forward and hung on to the reins and the horse's mane at the same time, holding on with her knees as well. It was a wild ride, and she didn't have time to worry about whether or not she was going to survive it. In the back of her mind she recalled Everett's sudden shout, but nothing registered after that.

The wind bit into her face, her hair came loose from its neat bun. She closed her eyes and began to pray. The jolting pressure was hurting, actually jarring her bones. If only she could keep from falling off!

She heard a second horse gaining on them, then, and she knew that everything would be all right. All she had to do was hold on until Everett could get to her.

But at that moment, the runaway gelding came to a fence and suddenly began to slow down. He balked at the fence, but Jennifer didn't. She sailed right over the animal's head to land roughly on her back in the pasture on the other side of the barbed wire.

The breath was completely knocked out of her. She lay there staring up at leaves and blue sky, feeling as if she'd never get a lungful of air again.

Nearby, Everett was cursing steadily, using words she'd never heard before, even from angry clients back in New York City. She saw his face come slowly into focus above her and was fascinated by its paleness. His eyes were colorful enough, though, like brown flames glittering at her.

"Not...my...fault," she managed to protest in a thin voice.

"I know that," he growled. "It was mine. Damned rattler, and me without a gun..."

"It didn't...bite you?" she asked apprehensively, her eyes widening with fear.

He blew out a short breath and chuckled. "No, it didn't. Sweet Jenny. Half dead in a fall, and you're worried about me. You're one in a million, honey."

He bent down beside her. "Hurt anywhere?" he asked gently.

"All over," she said. "Can't get...my breath."

"I'm not surprised. Damned horse. We'll put him in your next batch of chili, I promise," he said on a faint smile. "Let's see how much damage you did."

His lean, hard hands ran up and down her legs and arms, feeling for breaks. "How about your back?" he asked, busy with his task.

"Can't...feel it yet."

"You will," he promised ruefully.

She was still just trying to breathe. She'd heard of people having the breath knocked out of them, but never knew what it was until now. Her eyes searched Everett's quietly.

"Am I dead?" she asked politely.

"Not quite." He brushed the hair away from her cheeks. "Feel like sitting up?"

"If you'll give me a hand, I'll try," she said huskily.

He raised her up and that was when she noticed that her blouse had lost several buttons, leaving her chest quite exposed. And today of all days she hadn't worn a bra.

Her hands went protectively to the white curves of her breasts, which were barely covered.

"None of that," he chided. "We don't have that kind of relationship. I'm not going to embarrass you by staring. Now get up."

That was almost the final blow. Even half dressed, he still couldn't accept her as a woman. She wanted to sit down on the grass and bawl. It wouldn't have done any good, but it might have eased the sudden ache in her heart.

She let him help her to her feet and staggered unsteadily on them. Her pale eyes glanced toward the gelding, now happily grazing in the pasture across the fence.

"First," she sputtered, "I'm going to dig a deep pit. Then I'm going to fill it with six-foot rattlesnakes. Then I'm going to get a backhoe and shove that stupid horse in there!"

"Wouldn't you rather eat him?" he offered.

"On second thought, I'll gain weight," she muttered. "Lots of it. And I'll ride him two hours every morning."

"You could use a few pounds," he observed, studying her thinness. "You're almost frail."

"I'm not," she argued. "I'm just puny, remember? I'll get better."

"I guess you already have," he murmured dryly. "You sure do get through the housework."

"Slowly but surely," she agreed. She tugged her blouse together and tied the bottom edges together.

When she looked back up, his eyes were watching her hands with a strange, intent stare. He looked up and met her puzzled gaze.

"Are you okay now?" he asked.

"Just a little shaky," she murmured with a slight grin.

"Come here." He bent and lifted her easily into his arms, shifting her weight as he turned, and walked toward the nearby gate in the fence.

She was shocked by her reaction to being carried by him. She felt ripples of pleasure washing over her body like fire, burning where his chest touched her soft breasts. Even through two layers of fabric, the contact was wildly arousing, exciting. She clamped her teeth together hard to keep from giving in to the urge to grind her body against his. He was a man, after all, and not invulnerable. She could start something that she couldn't stop.

"I'm too heavy," she protested once.

"No," he said gently, glancing down into her eyes unsmilingly. "You're like feathers. Much too light."

"Most women would seem light to you," she murmured, lowering her eyes to his shirt. Where the top buttons were undone, she saw the white of his T-shirt and the curl of dark, thick hair. He smelled of leather and wind and tobacco and she wanted so desperately to curl up next to him and kiss that hard, chiseled mouth...

"Open the gate," he said, nodding toward the latch.

She reached out and unfastened it, and pushed until it came free of the post. He went through and let her fasten it again. When she finished, she noticed that his gaze had fallen to her body. She followed it, embarrassed to find that the edges of her blouse gaped so much, that one creamy pink breast was completely bare to his eyes.

Her hand went slowly to the fabric, tugging it into place. "Sorry," she whispered self-consciously.

"So am I. I didn't mean to stare," he said quietly, shifting her closer to his chest. "Don't be embarrassed, Jenny."

She drew in a slow breath, burying her red face in his throat. He stiffened before he drew her even closer, his arms tautening until she was crushed to his broad, warm chest.

He didn't say a word as he walked, and neither did she. But she could feel the hard beat of his heart, the ragged sigh of his breath, the stiffening of his body against her taut breasts. In ways she'd never expected, her body sang to her, exquisite songs of unknown pleasure, of soft touches and wild contact. Her hands clung to Everett's neck, her eyes closed. She wanted this to last forever.

All too soon, they reached the horses. Everett let her slide down his body in a much too arousing way, so that she could feel the impact of every single inch of him on the way to the ground. And then, his arms contracted, holding her, bringing her into the length of him, while his cheek rested on her hair and the wind blew softly around them.

She clung, feeling the muscles of his back tense under her hands, loving the strength and warmth and scent of him. She'd never wanted anything so much as she wanted this closeness. It was sweet and heady and satisfying in a wild new way.

Seconds later, he let her go, just as she imagined she felt a fine tremor in his arms.

"Are you all right?" he asked softly.

"Yes," she said, trying to smile, but she couldn't look up at him. It had been intimate, that embrace. As intimate as a kiss in some ways, and it had caused an unexpected shift in their relationship.

"We'd better get back," he said. "I've got work to do."

"So have I," she said quickly, mounting the gelding with more apprehension than courage. "All right, you ugly horse," she told it. "You do that to me again, and I'll back the pickup truck over you!"

The horse's ears perked up and it moved its head slightly to one side. She burst into laughter. "See, Rett, he heard me!"

But Everett wasn't looking her way. He'd already turned his mount and was smoking another cigarette. And all the way back to the house, he didn't say a word.

As they reached the yard she felt uncomfortably tense. To break the silence, she broached a subject she'd had on her mind all day.

"Rett, could I have a bucket of paint?"

He stared at her. "What?"

"Can I have a bucket of paint?" she asked. "Just one. I want to paint the kitchen."

"Now, look, lady," he said, "I hired you to cook and do housework and type." His eyes narrowed and she fought not to let her fallen spirits show. "I like my house the way it is, with no changes."

"Just one little bucket of paint," she murmured.

"No."

She glared at him, but he glared back just as hard. "If you want to spend money," he said curtly, "I'll buy you a new pair of jeans. But we aren't throwing money away on decorating." He made the word sound insulting.

"Decorating is an art," she returned, defending her professional integrity. She was about to tell him what she'd done for a living, but as she opened her mouth, he was speaking again.

"It's a high-class con game," he returned hotly. "And even if I had the money, I wouldn't turn one of those fools loose on my house. Imagine paying out good money to let some tasteless idiot wreck your home and charge you a fortune to do it!" He leaned forward in the saddle with a belligerent stare. "No paint. Do we understand each other, Miss King?"

Do we ever, she thought furiously. Her head lifted. "You'd be lucky to get a real decorator in here, anyway," she flung back. "One who wouldn't faint at the way you combine beautiful old oriental rugs with ashtrays made of old dead rattlesnakes!"

His dark eyes glittered dangerously. "It's my house," he said coldly.

"Thank God!" she threw back.

"If you don't like it, close your eyes!" he said. "Or pack your damned bag and go back to Atlanta and turn your nose up..."

"I'm not turning my nose up!" she shouted. "I just wanted a bucket of paint!"

"You know when you'll get it too, don't you?" he taunted. He tipped his hat and rode off, leaving her fuming on the steps.

Yes, she knew. His eyes had told her, graphically. When hell froze over. She remembered in the back of her mind that there was a place called Hell, and once it did freeze over and made national headlines. She only wished she'd saved the newspaper clipping. She'd shove it under his arrogant nose, and maybe then she'd get her paint!

She turned to go into the house, stunned to find Eddie coming out the front door.

He looked red-faced, but he doffed his hat. "Mornin', ma'am," he murmured. "I was just putting the mail on the table."

"Thanks, Eddie," she said with a wan smile.

He stared at her. "Boss lost his temper, I see."

"Yep," she agreed.

"Been a number of days before when he's done that."

"Yep."

"You going to keep it all to yourself, too, ain't you?"

"Yep."

He chuckled, tipped his hat, and went on down the steps. She walked into the house and burst out laughing. She was getting the hang of speaking Texan at last.

5

*

Jennifer spent the rest of the day feverishly washing down the kitchen walls. So decorators were con artists, were they? And he wouldn't turn one loose in his home, huh? She was so enraged that the mammoth job took hardly any time at all. Fortunately, the walls had been done with oil-based paint, so the dirt and grease came off without taking the paint along with them. When she was through, she stood back, worn out and damp with sweat, to survey her handiwork. She had the fan going full blast, but it was still hot and sticky, and she felt the same way herself. The pale yellow walls looked new, making the effort worthwhile.

Now, she thought wistfully, if she only had a few dollars' worth of fabric and some thread, and the use of the aging sewing machine upstairs, she could make curtains for the windows. She could even buy that out of her own pocket, and the interior-decorator-hating Mr. Everett Donald Culhane could just keep his nasty opinions to himself. She laughed, wondering what he'd have said if she'd used his full name while they were riding. Bib had told her his middle name. She wondered if anyone ever called him Donald.

She fixed a light supper of creamed beef and broccoli, remembering that he'd told her he hated both of those dishes. She deliberately made weak coffee. Then she sat down in the kitchen and pared apples while she waited for him to come home. Con artist, huh?

It was getting dark when he walked in the door. He was muddy and tired-looking, and in his lean, dark hand was a small bouquet of slightly wilted wildflowers.

"Here," he said gruffly, tossing them onto the kitchen table beside her coffee cup. The mad profusion of blue-

bonnets and Indian paintbrush and Mexican hat made
blue and orange and red swirls of color on the white tablecloth. "And you can have your damned bucket of
paint."

He strode toward the staircase, his face hard and unyielding, without looking back. She burst into tears, her
fingers trembling as they touched the unexpected gift.

Never in her life had she moved so fast. She dried her
tears and ran to pour out the pot of weak coffee. She put
on a pot of strong, black coffee and dragged out bacon
and eggs and flour, then put the broccoli and chipped
beef, covered, into the refrigerator.

By the time Everett came back down, showered and in
clean denims, she had bacon and eggs and biscuits on the
table.

"I thought you might like something fresh and hot for
supper," she said quickly.

He glanced at her as he sat down. "I'm surprised. I
was expecting liver and onions or broccoli tonight."

She flushed and turned her back. "Were you? How
strange." She got the coffeepot and calmly filled his cup
and her own. "Thank you for my flowers," she said
without looking at him.

"Don't start getting ideas, Miss King," he said curtly,
reaching for a biscuit. "Just because I backed down on
the paint, don't expect it to become a habit around here."

She lowered her eyes demurely to the platter of eggs she
was dishing up. "Oh, no, sir," she said.

He glanced around the room and his eyes darkened,
glittered. They came back to her. He laid down his knife.
"Did you go ahead and buy paint?" he asked in a softly
menacing tone.

"No, I did not," she replied curtly. "I washed down
the walls."

He blinked. "Washed down the walls?" He looked
around again, scowling. "In this heat?"

"Look good, don't they?" she asked fiercely, smiling. "I don't need the paint, but thank you anyway."

He picked up his fork, lifting a mouthful of eggs slowly
to his mouth. He finished his supper before he spoke

again. "Why did it matter so much about the walls?" he asked. "The house is old. It needs thousands of dollars' worth of things I can't afford to have done. Painting one room is only going to make the others look worse."

She shrugged. "Old habits," she murmured with a faint smile. "I've been fixing up houses for a long time."

That went right past him. He look preoccupied. Dark and brooding.

"Is something wrong?" she asked suddenly.

He sighed and pulled an envelope from his pocket and tossed it onto the table. "I found that on the hall table on my way upstairs."

She frowned. "What is it?"

"A notice that the first payment is due on the note I signed at the bank for my new bull." He laughed shortly. "I can't meet it. My tractor broke down and I had to use the money for the payment to fix it. Can't plant without the tractor. Can't feed livestock without growing feed. Ironically, I may have to sell the bull to pay back the money."

Her heart went out to him. Here she sat giving him the devil over a bucket of paint, and he was in serious trouble. She felt terrible.

"I ought to be shot," she murmured quietly. "I'm sorry I made such a fuss about the paint, Rett."

He laughed without humor. "You didn't know. I told you times were hard."

"Yes. But I didn't realize how hard until now." She sipped her coffee. "How much do you need... can I ask?" she said softly.

He sighed. "Six hundred dollars." He shook his head. "I thought I could swing it, I really did. I wanted to pay it off fast."

"I've got last week's salary," she said. "I haven't spent any of it. That would help a little. And you could hold back this week's..."

He stared into her wide, soft eyes and smiled. "You're quite a girl, Jenny."

"I want to help."

"I know. I appreciate it. But spend your money on yourself. At any rate, honey, it would hardly be a drop in the bucket. I've got a few days to work it out. I'll turn up something."

He got up and left the table and Jennifer stared after him, frowning. Well, she could help. There had to be an interior-design firm in Houston, which was closer than San Antonio or Austin. She'd go into town and offer her services. With any luck at all, they'd be glad of her expert help. She could make enough on one job to buy Everett's blessed bull outright. She was strong enough now to take on the challenge of a single job. And she would!

As luck would have it, the next morning Eddie mentioned that his wife Libby was going to drive into the city to buy a party dress for his daughter. Jennifer hitched a ride with her after Everett went to work.

Libby was a talker, a blond bearcat of a woman with a fine sense of humor. She was good company, and Jennifer took to her immediately.

"I'm so glad Everett's got you to help around the house," she said as they drove up the long highway to Houston. "I offered, but he wouldn't hear of it. Said I had enough to do, what with raising four kids. He even looks better since you've been around. And he doesn't cuss as much." She grinned.

"I was so delighted to have the job," Jennifer sighed, smiling. She brushed back a stray wisp of blond hair. She was wearing her best blue camisole with a simple navy-blue skirt and her polished white sling pumps with a white purse. She looked elegant, and Libby remarked on it.

"Where are you going, all dressed up?" she asked.

"To get a second job," Jennifer confessed. "But you mustn't tell Everett. I want to surprise him."

Libby looked worried. "You're not leaving?"

"Oh, no! Not until he makes me! This is only a temporary thing," she promised.

"Doing what?"

"Decorating."

"That takes a lot of schooling, doesn't it?" Libby asked, frowning.

"Quite a lot. I graduated from interior-design school in New York," Jennifer explained. "And I worked in the field for two years. My health gave out and I had to give it up for a while." She sighed. "There was so much pressure, you see. So much competition. My nerves got raw and my resistance got low, and I wound up flat on my back in a hospital with pneumonia. I went home to Atlanta to recuperate, got a job with a temporary talent agency, and met Robert Culhane on an assignment. He offered me a job, and I grabbed it. Getting to work in Texas was pretty close to heaven, for me."

Libby shook her head. "Imagine that."

"I was sorry about Robert," Jennifer said quietly. "I only knew him slightly, but I did like him. Everett still broods about it. He doesn't say much, but I know he misses his brother."

"He was forever looking out for Bobby," Libby confirmed. "Protecting him and such. A lot of the time, Bobby didn't appreciate that. And Bobby didn't like living low. He wanted Everett to sell off those oil rights and get rich. Everett wouldn't."

"I don't blame him," Jennifer said. "If it was my land, I'd feel the same way."

Libby looked surprised. "My goodness, another one."

"I don't like strip-mining, either," Jennifer offered. "Or killing baby seals for their fur or polluting the rivers."

Libby burst out laughing. "You and Everett were made for each other. He's just that way himself." She glanced at Jennifer as the Houston skyline came into view. "Did Bobby tell you what Everett did the day the oil man came out here to make him that offer, after the geologists found what they believe was oil-bearing land?"

"No."

"The little oil man wanted to argue about it, and Everett had just been thrown by a horse he was trying to saddle-break and was in a mean temper. He told the man to cut it off, and he wouldn't. So Everett picked him up," she said, grinning, "carried him out to his car, put him in, and walked away. We haven't seen any oil men at the ranch since."

Jennifer laughed. It sounded like Everett, all right. She sat back, sighing, and wondered how she was going to make him take the money she hoped to earn. Well, that worry could wait in line. First, she had to find a job.

While Libby went into the store, Jennifer found a telephone directory and looked up the addresses of two design shops. The first one was nearby, so she stopped to arrange a time and place to rendezvous with Libby that afternoon, and walked the two blocks.

She waited for fifteen minutes to see the man who owned the shop. He listened politely, but impatiently, while she gave her background. She mentioned the name of the firm she'd worked with in New York, and saw his assistant's eyebrows jump up. But the manager was obviously not impressed. He told her he was sorry but he was overstaffed already.

Crestfallen, she walked out and called a taxi to take her to the next company. This time, she had better luck. The owner was a woman, a veritable Amazon, thin and dark and personable. She gave Jennifer a cup of coffee, listened to her credentials, and grinned.

"Lucky me," she laughed. "To find you just when I was desperate for one more designer!"

"You mean, you can give me work?" Jennifer burst out, delighted.

"Just this one job, right now, but it could work into a full-time position," she promised.

"Part-time would be great. You see, I already have a job I'd rather not leave," Jennifer replied.

"Perfect. You can do this one in days. It's only one room. I'll give you the address, and you can go and see the lady yourself. Where are you staying?"

"Just north of Victoria," Jennifer said. "In Big Spur."

"How lovely!" the lady said. "The job's in Victoria! No transportation problem?"

She thought of asking Libby, and smiled. "I have a conspirator," she murmured. "I think I can manage." She glanced up. "Can you estimate my commission?"

Her new employer did, and Jennifer grinned. It would be more than enough for Everett to pay off his note. "Okay!"

"The client, Mrs. Whitehall, doesn't mind paying for quality work," came the lilting reply. "And she'll be tickled when she hears the background of her designer. I'll give her a ring now, if you like."

"Would I! Miss . . . Mrs . . . Ms . . . ?"

"Ms. Sally Ward," the owner volunteered. "I'm glad to meet you, Jennifer King. Now, let's get busy."

Libby was overjoyed when she heard what Jennifer was plotting, and volunteered to drive her back and forth to the home she'd be working on. She even agreed to pinch-hit in the house, so that Everett wouldn't know what was going on. It would be risky, but Jennifer felt it would be very much worth the risk.

As it turned out, Mrs. Whitehall was an elderly lady with an unlimited budget and a garage full of cars. She was more than happy to lend one to Jennifer so that she could drive back and forth to Victoria to get fabric and wallcoverings and to make appointments with painters and carpetlayers.

Jennifer made preliminary drawings after an interview with Mrs. Whitehall, who lived on an enormous estate called Casa Verde.

"My son Jason and his wife Amanda used to live with me," Mrs. Whitehall volunteered. "But since their marriage, they've built a house of their own further down the road. They're expecting their first child. Jason wants a boy and Amanda a girl." She grinned. "From the size of her, I'm expecting twins!"

"When is she due?" Jennifer asked.

"Any day," came the answer. "Jason spends part of the time pacing the floor and the other part daring Amanda to lift, move, walk, or breathe hard." She laughed delightedly. "You'd have to know my son, Miss King, to realize how out of character that is for him.

Jason was always such a calm person until Amanda got pregnant. I think it's been harder on him than it has on her."

"Have they been married long?"

"Six years," Mrs. Whitehall said. "So happily. They wanted a child very much, but it took a long time for Amanda to become pregnant. It's been all the world to them, this baby." She stared around the room at the fading wallpaper and the worn carpet. "I've just put this room off for so long. Now I don't feel I can wait any longer to have it done. Once the baby comes, I'll have so many things to think of. What do you suggest, my dear?"

"I have some sketches," Jennifer said, drawing out her portfolio.

Mrs. Whitehall looked over them, sighing. "Just what I wanted. Just exactly what I wanted." She nodded. "Begin whenever you like, Jennifer. I'll find somewhere else to sit while the workmen are busy."

And so it began. Jennifer spent her mornings at Casa Verde, supervising the work. Afternoons she worked at Everett's ranch. And amazingly, she never got caught.

It only took a few days to complete the work. Luckily, she found workmen who were between jobs and could take on a small project. By the end of the week, it was finished.

"I can't tell you how impressed I am," Mrs. Whitehall sighed as she studied the delightful new decor, done in soft green and white and dark green.

"It will be even lovelier when the furniture is delivered tomorrow." Jennifer grinned. "I'm so proud of it. I hope you like it half as much as I do."

"I do, indeed," Mrs. Whitehall said. "I . . ."

The ringing of the phone halted her. She picked up the extension at her side. "Hello?" She sat up straight. "Yes, Jason! When?" She laughed, covering the receiver. "It's a boy!" She moved her hand. "What are you going to name him? Oh, yes, I like that very much. Joshua Brand Whitehall. Yes, I do. How is Amanda? Yes, she's tough, all right. Dear, I'll be there in thirty minutes. Now you calm down, dear. Yes, I know it isn't every day a man has a son. I'll see you soon. Yes, dear."

She hung up. "Jason's beside himself," she said, smiling. "He wanted a boy so much. And they can have others. Amanda will get her girl yet. I must rush."

Jennifer stood up. "Congratulations on that new grandbaby," she said. "And I've enjoyed working with you very much."

"I'll drop you off at the ranch on my way," Mrs. Whitehall offered.

"It's a good little way," Jennifer began, wondering how she'd explain it to Everett. Mrs. Whitehall drove a Mercedes-Benz.

"Nonsense." Mrs. Whitehall laughed. "It's no trouble at all. Anyway, I want to talk to you about doing some more rooms. This is delightful. Very creative. I never enjoyed redecorating before, but you make it exciting."

After that, how could Jennifer refuse? She got in the car.

Luckily enough, Everett wasn't in sight when she reached the ranch. Mrs. Whitehall let her out at the steps and Jennifer rushed inside, nervous and wild-eyed. But the house was empty. She almost collapsed with relief. And best of all, on the hall table was an envelope addressed to her from Houston, from the interior-design agency. She tore it open and found a check and a nice letter offering more work. The check was for the amount Everett needed, plus a little. Jennifer endorsed it, grinning, and went in to fix supper.

6

*

Everett came home just before dark, but he didn't come into the house. Jennifer had a light supper ready, just cold cuts and bread so there wouldn't be anything to reheat. When he didn't appear after she heard the truck stop, she went out to look for him.

He was standing by the fence, staring at the big Hereford bull he'd wanted so badly. Jennifer stood on the porch and watched him, her heart aching for him. She'd decided already to cash her check first thing in the morning and give it to him at breakfast. But she wondered if she should mention it now. He looked so alone...

She moved out into the yard, the skirt of her blue shirtwaist dress blowing in the soft, warm breeze.

"Rett?" she called.

He glanced at her briefly. "Waiting supper on me again?" he asked quietly.

"No. I've only made cold cuts." She moved to the fence beside him and stared at the big, burly bull. "He sure is big."

"Yep." He took out a cigarette and lit it, blowing out a cloud of smoke. He looked very western in his worn jeans, batwing chaps, and close-fitting denim shirt, which was open halfway down his chest. He was a sensuous man, and she loved looking at him. Her eyes went up to his hard mouth and she wondered for what seemed the twentieth time how it would feel on her own. That made her burn with embarrassment, and she turned away.

"Suppose I offered you what I've saved?" she asked.

"We've been through all that. No. Thank you," he added. "I can't go deeper in debt, not even to save my bull. I'll just pay off the note and start over. The price of beef is expected to start going up in a few months. I'll stand pat until it does."

"Did anyone ever tell you that you have a double dose of pride?" she asked, exasperated.

He looked down at her, his eyes shadowed in the dusk by the brim of his hat. "Look who's talking about pride, for God's sake," he returned. "Don't I remember that you tried to walk back to town carrying a suitcase and a typewriter in the blazing sun with no hat? I had to threaten to tie you in the truck to get you inside it."

"I knew you didn't want me here," she said simply. "I didn't want to become a nuisance."

"I don't think I can imagine that. You being a nuisance, I mean." He took another draw from the cigarette and crushed it out. "I've had a good offer for the bull from one of my neighbors. He's coming over tomorrow to talk to me about it."

Well, that gave her time to cash the check and make one last effort to convince him, she thought.

"Why are you wearing a dress?" he asked, staring down at her. "Trying to catch my eye, by any chance?"

"Who, me?" she laughed. "As you told me the other day, we don't have that kind of relationship."

"You were holding me pretty hard that day the rattlesnake spooked your horse," he said unexpectedly, and he didn't smile. "And you didn't seem to mind too much that I saw you without your shirt."

She felt the color work its way into her hairline. "I'd better put supper on the ... oh!"

He caught her before she could move away and brought her gently against the length of his body. His hand snaked around her waist, holding her there, and the other one spread against her throat, arching it.

"Just stand still," he said gently. "And don't start anything. I know damned good and well you're a virgin. I'm not going to try to seduce you."

Her breath was trapped somewhere below her windpipe. She felt her knees go wobbly as she saw the narrowness of his eyes, the hard lines of his face. She'd wanted it so much, but now that it was happening, she was afraid.

She stilled and let her fingers rest over his shirt, but breathing had become difficult. He felt strong and warm and she wanted to touch his hair-roughened skin. It looked so tantalizing to her innocent eyes.

He was breathing slowly, steadily. His thumb nudged her chin up so that he could look into her eyes. "You let me look at you," he said under his breath. "I've gone half mad remembering that, wondering how many other men have seen you that way."

"No one has," she replied quietly. She couldn't drag her eyes from his. She could feel his breath, taste the smokiness of it, smell the leather and tobacco smells of his big, hard body so close to hers. "Only you."

His chest rose heavily. "Only me?"

"I was career-minded," she said hesitantly. "I didn't want commitment, so I didn't get involved. Everett..."

"No. I don't want to fight." He took her hands and slid them up and down over the hard muscles of his chest. His breathing changed suddenly.

He bent and drew her lower lip down with the soft pressure of his thumb. He fit his own mouth to it with exquisite patience, opening it slowly, tempting it, until she stood very still and closed her eyes.

His free hand brought her body close against his. The other one slowly undid the top two buttons of her dress and moved inside to her throat, her shoulder, her collarbone. His mouth increased its ardent pressure as his fingers spread, and his breathing became suddenly ragged as he arched her body and found the soft rise of her breast with his whole hand.

She gasped and instinctively caught his wrist. But he lifted his mouth and looked into her eyes and slowly shook his head. "You're old enough to be taught this," he said quietly. "I know how delicate you are here," he breathed, brushing his fingers over the thin lace. "I'm going to be very gentle, and you're going to enjoy what I do to you. I promise. Close your eyes, honey."

His mouth found hers again, even as he stopped speaking. It moved tenderly on her trembling lips, nibbling, demanding, in a silence bursting with new sensations and promise.

She clung to his shirtfront, shocked to find that her legs were trembling against his, that her breath was coming quick enough to be audible. She tried to pull away, but his fingers slid quietly under the bra and found bare, vulnerable skin, and she moaned aloud.

Her nails bit into his chest. "Rett!" she gasped, on fire with hunger and frightened and embarrassed that he could see and feel her reaction to him.

"Shhhh," he whispered at her mouth, gentling her. "It's all right. It's all right to let me see. You're so sweet, Jenny Wren. Like a bright new penny without a single fingerprint except mine." His mouth touched her closed eyelids, her forehead. His fingers contracted gently, his palm feeling the exquisite tautening of her body as she clung to him and shuddered. "Yes, you like that, don't you?" he breathed. His mouth brushed her eyelids again, her nose, her mouth. "Jenny, put your hand inside my shirt."

His voice was deep and low and tender. She obeyed him blindly, on fire with reckless hunger, needing to touch and taste and feel him. Her hands slid under his shirt and flattened on hair and warm muscle, and he tautened.

"Does that...make you feel the way...I feel?" she whispered shakily, looking up at him.

"Exactly," he whispered back. He moved his hand from her breast to her neck and pressed her face slowly against his bare chest.

She seemed to sense what he wanted. Her mouth touched him there tentatively, shyly, and he moaned. He smelled of faint cologne and tobacco, and she liked the way his hard muscles contracted where she touched them with her hands and her lips. He was all man. All man. And her world was suddenly narrowed to her senses, and Everett.

He took her face in his hands and tilted it, bending to kiss her with a hungry ferocity that would have frightened her minutes before. But she went on tiptoe and linked her arms around his neck and gave him back the kiss, opening her mouth under his to incite him to further intimacy, shivering wildly when he accepted the invitation and his tongue went into the sweet darkness in a slow, hungry tasting.

When he finally released her, he was shaking too. His eyes burned with frustrated desire, his hands framed her face, hot and hard.

"We have to stop. Now."

She took a slow, steadying breath. "Yes."

He took his hands away and moved toward the house, lighting a cigarette eventually after two fumbles.

She followed him, drunk on sensual pleasure, awed by what she'd felt with him, by what she'd let him do. She felt shy when they got into the house, into the light, and she couldn't quite meet his eyes.

"I'll get supper on the table," she said.

He didn't even reply. He followed her into the kitchen, and with brooding dark eyes watched her move around.

She poured coffee and he sat down, still watching her.

Her hand trembled as she put the cream pitcher beside his cup. He caught her fingers, looking up at her with a dark, unsmiling stare.

"Don't start getting self-conscious with me," he said quietly. "I know you've never let another man touch you like that. I'm proud that you let me."

She stared at him, eyes widening. Of all the things she'd expected he might say, that wasn't one of them.

His nostrils flared and his hand contracted. "After supper," he said slowly, holding her eyes, "I'm going to carry you into the living room and lay you down on the sofa. And I'm going to make love to you, in every way I know. And when I get through, you'll shudder at the thought of another man's hands on you."

His eyes were blazing, and her own kindled. Her lips parted. "Rett, I can't...you know."

He nodded. "We won't go that far." His fingers caressed her wrist and his face hardened. "How hungry are you?" he asked under his breath.

Her heart was beating wildly. She looked at him and it was suicide. She felt shaky to her toes.

"Make love to me," she whispered blindly as she reached for him.

He twisted her down across his lap and found her mouth in a single motion. He groaned as he kissed her, his breath sighing out raggedly.

"Oh, God, I need you," he ground out, standing with her in his arms. "I need you so much!"

He turned, still kissing her, and carried her through into the living room, putting her gently down on the worn couch. After giving her a hot stare, he turned and methodically drew all the curtains and closed and locked the door. Then he came back, sitting down so that he was facing her.

"Now," he whispered, bending with trembling hands to the bodice of her dress. "Now, let's see how much damage we can do to each other's self-control, Jenny Wren. I want to look at you until I ache to my toes!"

He unbuttoned it and she sank back against the pillows, watching unprotestingly. He half lifted her and slipped the dress down her arms. Her bra followed it. And then he leaned over her, just looking at the soft mounds he'd uncovered.

His fingers stroked one perfect breast, lingering on the tip until she cried out.

"Does that hurt?" he whispered, looking into her eyes.

She was trembling, and it was hard to talk. "No," she breathed.

He smiled slowly, in a tender, purely masculine way, and repeated the brushing caress. She arched up, and his eyes blazed like dark fires.

"Jenny!" he growled. He lifted her body up to his hard mouth. He took her by surprise, and she moaned wildly as she felt the warm moistness envelop her. Her hands dug into his hair and she dragged his head closer, whimpering as if she were being tortured.

"Not so hard, baby," he whispered raggedly, lifting his head. "You're too delicate for that, Jenny."

"Rett," she moaned, her eyes wild.

"Like this, then," he whispered, bending to grind his mouth into hers. His hand swallowed her, stroking, molding, and she trembled all over as if with a fever, clinging to him, needing something more than this, something closer, something far, far more intimate...

Her hands moved against his chest, trembling as they explored the hard muscles.

"Be still now," he whispered, easing her back into the cushions. "Don't move under me. Just lie still, Jenny Wren, and let me show you...how bodies kiss."

She held her breath as his body moved completely onto hers. She felt the blatant maleness of it, the warmth, the tickle of hair against her soft breasts, the exquisite weight, and her hungry eyes looked straight into his as they joined.

"Oh," she whispered jerkily.

"Sweet, sweet Jenny," he breathed, cupping her face in his hands. "It's like moving on velvet. Do you feel me...all of me?"

"Yes." Her own hands went to his back, found their way under his shirt. "Rett, you're very heavy," she said with a shaky smile.

"Too heavy?" he whispered.

"Oh, no," she said softly. "I...like the way it feels."

"So do I." He bent and kissed her tenderly, in a new and delicious way. "Not afraid?"

"No."

"You will be," he whispered softly. His hands moved down, sliding under her hips. He lifted his head and looked down at her just as his fingers contracted and ground her hips up into his in an intimacy that made her gasp and cry out.

He shuddered, and she buried her face in his hot throat, dizzy and drowning in deep water, burning with exquisite sensation and blinding pleasure.

"Jenny," he groaned. His hands hurt. "Jenny, Jenny, if you weren't a virgin, I'd take you. I'd take you, here, now, in every way there is . . . !"

She barely heard him, she was shaking so badly. All at once, he eased himself down beside her and folded her into his arms in a strangely protective way. His hands smoothed her back, his lips brushed over her face in tiny, warm kisses. All the passion was suddenly gone, and he was comforting her.

"I never believed . . . what my mother used to say about . . . passion," Jenny whispered at his ear, still trembling. "Rett, it's exquisite . . . isn't it? So explosive and sweet and dangerous!"

"You've never wanted a man before?" he breathed.

"No."

"I'll tell you something, Jenny. I've never wanted a woman like this. Not ever." He kissed her ear softly. "I want you to know something. If it ever happened, even accidentally, you'd never want to forget it. I'd take you so tenderly, so slowly, that you'd never know anything about pain."

"Yes, I know that," she murmured, smiling. Her arms tightened. "You could have had me, then, lofty principles and all," she added ruefully. "I didn't realize how easy it was to throw reason to the wind."

"You're a very passionate woman." He lifted his head and searched her eyes. "I didn't expect that."

"You didn't seem much like a passionate man either," she confessed, letting her eyes wander slowly over his hard, dark face. "Oh, Rett, I did want you in the most frightening way!"

His chest expanded roughly. "Jenny, I think we'd better get up from here. My good intentions only seem to last until I get half your clothes off."

She watched him draw away, watched how his eyes clung to her bare breasts, and she smiled and arched gently.

"Oh, God, don't do that!" he whispered, shaken, as he turned away.

She laughed delightedly and sat up, getting back into her clothes as she stared at his broad back. He was smoking a cigarette, running a restless hand through his hair. And he was the handsomest man she'd ever seen in her life. And the most . . . loved.

I love you, she thought dreamily. I love every line and curve and impatient gesture you make. I'd rather live here, in poverty, with you than to have the world in the bank.

"I'm decent now," she murmured, smiling when he turned hesitantly around. "My gosh, you make me feel good. I was always self-conscious about being so small."

His eyes narrowed. "You're not small, baby," he said in a gruff tone. "You're just delicate."

Her face glowed with pride. "Thank you, Rett."

"Let's see if the coffee's still warm," he said softly, holding out his hand.

She took it, and he pulled her up, pausing to bend and kiss her slowly, lingering over the soft, swollen contours of her warm mouth.

"I've bruised your lips," he whispered. "Are they sore?"

"They're delightfully sensitive," she whispered back, going on tiptoe. "You know a lot about kissing for a cattleman."

"You know a lot for a virgin," he murmured, chuckling.

"Pat yourself on the back, I'm a fast study." She slid her hand pertly inside his shirt and stroked him. "See?"

He took her hand away and buttoned his shirt to the throat. "I'm going to have to watch you, lady," he murmured, "or you'll wrestle me down on the couch and seduce me one dark night."

"It's all right," she whispered. "I won't get you pregnant. You can trust me, honey," she added with a wicked smile.

He burst out laughing and led her into the kitchen. "Feed me," he said, "before we get in over our heads."

"Spoilsport. Just when things were getting interesting."

"Another minute, and they'd have gone past interesting to educational," he murmured dryly, with a pointed glance. "Men get hot pretty fast that way, Jenny. Don't rely on my protective instincts too far. I damned near lost my head."

"Did you, really?" she asked, all eyes. "But I don't know anything."

"That's why," he sighed. "I . . . haven't touched a virgin since I was one myself. Funny, isn't it, that these days it's become a stigma. Back when I was a kid, decent boys wouldn't be seen with a girl who had a reputation for being easy. Now it's the virgins who take all the taunting." He stopped, turning her, and his face was solemn. "I'm glad you're still innocent. I'm glad that I can look at you and make you blush, and watch all those first reactions that you've never shown anybody else. To hell with modern morality, Jenny. I love the fact that you're as old-fashioned as I am."

"So do I. Now," she added, studying him warmly. "Rett . . ." Her fingers went up and touched his hard mouth. "Rett, I think I . . ." She was about to say "love you" when a piece of paper on the floor caught his eye.

"Hey, what's this?" he asked, bending to pick it up.

Her heart stopped. It was the check she'd gotten in the mail. She'd stuck it in her pocket, but it must have fallen out. She watched him open it and read the logo at the top with a feeling of impending disaster. She hadn't meant to tell him where it came from just yet. . . .

His lean hand closed around the check, crumpling it. "Where did you get this kind of money, and what for?" he demanded.

"I . . . I worked part-time for a design house in Houston, decorating a lady's living room," she blurted out. "It's for you. To pay off your bull," she said, her face bright, her eyes shining. "I went to Houston and got a part-time job decorating a living room. That's my commission. Surprise! Now you won't have to sell that mangy old Hereford bull!"

He looked odd. As if he'd tried to swallow a watermelon and couldn't get it down. He stood up, still staring at the crumpled check, and turned away. He walked to the sink, staring out the darkened window.

"How did you get a job decorating anything?"

"I studied for several years at an excellent school of interior design in New York," she said. "I got a job with one of the leading agencies and spent two years developing my craft. That's why I got so angry when you made the remark about interior decorators being con artists," she added. "You see, I am one."

"New York?"

"Yes. It's the best place to learn, and to work."

"And you got pneumonia . . ."

"And had to give it up temporarily," she agreed. She frowned. He sounded strange. "Thanks to you, I'm back on my feet now and in fine form. The lady I did the design for was really pleased with my work, too. But the reason I did it was to get you enough money to pay off your note . . ."

"I can't take this," he said in a strained tone. He put it gently on the table and started out the door.

"But, Everett, your supper . . . !" she called.

"I'm not hungry." He kept walking. A moment later, the front door slammed behind him.

She sat there at the table, alone, staring at the check for a long time, until the numbers started to blur. Her eyes burned with unshed tears. She loved him. She loved Everett Culhane. And in the space of one night, her good intentions had lost her the pleasure of being near him. She knew almost certainly that he was going to fire her now. Too late, she remembered his opinion of city women. She hadn't had time to explain that it was her parents' idea for her to study and work in New York, not her own. Nor that the pressure had been too much. He thought it was only pneumonia. Could she convince him in time that she wasn't what he was sure she was? That she wanted to stay here forever, not just as a temporary thing? She glanced toward the door with a quiet sigh. Well, she'd just sit here and wait until the shock wore off and he came back.

She did wait. But when three o'clock in the morning came, with no sign of Everett, she went reluctantly upstairs and lay down. It didn't help that she still smelled leather and faint cologne, and that her mind replayed the fierce ardor she'd learned from him until, exhausted, she slept.

When her eyes slowly opened the next morning, she felt as if she hadn't slept at all. And the first thing she remembered was Everett's shocked face when she'd told him what she used to do for a living. She couldn't understand why he'd reacted that way. After the way it had been between them, she hadn't expected him to walk off without at least discussing it. She wondered if it was going to be that way until he fired her. Because she was sure he was going to. And she knew for a certainty that she didn't want to go. She loved him with all her heart.

7

*

If she'd hoped for a new start that morning, she was disappointed. She fixed breakfast, but Everett went out the front door without even sticking his head in the kitchen. Apparently, he'd rather have starved than eat what she'd cooked for him.

That morning set the pattern for the next two days. Jennifer cooked and wound up eating her efforts by herself. Everett came home in the early hours of the morning, arranging his schedule so that she never saw him at all.

He'd sold the bull. She found it out from Eddie, who was in a nasty temper of his own.

"I practically begged him to wait and see what happened," Eddie spat as he delivered the eggs to Jennifer the second morning. "When that neighbor didn't want the bull, Everett just loaded it up and took it to the sale without a word. He looks bad. He won't talk. Do you know what's eating him?"

She avoided that sharp look. "He's worried about money, I think," she said. "I offered him what I had. He got mad and stomped off and he hasn't spoken to me since."

"That don't sound like Everett."

"Yes, I know." She sighed, smiling at him. "I think he wants me to go away, Eddie. He's done everything but leave the ranch forever to get his point across."

"Money troubles are doing it, not you." Eddie grinned. "Don't back off now. He needs us all more than ever."

"Maybe he does," Jennifer said. "I just wish he'd taken the money I offered to lend him."

"That would be something, all right, to watch Everett take money from a lady. No offense, Miss Jenny, but he's too much man. If you know what I mean."

She did, unfortunately. She'd experienced the male in him, in ways that would haunt her forever. And worst of all was the fact that she was still hungry for him. If anything, that wild little interlude on the sofa had whetted her appetite, not satisfied it.

For lunch, she put a platter of cold cuts in the refrigerator and left a loaf of bread on the table along with a plate and cup; there was coffee warming on the stove. She pulled on a sweater and went down to visit Libby. It was like baiting a trap, she thought. Perhaps he'd enjoy eating if he didn't have to look at a city woman.

Libby didn't ask any obvious questions. She simply enjoyed the visit, since the children were in school and she could talk about clothes and television programs with the younger woman.

At one o'clock, Jennifer left the house and walked slowly back up to see if Everett had eaten. It was something of a shock to find him wandering wildly around the kitchen, smoking like a furnace.

"So there you are!" he burst out, glaring at her with menacing brown eyes. "Where in hell have you been? No note, no nothing! I didn't know if you'd left or been kidnapped, or stepped into a hole . . ."

"What would you care if I had?" she demanded. "You've made it obvious that you don't care for my company!"

"What did you expect?" he burst out, his eyes dangerous. "You lied to me."

"I didn't," she said in defense.

"I thought you were a poor little secretary in danger of starving if I didn't take you in," he said through his teeth. He let his eyes wander with slow insolence over the white blouse and green skirt she was wearing. "And what do I find out? That you lived and worked in New York at a job that would pay you more in one week than I can make here in two months!"

So that was it. His pride was crushed. He was poor and she wasn't, and that cut him up.

But knowing it wasn't much help. He was as unapproachable as a coiled rattler. In his dusty jeans and denim shirt, he looked as wild as an outlaw.

"I had pneumonia," she began. "I had to come south..."

"Bobby didn't know?" he asked.

"No," she said. "I didn't see any reason to tell him. Everett...!"

"Why didn't you say something at the beginning?" he demanded, ramming his hand into his pocket to fish for another cigarette.

"What was there to say?" she asked impotently. She took the sweater from around her shoulders, and her green eyes pleaded with him. "Everett, I'm just the same as I always was."

"Not hardly," he said. His jaw clenched as he lit the cigarette. "You came here looking like a straggly little hen. And now..." He blew out a cloud of smoke, letting his eyes savor the difference. They lingered for a long time on her blouse, narrowing, burning. "I brought a city girl here once," he said absently. His eyes caught hers. "When she found out that I had more ideas than I had money, she turned around and ran. We were engaged," he said on a short laugh. "I do have the damndest blind spot about women."

She wrapped her arms around her chest. "Why does it make so much difference?" she asked. "I only took the designing job to help, Rett," she added. She moved closer. "I just wanted to pay you back, for giving me a job when I needed it. I knew you couldn't afford me, but I was in trouble, and you sacrificed for me." Her eyes searched his dark, hard face. "I wanted to do something for you. I wanted you to have your bull."

His face hardened and he turned away, as if he couldn't bear the sight of her. He raised the cigarette to his lips and his back was ramrod straight.

"I want you to leave," he said.

"Yes, I know," she said on a soft little sigh. "When?"

"At the end of the week."

So soon, she thought miserably? Her eyes clouded as she stared at his back, seeing the determination in every hard line of it. "Do you hate me?" she asked in a hurting tone.

He turned around slowly, the cigarette held tautly in one hand, and his eyes slashed at her. He moved closer, with a look in his dark eyes that was disturbing.

With a smooth motion, he tossed the unfinished cigarette into an ashtray on the table and reached for her.

"I could hate you," he said harshly. "If I didn't want you so damned much." He bent his head and caught her mouth with his.

She stiffened for an instant, because there was no tenderness in this exchange. He was rough and hurting, deliberately. Even so, she loved him. If this was all he could give, then it would be enough. She inched her trapped hands up to his neck and slid them around it. Her soft mouth opened, giving him all he wanted of it. She couldn't respond, he left her no room. He was taking without any thought of giving back the pleasure.

His hard hands slid roughly over her breasts and down to her hips and ground her against him in a deep, insolent rhythm, letting her feel what she already knew—that he wanted her desperately.

"Was it a lie?" he ground out against her mouth. "Are you really a virgin?"

Her lips felt bruised when she tried to speak. "Yes," she said shakily. He was still holding her intimately, and when she tried to pull back, he only crushed her hips closer.

"No, don't do that," he said with a cruel smile. "I like to feel you. Doesn't it give you a sense of triumph, city girl, knowing how you affect me?"

Her hands pushed futilely at his hard chest. "Everett, don't make me feel cheap," she pleaded.

"Could I?" He laughed coldly. "With your prospects?" His hands tightened, making her cry out. His mouth lowered. This time it was teasing, tantalizing. He brushed it against her own mouth in whispery motions that worked like a narcotic, hypnotizing her, weakening her. She began to follow those hard lips with her own, trying to capture them in an exchange that would satisfy the ache he was creating.

"Do you want to stay with me, Jenny?" he whispered.

"Yes," she whispered back, her whole heart in her response. She clutched at his shirtfront with trembling fingers. Her mouth begged for his. "Yes, Everett, I want to stay...!"

His breath came hard and fast at her lips. "Then come upstairs with me, now, and I'll let you," he breathed.

It took a minute for his words to register, and then she realized that his hands had moved to the very base of her spine, to touch her in ways that shocked and frightened her.

She pulled against his hands, her face red, her eyes wild. "What do you mean?" she whispered.

He laughed, his eyes as cold as winter snow. "Don't you know? Sleep with me. Or would you like to hear it in a less formal way?" he added, and put it in words that made her hand come up like a whip.

He caught it, looking down at her with contempt and desire and anger all mixed up in his hard face. "Not interested?" he asked mockingly. "You were a minute ago. You were the other night, when you let me strip you."

Her teeth clenched as she tried to hang on to her dignity and her pride. "Let me go," she whispered shakily.

"I could please you, city girl," he said with a bold, slow gaze down her taut body. "You're going to give in to a man someday. Why not me? Or do I need to get rich first to appeal to you?"

Tears welled up in her eyes. His one hand was about to crack the delicate bone in her wrist, and the other was hurting her back. She closed her eyelids to shut off the sight of his cold face. She loved him so. How could he treat her this way? How could he be so cruel after that tenderness they'd shared!

"No comment?" he asked. He dropped his hands and retrieved his still-smoking cigarette from the ashtray.

"Well, you can't blame a man for trying. You seemed willing enough the other night. I thought you might like some memories to carry away with you."

She'd had some beautiful ones, she thought miserably, until now. Her hands reached, trembling, for her sweater. She held it over her chest and wouldn't look up.

"I've got some correspondence on the desk you can type when you run out of things to do in the kitchen," he said, turning toward the door. He looked back with a grim smile on his lips. "That way you can make up some of the time you spent decorating that woman's house for her."

She still didn't speak, didn't move. The world had caved in on her. She loved him. And he could treat her like this, like some tramp he'd picked up on the street!

He drew in a sharp breath. "Don't talk, then," he said coldly. "I don't give a damn. I never did. I wanted you, that's all. But if I had the money, I could have you and a dozen like you, couldn't I?"

She managed to raise her ravaged face. He seemed almost to flinch at the sight of it, but he was only a blur through the tears in her eyes, and she might have been mistaken.

"Say something!" he ground out.

She lifted her chin. Her pale, swollen eyes just stared at him accusingly, and not one single word left her lips. Even if he threw her against the wall, she wouldn't give him the satisfaction of even one syllable!

He drew in a furious breath and whirled on his heel, slamming out the door.

She went upstairs like a zombie, hardly aware of her surroundings at all. She went into her room and took the uncashed checks that he'd signed for her salary and put them neatly on her dresser. She packed very quickly and searched in her purse. She had just enough pocket money left to pay a cab. She could cash the design firm's check in town when she got there. She called the cab company and then lifted her case and went downstairs to wait for it.

Everett was nowhere in sight, neither were Eddie and Bib, when the taxi came winding up the driveway. She walked down the steps, her eyes dry now, her face resolved, and got inside.

"Take me into town, please," she said quietly.

The cab pulled away from the steps, and she scanned the ranchhouse and the corrals one last time. Then she turned away and closed her eyes. She didn't look back, not once.

Fortunately, Jennifer had no trouble landing a job. Sally Wade had been so impressed with the work that she'd done for Mrs. Whitehall that she practically created a position for Jennifer in her small, and still struggling, design firm. Jennifer loved the work, but several weeks had passed before she was able to think about Everett without crying.

The cup of coffee at Jennifer's elbow was getting cold. She frowned at it as her hand stilled on the sketch she was doing for a new client.

"Want some fresh?" Sally Wade asked from the doorway, holding her own cup aloft. "I'm just going to the pot."

"Bless you," Jennifer laughed.

"That's the first time you've really looked happy in the three months since you've been here," Sally remarked, cocking her head. "Getting over him?"

"Over whom?" came the shocked reply.

"That man, whoever he was, who had you in tears your first week here. I didn't pry, but I wondered," the older woman confessed. "I kept waiting for the phone to ring, or a letter to come. But nothing did. I kind of thought that he had to care, because you cared so much."

"He wanted a mistress," Jennifer said, putting it into words. "And I wanted a husband. We just got our signals crossed. Besides," she added with a wan smile, "I'm feeling worlds better. I've got a great job, a lovely boss, and even a part-time boyfriend. If you can call Drew a boy."

"He's delightful." Sally sighed. "Just what you need. A live wire."

"And not a bad architect, either. You must be pleased he's working with us." She grinned. "He did a great job on that office project last month."

"So did you," Sally said, smiling. She leaned against the doorjamb. "I thought it a marvelous idea, locating a group of offices in a renovated mansion. It only needed the right team, and you and Drew work wonderfully well together."

"In business, yes." Jennifer twirled her pencil around in her slender fingers. "I just don't want him getting serious about me. If it's possible for him to get serious about anyone." She laughed.

"Don't try to bury yourself."

"Oh, I'm not. It's just..." She shrugged. "I'm only now getting over... I don't want any more risks. Not for a long time. Maybe not ever."

"Some men are kind-hearted," Sally ventured.

"So why are you single?" came the sharp reply.

"I'm picky," Sally informed her with a sly smile. "Very, very picky. I want Rhett Butler or nobody."

"Wrong century, wrong state."

"You're from Georgia. Help me out!"

"Sorry," Jennifer murmured. "If I could find one, do you think I'd tell anybody?"

"Point taken. Give me that cup and I'll fill it for you."

"Thanks, boss."

"Oh, boy, coffee!" a tall, redheaded man called from the doorway as he closed the door behind him. "I'll have mine black, with two doughnuts, a fried egg..."

"The breakfast bar is closed, Mr. Peterson," Jennifer told him.

"Sorry, Drew," Sally added. "You'll just have to catch your own chicken and do it the hard way."

"I could starve," he grumbled, ramming his hands in his pockets. He had blue eyes, and right now they were glaring at both women. "I don't have a wife or a mother. I live alone. My cook hates me..."

"You're breaking my heart," Sally offered.

"You can have the other half of my doughnut," Jennifer said, holding up a chunk of doughnut with chocolate clinging to it.

"Never mind." Drew sighed. "Thanks all the same, but I'll just wither away."

"That wouldn't be difficult," Jennifer told him. "You're nothing but skin and bones."

"I gained two pounds this week," he said, affronted.

"Where is it," Sally asked with a sweeping glance, "in your big toe?"

"Ha, ha," he laughed as she turned to go to the coffeepot.

"You *are* thin," Jennifer remarked.

He glared at her. "I'm still a growing boy." He stretched lazily. "Want to ride out to the new office building with me this morning?"

"No, thanks. I've got to finish these drawings. What do you think?"

She held one up, and he studied it with an architect's trained eye. "Nice. Just remember that this," he said, pointing to the vestibule, "is going to be a heavy-traffic area, and plan accordingly."

"There goes my white carpet," she teased.

"I'll white carpet you," he muttered. He pursed his lips as he studied her. "Wow, lady, what a change."

She blinked up at him. "What?"

"You. When you walked in here three months ago, you looked like a drowned kitten. And now..." He only sighed.

She was wearing a beige suit with a pink candy-striped blouse and a pink silk scarf. Her blond hair was almost platinum with its new body and sheen, and she'd had it trimmed so that it hung in wispy waves all around her shoulders. Her face was creamy and soft and she was wearing makeup again. She looked nice, and his eyes told her so.

"Thanks."

He pursed his lips. "What for?"

"The flattery," she told him. "My ego's been even with my ankles for quite awhile."

"Stick with me, kid, I'll get it all the way up to your ears," he promised with an evil leer.

"Sally, he's trying to seduce me!" she called toward the front of the office.

She expected some kind of bantering reply, but none was forthcoming. She looked up at Drew contemplatively. "Reckon she's left?"

"No. She's answered the phone. You still aren't used to the musical tone, are you?"

No, she wasn't. There were quite a lot of things she wasn't used to, and the worst of them was being without Everett. She had a good job, a nice apartment, and some new clothes. But without him, none of that mattered. She was going through the motions, and little more. His contempt still stung her pride when she recalled that last horrible scene. But she couldn't get him out of her mind, no matter how she tried.

"Well!" Sally said, catching her breath as she rejoined them. "If the rest of him looks like his voice, I may get back into the active part of the business. That was a potential client, and I think he may be the Rhett Butler I've always dreamed of. What a silky, sexy voice!"

"Dream on," Jennifer teased.

"He's coming by in the morning to talk to us. Wants his whole house done!" the older woman exclaimed.

"He must have a sizeable wallet, then," Drew remarked.

Sally nodded. "He didn't say where the house was, but I assume it's nearby. It didn't sound like a long-distance call." She glanced at Jennifer with a smile. "Apparently your reputation has gotten around, too," she laughed. "He asked if you'd be doing the project. I had the idea he wouldn't have agreed otherwise." She danced around with her coffee cup in her hand. "What a godsend. With the office building and this job, we'll be out of the red, kids! What a break!"

"And you were groaning about the bills just yesterday," Jennifer laughed. "I told you something would turn up, didn't I?"

"You're my lucky charm," Sally told her. "If I hadn't hired you, I shudder to think what would have happened."

"You know how much I appreciated getting this job," Jennifer murmured. "I was in pretty desperate circumstances."

"So I noticed. Well, we did each other a lot of good. We still are," Sally said warmly. "Hey, let's celebrate. Come on. I'll treat you two to lunch."

"Lovely!" Jennifer got up and grabbed her purse. "Come on, Drew, let's hurry before she changes her mind!"

She rushed out the door, with Drew in full pursuit, just ahead of Sally. And not one of them noticed the man sitting quietly in the luxury car across the street, his fingers idly caressing a car phone in the back seat as he stared intently after them.

8
*

Drew had asked Jennifer to go out with him that night, but she begged off with a smile. She didn't care for the nightlife anymore. She went to company functions with Sally when it was necessary to attract clients or discuss new projects, but that was about the extent of her social consciousness. She spent most of her time alone, in her modest apartment, going over drawings and planning rooms.

She enjoyed working for Sally. Houston was a big city, but much smaller than New York. And while there was competition, it wasn't as fierce. The pressure was less. And best of all, Jennifer was allowed a lot of latitude in her projects. She had a free hand to incorporate her own ideas as long as they complemented the client's requirements. She loved what she did, and in loving it, she blossomed into the woman she'd once been. But this time she didn't allow herself to fall into the trap of overspending. She budgeted, right down to the pretty clothes she loved—she bought them on sale, a few at a time, and concentrated on mix-and-match outfits.

It was a good life. But part of her was still mourning Everett. Not a day went by when she couldn't see him, tall and unnerving, somewhere in her memory. They'd been so good for each other. She'd never experienced such tenderness in a man.

She got up from the sofa and looked out at the skyline of Houston. The city was bright and beautiful, but she remembered the ranch on starry nights. Dogs would howl far in the distance, crickets would sing at the steps. And all around would be open land and stars and the silhouettes of Everett's cattle.

She wrapped her arms around her body and sighed. Perhaps someday the pain would stop and she could really forget him. Perhaps someday she could remember his harsh accusations and not be wounded all over again. But right now, it hurt terribly. He'd been willing to let her stay as his mistress, as a possession to be used when he wanted her. But he wouldn't let her be part of his life. He couldn't have told her more graphically how little he thought of her. That had hurt the most. That even after all the caring, all the tenderness, she hadn't reached him at all. He hadn't seen past the shape of her body and his need of it. He hadn't loved her. And he'd made sure she knew it.

There were a lot of nights, like this one, when she paced and paced and wondered if he thought of her at all, if he regretted what had happened. Somehow, she doubted it. Everett had a wall like steel around him. He wouldn't let anyone inside it. Especially not a city woman with an income that could top his.

She laughed bitterly. It was unfortunate that she had fallen in love for the first time with such a cynical man. It had warped the way she looked at the world. She felt as if she, too, were impregnable now. Her emotions were carefully wrapped up, where they couldn't be touched. Nobody could reach her now. She felt safe in her warm cocoon. Of course, she was as incapable of caring now as he'd been. And in a way, that was a blessing. Because she couldn't be hurt anymore. She could laugh and carry on with Drew, and it didn't mean a thing. There was no risk in dating these days. Her heart was safely tucked away.

With a last uncaring look at the skyline, she turned off the lights and went to bed. Just as she drifted off, she wondered who the new client was going to be, and grinned at the memory of Sally's remark about his sexy voice.

She overslept the next morning for the first time in months. With a shriek as she saw the time, she dressed hastily in a silky beige dress and high heels. She moaned over her unruly hair that would curl and feather all around her shoulders instead of going into a neat bun.

She touched up her face, stepped into her shoes, and rushed out into the chill autumn morning without a jacket or a sweater. Oh, well, maybe she wouldn't freeze, she told herself as she jumped into the cab she'd called and headed for the office.

"So there you are," Drew said with mock anger as she rushed breathlessly in the door, her cheeks flushed, her eyes sparkling, her hair disheveled and sexy around her face. "I ought to fire you."

"Go ahead. I dare you." She laughed up at him. "And I'll tell Sally all about that last expense voucher you faked."

"Blackmailer!" he growled. He reached out and lifted her up in the air, laughing at her.

"Put me down, you male chauvinist." She laughed gaily. Her face was a study in beauty, her body lusciously displayed in the pose, her hands on his shoulders, her hair swirling gracefully as she looked down at him. "Come on, put me down," she coaxed. "Put me down, Drew, and I'll take you to lunch."

"In that case," he murmured dryly.

"Jennifer! Drew!" Sally exclaimed, entering the room with a nervous laugh. "Stop clowning. We've got business to discuss, and you're making a horrible first impression."

"Oops," Drew murmured. He turned his head just as Jennifer turned hers, and all the laughter and brightness drained out of her like air out of a balloon. She stared down at the newcomer with strained features and eyes that went from shock to extreme anger.

Drew set her down on her feet and turned, hand extended, grinning. "Sorry about that. Just chastising the staff for tardiness." He chuckled. "I'm Andrew Paterson, resident architect. This is my associate, Jennifer King."

"I know her name," Everett Culhane said quietly. His dark eyes held no offer of peace, no hint of truce. They were angry and cold, and he smiled mockingly as his eyes went from Jennifer to Drew. "We've met."

Sally looked poleaxed. It had just dawned on her who Everett was, when she got a look at Jennifer's white face.

"Uh, Mr. Culhane is our new client," Sally said hesitantly. Jennifer looked as if she might faint. "You remember, Jenny, I mentioned yesterday that he'd called."

"You didn't mention his name," Jennifer said in a cool voice that shook with rage. "Excuse me, I have a phone call to make."

"Not so fast," Everett said quietly. "First we talk."

Her eyes glittered at him, her body trembled with suppressed tension. "I have nothing to say to you, Mr. Culhane," she managed. "And you have nothing to say to me that I care to hear."

"Jennifer..." Sally began nervously.

"If my job depends on working for Mr. Culhane, you can have my resignation on the spot," Jennifer said unsteadily. "I will not speak to him, much less work with him. I'm sorry."

She turned and went on wobbly legs to her office, closing the door behind her. She couldn't even sit down. She was shaking like a leaf all over and tears were burning her eyes. She heard voices outside, but ignored them. She stared at an abstract painting on the wall until she thought she'd go blind.

The sound of the door opening barely registered. Then it closed with a firm snap, and she glanced over her shoulder to find Everett inside.

It was only then that she noticed he was wearing a suit. A very expensive gray one that made his darkness even more formidable; his powerful body was streamlined and elegant in its new garments. He was holding a silverbelly Stetson in one lean hand and staring at her quietly, calculatingly.

"Please go away," she said with as much conviction as she could muster.

"Why?" he asked carelessly, tossing his hat onto her desk. He dropped into an armchair and crossed one long leg over the other. He lit a cigarette and pulled the ashtray on her desk closer, but his eyes never left her ravaged face.

"If you want your house redone, there are other firms," she told him, turning bravely, although her legs were still trembling.

He saw that, and his eyes narrowed, his jaw tautened. "Are you afraid of me?" he asked quietly.

"I'm outraged," she replied in a voice that was little more than a whisper. Her hand brushed back a long, unruly strand of hair. "You might as well have taken a bullwhip to me, just before I left the ranch. What do you want now? To show me how prosperous you are? I've noticed the cut of your suit. And the fact that you can afford to hire this firm to redo the house does indicate a lot of money." She smiled unsteadily. "Congratulations. I hope your sudden wealth makes you happy."

He didn't speak for a long minute. His eyes wandered over her slowly, without any insult, as if he'd forgotten what she looked like and needed to stare at her, to fill his eyes. "Aren't you going to ask me how I came by it?" he demanded finally.

"No. Because I don't care," she said.

One corner of his mouth twitched a little. He took a draw from the cigarette and flicked an ash into the ashtray. "I sold off the oil rights."

So much for sticking to your principles, she wanted to say. But she didn't have the strength. She went behind her desk and sat down carefully.

"No comment?" he asked.

She blanched, remembering with staggering clarity the last time he'd said that. He seemed to remember it, too, because his jaw tautened and he drew in a harsh breath.

"I want my house done," he said curtly. "I want you to do it. Nobody else. And I want you to stay with me while you work on the place."

"Hell will freeze over first," she said quietly.

"I was under the impression that the firm wasn't operating in the black," he said with an insolent appraisal of her office. "The commission on this project will be pretty large."

"I told you once that you couldn't buy me," she said on a shuddering breath. "I'd jump off a cliff before I'd stay under the same roof with you!"

His eyes closed. When they opened again, he was staring down at his boot. "Is it that redheaded clown outside?" he asked suddenly, jerking his gaze up to catch hers.

Her lips trembled. "That's none of your business."

His eyes wandered slowly over her face. "You looked different with him," he said deeply. "Alive, vibrant, happy. And then, the minute you spotted me, every bit of life went out of you. It was like watching water drain from a glass."

"What did you expect, for God's sake!" she burst out, her eyes wild. "You cut me up!"

He drew in a slow breath. "Yes. I know."

"Then why are you here?" she asked wearily. "What do you want from me?"

He stared at the cigarette with eyes that barely saw it. "I told you. I want my house done." He looked up. "I can afford the best, and that's what I want. You."

There was an odd inflection in his voice, but she was too upset to hear it. She blinked her eyes, trying to get herself under control. "I won't do it. Sally will just have to fire me."

He got to his feet and loomed over the desk, crushing out the cigarette before he rammed his hands into his pockets and glared at her. "There are less pleasant ways to do this," he said. "I could make things very difficult for your new employer." His eyes challenged her. "Call my bluff. See if you can skip town with that on your conscience."

She couldn't, and he knew it. Her pride felt lacerated. "What do you think you'll accomplish by forcing me to come back?" she asked. "I'd put a knife in you if I could. I won't sleep with you, no matter what you do. So what will you get out of it?"

"My house decorated, of course," he said lazily. His eyes wandered over her. "I've got over the other. Out of sight, out of mind, don't they say?" He shrugged and turned away with a calculating look on his face. "And one body's pretty much like another in the dark," he added, reaching for his Stetson. His eyes caught the flutter of her lashes and he smiled to himself as he reached for the doorknob. "Well, Miss King, which is it? Do you come back to Big Spur with me or do I give Ms. Wade the sad news that you're leaving her in the lurch?"

Her eyes flashed green sparks at him. What choice was there? But he'd pay for this. Somehow, she'd make him. "I'll go," she bit off.

He didn't say another word. He left her office as though he were doing her a favor by letting her redecorate his house!

Sally came in the door minutes later, looking troubled and apologetic.

"I had no idea," she told Jennifer. "Honest to God, I had no idea who he was."

"Now you know," Jennifer said on a shaky laugh.

"You don't have to do it," the older woman said curtly.

"Yes, I'm afraid I do. Everett doesn't make idle threats," she said, rising. "You've been too good to me, Sally. I can't let him cause trouble for you on my account. I'll go with him. After all, it's just another job."

"You look like death warmed over. I'll send Drew with you. We'll do something to justify him . . ."

"Everett would eat him alive," she told Sally with a level stare. "And don't pretend you don't know it. Drew's a nice man but he isn't up to Everett's weight or his temper. This is a private war."

"Unarmed combat?" Sally asked sadly.

"Exactly. He has this thing about city women, and I wasn't completely honest with him. He wants to get even."

"I thought revenge went out with the Borgias," Sally muttered.

"Not quite. Wish me luck. I'm going to need it."

"If it gets too rough, call for reinforcements," Sally said. "I'll pack a bag and move in with you, Everett or no Everett."

"You're a pal," Jennifer said warmly.

"I'm a rat," came the dry reply. "I wish I hadn't done this to you. If I'd known who he was, I'd never have told him you worked here."

Jennifer had hoped to go down to Big Spur alone, but Everett went back to her apartment with her, his eyes daring her to refuse his company.

He waited in the living room while she packed, and not one corner escaped his scrutiny.

"Looking for dust?" she asked politely, case in hand.

He turned, cigarette in hand, studying her. "This place must cost you an arm," he remarked.

"It does," she said with deliberate sarcasm. "But I can afford it. I make a lot of money, as you reminded me."

"I said a lot of cruel things, didn't I, Jenny Wren?" he asked quietly, searching her shocked eyes. "Did I leave deep scars?"

She lifted her chin. "Can we go? The sooner we get there, the sooner I can get the job done and come home."

"Didn't you ever think of the ranch as home?" he asked, watching her. "You seemed to love it at first."

"Things were different then," she said noncommittally, and started for the door.

He took her case, his fingers brushing hers in the process, and producing electric results.

"Eddie and Bib gave me hell when they found out you'd gone," he said as he opened the door for her.

"I imagine you were too busy celebrating to notice."

He laughed shortly. "Celebrating? You damned little fool, I . . . !" He closed his mouth with a rough sigh. "Never mind. You might have left a nasty note or something."

"Why, so you'd know where I went?" she demanded. "That was the last thing I wanted."

"So I noticed," he agreed. He locked the door, handed her the key, and started down the hall toward the elevator. "Libby told me the name of the firm you'd worked for. It wasn't hard to guess you'd get a job with them."

She tossed her hair. "So that was how you found me."

"We've got some unfinished business," he replied as they waited for the elevator. His dark eyes held hers and she had to clench her fists to keep from kicking him. He had a power over her that all her anger couldn't stop. Deep beneath the layer of ice was a blazing inferno of hunger and love, but she'd die before she'd show it to him.

"I hate you," she breathed.

"Yes, I know you do," he said with an odd satisfaction.

"Mr. Culhane..."

"You used to call me Rett," he recalled, studying her. "Especially," he added quietly, "when we made love."

Her face began to color and she aimed a kick at his shins. He jumped back just as the elevator door opened.

"Pig!" she ground out.

"Now, honey, think of the kids," he drawled, aiming a glance at the elevator full of fascinated spectators. "If you knock me down, how can I support the ten of you?"

Red-faced, she got in ahead of him and wished with all her heart that the elevator doors would close right dead center on him. They didn't.

He sighed loudly, glancing down at her. "I begged you not to run off with that salesman," he said in a sad drawl. "I told you he'd lead you into a life of sin!"

There were murmured exclamations all around and a buzz of conversation. She glared up at him. Two could play that game.

"Well, what did you expect me to do, sit at home and knit while you ran around with that black-eyed hussy?" she drawled back. "And me in my delicate condition..."

"Delicate condition...?" he murmured, shocked at her unexpected remark.

"And it's your baby, too, you animal," she said with a mock sob, glaring up at him.

"Darling!" he burst out. "You didn't tell me!"

And he grabbed her and kissed her hungrily right there in front of the whole crowd while she gasped and counted to ten and tried not to let him see that she was melting into the floor from the delicious contact with his mouth.

The elevator doors opened and he lifted his head as the other occupants filed out. He was breathing unsteadily and his eyes held hers. "No," he whispered when she tried to move away. His arm caught her and his head bent. "I need you," he whispered shakily. "Need you so...!"

That brought it all back. Need. He needed her. He just needed a body, that was all, and she knew it! She jerked herself out of his arms and stomped off the elevator.

"You try that again and I'll vanish!" she threatened, glaring up at him when they were outside the building. Her face was flushed, her breath shuddering. "I mean it! I'll disappear and you won't find me this time!"

He shrugged. "Suit yourself." He walked alongside her, all the brief humor gone out of his face. She wondered minutes later if it had been there at all.

9
*

He had a Lincoln now. Not only the car, but a driver to go with it. He handed her bag to the uniformed driver and put Jennifer in the back seat beside him.

"Aren't we coming up in the world, though?" she asked with cool sarcasm.

"Don't you like it?" he replied mockingly. He leaned back against the seat facing her and lit a cigarette. "I didn't think a woman alive could resist flashy money."

She remembered reluctantly how he'd already been thrown over once for the lack of wealth. Part of her tender heart felt sorry for him. But not any part that was going to show, she told herself.

"You could buy your share now, I imagine," she said, glancing out the window at the traffic.

He blew out a thin cloud of smoke. The driver climbed in under the wheel and, starting the powerful car, pulled out into the street.

"I imagine so."

She stared at the purse in her lap. "They really did find oil out there?" she asked.

"Sure did. Barrels and barrels." He glanced at her over his cigarette. "The whole damned skyline's cluttered with rigs these days. Metal grasshoppers." He sighed. "The cattle don't even seem to mind them. They just graze right on."

Wouldn't it be something if a geyser blew out under one of his prize Herefords one day, she mused. She almost told him, and then remembered the animosity between them. It had been a good kind of relationship that they'd had. If only Everett hadn't ruined it.

"It's a little late to go into it now," he said quietly. "But I didn't mean to hurt you that much. Once I cooled down, I would have apologized."

"The apology wouldn't have meant much after what you said to me!" she said through her teeth, flushing at the memory of the crude phrase.

He looked away. For a long minute he just sat and smoked. "You're almost twenty-four years old, Jenny," he said finally. "If you haven't heard words like that before, you're overdue."

"I didn't expect to hear them from you," she shot back, glaring at him. "Much less have you treat me with less respect than a woman you might have picked up on the streets with a twenty-dollar bill!"

"One way or another, I'd have touched you like that eventually!" he growled, glaring at her. "And don't sit there like lily white purity and pretend you don't know what I'm talking about. We were on the verge of becoming lovers that night on the sofa."

"You wouldn't have made me feel ashamed if it had happened that night," she said fiercely. "You wouldn't have made me feel cheap!"

He seemed about to explode. Then he caught himself and took a calming draw from the cigarette. His dark eyes studied the lean hand holding it. "You hurt me."

It was a shock to hear him admit it. "What?"

"You hurt me." His dark eyes lifted. "I thought we were being totally honest with each other. I trusted you. I let you closer than any other woman ever got. And then out of the blue, you hit me with everything at once. That you were a professional woman, a career woman. Worse," he added quietly, "a city woman, used to city men and city life and city ways. I couldn't take it. I'd been paying you scant wages, and you handed me that check . . ." He sighed wearily. "My God, I can't even tell you how I felt. My pride took one hell of a blow. I had nothing, and you were showing me graphically that you could outdo me on every front."

"I only wanted to help," she said curtly. "I wanted to buy you the damned bull. Sorry. If I had it to do all over again, I wouldn't offer you a dime."

"Yes, it shows." He sighed. He finished the cigarette and crushed it out. "Who's the redhead?"

"Drew? Sally told you. He's our architect. He has his own firm, of course, but he collaborates with us on big projects."

"Not on mine," he said menacingly, and his eyes darkened. "Not in my house."

She glared back. "That will depend on how much renovation the projects calls for, I imagine."

"I won't have him on my place," he said softly.

"Why?"

"I don't like the way he looks at you," he said coldly. "Must less the way he makes free with his hands."

"I'm twenty-three years old," she reminded him. "And I like Drew, and the way he looks at me! He's a nice man."

"And I'm not," he agreed. "Nice is the last thing I am. If he ever touches you that way again when I'm in the same room, I'll break his fingers for him."

"Everett Donald Culhane!" she burst out.

His eyebrows arched. "Who told you my whole name?"

She looked away. "Never mind," she said, embarrassed.

His hand brushed against her hair, caressing it. "God, your hair is glorious," he said quietly. "It was nothing like this at the ranch."

She tried not to feel his touch. "I'd been ill," she managed.

"And now you aren't. Now you're…fuller and softer-looking. Even your breasts…"

"Stop it!" she cried, red-faced.

He let go of her hair reluctantly, but his eyes didn't leave her. "I'll have you, Jenny," he said quietly, his tone as soft as it had been that night when he was loving her.

"Only if you shoot me in the leg first!" she told him.

"Not a chance," he murmured, studying her. "I'll want you healthy and strong, so that you can keep up with me."

Her face did a slow burn again. She could have kicked him, but they were sitting down. "I don't want you!"

"You did. You will. I've got a whole campaign mapped out, Miss Jenny," he told her with amazing arrogance. "You're under siege. You just haven't realized it yet."

She looked him straight in the eye. "My grandfather held off a whole German company during World War I rather than surrender."

His eyebrows went up. "Is that supposed to impress me?"

"I won't be your mistress," she told him levelly. "No matter how many campaigns you map out or what kind of bribes or threats you try to use. I came with you to save Sally's business. But all this is to me is a job. I am not going to sleep with you."

His dark, quiet eyes searched over her face. "Why?"

Her lips opened and closed, opened again. "Because I can't do it without love," she said finally.

"Love isn't always possible," he said softly. "Sometimes, other things have to come first. Mutual respect, caring, companionship..."

"Can we talk about something else?" she asked tautly. Her fingers twisted the purse out of shape.

He chuckled softly. "Talking about sex won't get you pregnant."

"You've got money now. You can buy women," she ground out. "You said so."

"Honey, would you want a man you had to buy?" he asked quietly, studying her face.

Her lips parted. "Would I..." She searched his eyes. "Well, no."

"I wouldn't want a woman I had to buy," he said simply. "I'm too proud, Jenny. I said and did some harsh things to you," he remarked. "I can understand why you're angry and hurt about it. Someday I'll try to explain why I behaved that way. Right now, I'll settle for regaining even a shadow of the friendship we had. Nothing more. Despite all this wild talk, I'd never deliberately try to seduce you.''

"Wouldn't you?'' she asked bitterly. "Isn't that the whole point of getting me down here?''

"No.'' He lit another cigarette.

"You said you were going to...'' she faltered.

"I want to,'' he admitted quietly. "God, I want to! But I can't quite take a virgin in my stride. Once, I thought I might,'' he confessed, his eyes searching her face. "That night... You were so eager, and I damned near lost my head when I realized that I could have you.'' He stared at the tip of his cigarette with blank eyes. "Would you have hated me if I hadn't been able to stop?''

Her eyes drilled into her purse. "There's just no point in going over it,'' she said in a studiously polite tone. "The past is gone.''

"Like hell it's gone,'' he ground out. "I look at you and start aching,'' he said harshly.

Her lower lip trembled as she glared at him. "Then stop looking. Or take cold showers! Just don't expect me to do anything about it. I'm here to work, period!''

His eyebrows arched, and he was watching her with a faintly amused expression. "Where did you learn about cold showers?''

"From watching movies!''

"Is that how you learned about sex, from the movies?'' he taunted.

"No, I learned in school! Sex education,'' she bit off.

"In my day, we had to learn it the hard way,'' he murmured. "It wasn't part of the core curriculum.''

She glanced at him. "I can see you, doing extracurricular work in somebody's backseat.''

He reached out and caught her hair again, tugging on it experimentally. "In a haystall, actually,'' he said, his voice low and soft and dark. Her head turned and he held her eyes. "She was two years older than I was, and she taught me the difference between sex and making love.''

Her face flushed. He affected her in ways nobody else could. She was trembling from the bare touch of his fin-

gers on her hair; her heart was beating wildly. How was
she going to survive being in the same house with him?

"Everett . . ." she began.

"I'm sorry about what I said to you that last day,
Jenny," he said quietly. "I'm sorry I made it into something cheap and sordid between us. Because that's the last
thing it would have been if you'd given yourself to me."

She pulled away from him with a dry little laugh. "Oh,
really?" she said shakenly, turning her eyes to the window. They were out of Houston now, heading south.
"The minute you'd finished with me, you'd have kicked
me out the door, and you know it, Everett Culhane. I'd
have been no different from all the other women you've
held in contempt for giving in to you."

"It isn't like that with you."

"And how many times have you told that story?" she
asked sadly.

"Once. Just now."

He sounded irritated, probably because she wasn't
falling for his practiced line. She closed her eyes and
leaned her head against the cool window pane.

"I'd rather stay in a motel," she said, "if you don't
mind."

"No way, lady," he said curtly. "The same lock's still
on your door, if you can't trust me that far. But staying
at Big Spur was part of the deal you and I negotiated."

She turned her head to glance at his hard, set profile.
He looked formidable again, all dark, flashing eyes and
coldness. He was like the man she'd met that first day at
the screen door.

"What would you have done, if I'd given in?" she
asked suddenly, watching him closely. "What if I'd gotten pregnant?"

His head turned and his eyes glittered strangely. "I'd
have gotten down on my knees and thanked God for it,"
he said harshly. "What did you think I'd do?"

Her lips parted. "I hadn't really thought about it."

"I want children. A yardfull."

That was surprising. Her eyes dropped to his broad
chest, to the muscles that his gray suit barely contained,

and she remembered how it was to be held against him in passion.

"Libby said you loved the ranch," he remarked.

"I did. When I was welcome."

"You still are."

"Do tell?" She cocked her head. "I'm a career woman, remember? And I'm a city girl."

His mouth tugged up. "I think city girls are sexy." His dark eyes traveled down to her slender legs encased in pink hose. "I didn't know you had legs, Jenny Wren. You always kept them in jeans."

"I didn't want you leering at me."

"Ha!" he shot back. "You knew that damned blouse was torn, the day you fell off your horse." His eyes dared her to dispute him. "You wanted my eyes on you. I'll never forget the way you looked when you saw me staring at you."

Her chest rose and fell quickly. "I was shocked."

"Shocked, hell. Delighted." He lifted the cigarette to his mouth. "I didn't realize you were a woman until then. I'd seen you as a kid. A little helpless thing I needed to protect." His eyes cut sideways and he smiled mockingly. "And then that blouse came open and I saw a body I'd have killed for. After that, the whole situation started getting impossible."

"So did you."

"I know," he admitted. "My brain was telling me to keep away, but my body wouldn't listen. You didn't help a hell of a lot, lying there on that couch with your mouth begging for mine."

"Well, I'm human!" she burst out furiously. "And I never asked you to start kissing me."

"You didn't fight me."

She turned away. "Can't we get off this subject?"

"Just when it's getting interesting?" he mused. "Why? Don't you like remembering it?"

"No, I don't!"

"Does he kiss you the way I did?" he asked shortly, jerking her around by the arm, his lean hand hurting. "That redhead, have you let him touch you like I did!"

"No!" she whispered, shocking herself with the disgust she put into that one, telling syllable.

His nostrils flared and his dark eyes traveled to the bodice of her dress, to her slender legs, her rounded hips, and all the way back up again to her eyes. "Why not?" he breathed unsteadily.

"Maybe I'm terrified of men now," she muttered.

"Maybe you're just terrified of other men," he whispered. "It was so good, when we touched each other. So good, so sweet . . . I rocked you under me and felt you swell, here . . ." His fingers brushed lightly against the bodice of her dress.

Coming to her senses all at once, she caught his fingers and pushed them away.

"No!" she burst out.

His fingers curled around her hand. He brought her fingers to his mouth and nibbled at them softly, staring into her eyes. "I can't even get in the mood with other women," he said quietly. "Three long months and I still can't sleep for thinking how you felt in my arms."

"Don't," she ground out, bending her head. "You won't make me feel guilty."

"That isn't what I want from you. Not guilt."

Her eyes came up. "You just want sex, don't you? You want me because I haven't been with anyone else!"

He caught her face in his warm hands and searched it while the forgotten cigarette between his fingers sent up curls of smoke beside her head.

"Someday, I'll tell you what I really want," he said, his voice quiet and soft and dark. "When you've forgotten, and forgiven what happened. Until then, I'll just go on as I have before." His mouth twisted. "Taking cold showers and working myself into exhaustion."

She wouldn't weaken; she wouldn't! But his hands were warm and rough, and his breath was smoky against her parted lips. And her mouth wanted his.

He bent closer, just close enough to torment her. His eyes closed. His nose touched hers.

She felt reckless and hungry, and all her willpower wasn't proof against him.

"Jenny," he groaned against her lips.

"Isn't . . . fair," she whispered shakily.

"I know." His hands were trembling. They touched her face as if it were some priceless treasure. His mouth trembled, too, while it brushed softly over hers. "Oh, God, I'll die if I don't kiss you . . . !" he whispered achingly.

"No . . ." But it was only a breath, and he took it from her with the cool, moist pressure of his hard lips.

She hadn't dreamed of kisses this tender, this soft. He nudged her mouth with his until it opened. She shuddered with quickly drawn breaths. Her eyes slid open and looked into his slitted ones.

"Oh," she moaned in a sharp whisper.

"Oh," he whispered back. His thumbs brushed her cheeks. "I want you. I want to lie with you and touch you and let you touch me. I want to make love with you and to you."

"Everett . . . you mustn't," she managed in a husky whisper as his mouth tortured hers. "Please, don't do this . . . to me. The driver . . ."

"I closed the curtain, didn't you notice?" he whispered.

She looked past him, her breath jerky and quick, her face flushed, her eyes wild.

"You see?" he asked quietly.

She swallowed, struggling for control. Her eyes closed and she pulled carefully away from his warm hands.

"No," she said then.

"All right." He moved back and finished his cigarette in silence.

She glanced at him warily, tucking back a loose strand of hair.

"There's nothing to be afraid of," he said, as if he sensed all her hidden fears. "I want nothing from you that you don't want to give freely."

She clasped her hands together. Her tongue touched her dry lips, and she could still taste him on them. It was so intimate that she caught her breath.

"I can't go with you," she burst out, all at once.

"Your door has a lock," he reminded her. "And I'll even give you my word that I won't force you."

Her troubled eyes sought his and he smiled reassuringly.

"Let me rephrase that," he said after a minute. "I won't take advantage of any...lapses. Is that better?'

She clutched her purse hard enough to wrinkle the soft leather wallet inside. "I hate being vulnerable!"

"Do you think I don't?" he growled, his eyes flashing. He crushed out his cigarette. "I'm thirty-five, and it's never happened to me before." He glared at her. "And it had to be with a damned virgin!"

"Don't you curse at me!"

"I wasn't cursing," he said harshly. He reached for another cigarette.

"Will you please stop that?" she pleaded. "I'm choking on the smoke as it is."

He made a rough sound and repocketed the cigarette. "You'll be carrying a noose around with you next."

"Not for your neck," she promised him with a sweet smile. "Confirmed bachelors aren't my cup of tea."

"Career women aren't mine."

She turned her eyes out the window. And for the rest of the drive to the ranch she didn't say another word.

The room he gave her was the one she'd had before. But she was surprised to see that the linen hadn't been changed. And the checks he'd written for her were just where she'd left them, on the dresser.

She stared at him as he set her bag down. "It's...you haven't torn them up," she faltered.

He straightened, taking off his hat to run a hand through his thick, dark hair. "So what?" he growled, challenge in his very posture. He towered over her.

"Well, I don't want them!" she burst out.

"Of course not," he replied. "You've got a good paying job now, don't you?"

Her chin lifted. "Yes, I do."

He tossed his hat onto the dresser and moved toward her.

"You promised!" she burst out.

"Sure I did," he replied. He reached out and jerked her up into his arms, staring into her eyes. "What if I lied?" he whispered gruffly. "What if I meant to throw you on that bed, and strip you, and make love to you until dawn?"

He was testing her. So that was how it was going to be. She stared back at him fearlessly. "Try it," she invited.

His mouth curled up. "No hysterics?"

"I stopped having hysterics the day that horse threw me and you got an anatomy lesson," she tossed back. "Go ahead, rape me."

His face darkened. "It wouldn't be rape. Not between you and me."

"If I didn't want you, it would be."

"Honey," he said softly, "you'd want me. Desperately."

She already did. The feel of him, the clean smell of his body, the coiled strength in his powerful muscles were all working on her like drugs. But she was too afraid of the future to slide backwards now. He wanted her. But nothing more. And without love, she wanted nothing he had to offer.

"You promised," she said again.

He sighed. "So I did. Damned fool." He set her down on her feet and moved away with a long sigh to pick up his hat. His eyes studied her from the doorway. "Well, come on down when you're rested, and I'll have Consuelo fix something to eat."

"Consuelo?"

"My housekeeper." His eyes watched the expressions that washed over her face. "She's forty-eight, nicely plump, and happily married to one of my new hands. All right?"

"Did you hope I might be jealous?" she asked.

His broad chest rose and fell swiftly. "I've got a lot of high hopes about you. Care to hear a few of them?"

"Not particularly."

"That's what I was afraid of." He went out and closed the door behind him with an odd laugh.

10
*

Consuelo was a treasure. Small, dark, very quick around the kitchen, and Jennifer liked her on sight.

"It is good that you are here, senorita," the older woman said as she put food on the new and very elegant dining room table. "So nice to see the senor do something besides growl and pace."

Jennifer laughed as she put out the silverware.

"Yes, now he's cursing at the top of his lungs," she mused, cocking her ear toward the window. "Hear him?"

It would have been impossible not to. He was giving somebody hell about an open gate, and Jennifer was glad it wasn't her.

"Such a strange man," Consuelo sighed, shaking her head. "The room he has given you, senorita, he would not let me touch it. Not to dust, not even to change the linen."

"Did he say why?" Jennifer asked with studied carelessness.

"No. But sometimes at night..." she hesitated.

"Yes?"

Consuelo shrugged at the penetrating look she got from the younger woman. "Sometimes at night, the senor, he would go up there and just sit. For a long time. I wonder, you see, but the only time I mention this strange habit, he says to mind my own business. So I do not question it."

How illuminating that was. Jennifer pondered on it long and hard. It was almost as if he'd missed her. But then, if he'd missed her, he'd have to care. And he didn't. He just wanted her because she was something different, a virgin. And perhaps because she was the only woman who'd been close to him for a long time. Under the same circumstances, it could very well have been any young, reasonably attractive woman.

He came in from the corral looking dusty and tired and out of humor. Consuelo glanced at him and he glared at her as he removed his wide-brimmed hat and sat down at the table with his chaps still on.

"Any comments?" he growled.

"Not from me, senor," Consuelo assured him. "As far as I am concerned, you can sit there in your overcoat. Lunch is on the table. Call if you need me."

Jennifer put a hand over her mouth to keep from laughing. Everett glared at her.

"My, you're in a nasty mood," she observed as she poured him a cup of coffee from the carafe. She filled her own cup, too.

"Pat yourself on the back," he returned.

She raised her eyebrows. "Me?"

"You." He picked up a roll and buttered it.

"I can leave?" she suggested.

"Go ahead."

She sat back in her chair, watching him. "What's wrong?" she asked quietly. "Something is."

"Bull died."

She caught her breath. "The big Hereford?"

He nodded. "The one I sold and then bought back when I leased the oil rights." He stared at his roll blankly. "The vet's going to do an autopsy. I want to know why. He was healthy."

"I'm sorry," she said gently. "You were very proud of him."

His jaw tautened. "Well, maybe some of those heifers I bred to him will throw a good bull."

She dished up some mashed potatoes and steak and gravy. "I thought heifers were cows that hadn't grown up," she murmured. "Isn't that what you told me?"

"Heifers are heifers until they're two years old and bred for the first time. Which these just were."

"Oh."

He glanced at her. "I'm surprised you'd remember that."

"I remember a lot about the ranch," she murmured as she ate. "Are you selling off stock before winter?"

"Not a lot of it," he said. "Now that I can afford to feed the herd."

"It's an art, isn't it?" she asked, lifting her eyes to his. "Cattle-raising, I mean. It's very methodical."

"Like decorating?" he muttered.

"That reminds me." She got up, fetched her sketch pad, and put it down beside his plate. "I did those before I came down. They're just the living room and kitchen, but I'd like to see what you think."

"You're the decorator," he said without opening it. "Do what you please."

She glared at him and put down her fork. "Everett, it's your house. I'd at least like you to approve the suggestions I'm making."

He sighed and opened the sketch pad. He frowned. His head came up suddenly. "I didn't know you could draw like this."

"It kind of goes with the job," she said, embarrassed.

"Well, you're good. Damned good. Is this what it will look like when you're finished?" he asked.

"Something like it. I'll do more detailed drawings if you like the basic plan."

"Yes, I like it," he said with a slow smile. He ran a finger over her depiction of the sofa and she remembered suddenly that instead of drawing in a new one, she'd sketched the old one. The one they'd lain on that night....

She cleared her throat. "The kitchen sketch is just under that one."

He looked up. "Was that a Freudian slip, drawing that particular sofa?" he asked.

Her face went hot. "I'm human!" she grumbled.

His eyes searched hers. "No need to overheat, Miss King. I was just asking a question. I enjoyed what we did, too. I'm not throwing stones." He turned the page and pursed his lips. "I don't like the breakfast bar."

Probably because it would require the services of an architect, she thought evilly.

"Why?" she asked anyway, trying to sound interested.

He smiled mockingly. "Because, as I told you already, I won't have that redhead in my house."

She sighed angrily. "As you wish." She studied his hard face. "Will you have a few minutes to go over some ideas with me tonight? Or are you still trying to work yourself into an early grave?"

"Would you mind if I did, Jenny?" he mused.

"Yes. I wouldn't get paid," she said venomously.

He chuckled softly. "Hardhearted little thing. Yes, I'll have some free time tonight." He finished his coffee. "But not now." He got up from the table.

"I'm sorry about your bull."

He stopped by her chair and tilted her chin up. "It will all work out," he said enigmatically. His thumb brushed over her soft mouth slowly, with electrifying results. She stared up with an expression that seemed to incite violence in him.

"Jenny," he breathed gruffly, and started to bend.

"Senor," Consuelo called, coming through the door in time to break the spell holding them, "do you want dessert now?"

"I'd have had it but for you, woman," he growled. And with that he stomped out the door, rattling the furniture as he went.

Consuelo stared after him, and Jennifer tried not to look guilty and frustrated all at once.

For the rest of the day, Jennifer went from room to room, making preliminary sketches. It was like a dream come true. For a long time, ever since she'd first seen the big house, she'd wondered what it would be like to redo it. Now she was getting the chance, and she was overjoyed. The only sad part was that Everett wouldn't let her get Drew in to do an appraisal of the place. It would be a shame to redo it if there were basic structural problems.

That evening after a quiet supper she went into the study with him and watched him build a fire in the fireplace. It was late autumn and getting cold at night. The fire crackled and burned in orange and yellow glory and smelled of oak and pine and the whole outdoors.

"How lovely," she sighed, leaning back in the armchair facing it with her eyes closed. She was wearing jeans again, with a button-down brown patterned shirt, and she felt at home.

"Yes," he said.

She opened her eyes lazily to find him standing in front of her, staring quietly at her face.

"Sorry, I drifted off," she said quickly, and started to rise.

"Don't get up. Here." He handed her the sketch pad and perched himself on the arm of the chair, just close enough to drive her crazy with the scent and warmth and threat of his big body. "Show me."

She went through the sketches with him, showing the changes she wanted to make. When they came to his big bedroom, her voice faltered as she suggested new Mediterranean furnishings and a king-sized bed.

"You're very big," she said, trying not to look at him. "And the room is large enough to accommodate it."

"By all means," he murmured, watching her. "I like a lot of room."

It was the way he said it. She cleared her throat. "And I thought a narrow chocolate-and-vanilla-stripe wallpaper would be nice. With a thick cream carpet and chocolate-colored drapes."

"Am I going to live in the room, or eat it?"

"Hush. And you could have a small sitting area if you like. A desk and a chair, a lounge chair..."

"All I want in my bedroom is a bed," he grumbled. "I can work down here."

"All right." She flipped the page, glad to be on to the next room, which was a guest bedroom. "This..."

"No."

She glanced up. "What?"

"No. I don't want another guest room there." He looked down into her eyes. "Make it into a nursery."

She felt her body go cold. "A nursery?"

"Well, I've got to have someplace to put the kids," he said reasonably.

"Where are they going to come from?" she asked blankly.

He sighed with exaggerated patience. "First you have a man. Then you have a woman. They sleep together and—"

"I know that!"

"Then why did you ask me?"

"Forgive me if I sound dull, but didn't you swear that you'd rather be dead than married?" she grumbled.

"Sure. But being rich has changed my ideas around. I've decided that I'll need somebody to leave all this to." He pulled out a cigarette and lit it.

She stared at her designs with unseeing eyes. "Do you have a candidate already?" she asked with a forced laugh.

"No, not yet. But there are plenty of women around." His eyes narrowed as he studied her profile. "As a matter of fact, I had a phone call last week. From the woman I used to be engaged to. Seems her marriage didn't work out. She's divorced now."

That hurt. She hadn't expected that it would, but it went through her like a dagger. "Oh?" she said. Her pencil moved restlessly on the page as she darkened a line. "Were you surprised?"

"Not really," he said with cynicism. "Women like that are pretty predictable. I told you how I felt about buying them."

"Yes." She drew in a slow breath. "Well, Houston is full of debutantes. You shouldn't have much trouble picking out one."

"I don't want a child."

She glanced up. "Picky, aren't you?"

His mouth curled. "Yep."

She laughed despite herself, despite the cold that was numbing her heart. "Well, I wish you luck. Now, about the nursery, do you want it done in blue?"

"No. I like girls, too. Make it pink and blue. Or maybe yellow. Something unisex." He got up, stretching lazily, and yawned. "God, I'm tired. Honey, do you mind if we cut this short? I'd dearly love a few extra hours' sleep."

"Of course not. Do you mind if I go ahead with the rooms we've discussed?" she asked. "I could go ahead and order the materials tomorrow. I've already arranged to have the wallpaper in the living room stripped."

"Go right ahead." He glanced at her. "How long do you think it will take, doing the whole house?"

"A few weeks, that's all."

He nodded. "Sleep well, Jenny. Good night."

"Good night."

He went upstairs, and she sat by the fire until it went out, trying to reconcile herself to the fact that Everett was going to get married and have children. It would be to somebody like Libby, she thought. Some nice, sweet country girl who had no ambition to be anything but a wife and mother. Tears dripped down her cheeks and burned her cool flesh. What a pity it wouldn't be Jennifer.

She decided that perhaps Everett had had the right idea in the first place. Exhaustion was the best way in the world to keep one's mind off one's troubles. So she got up at dawn to oversee the workmen who were tearing down wallpaper and repairing plaster. Fortunately the plasterwork was in good condition and wouldn't have to be redone. By the time they were finished with the walls, the carpet people had a free day and invaded the house. She escaped to the corral and watched Eddie saddle-break one of the new horses Everett had bought.

Perched on the corral fence in her jeans and blue sweatshirt, with her hair in a ponytail, she looked as outdoorsy as he did.

"How about if I yell 'ride 'em, cowboy,' and cheer you on, Eddie?" she drawled.

He lifted a hand. "Go ahead, Miss Jenny!"

"Ride 'em, cowboy!" she hollered.

He chuckled, bouncing around on the horse. She was so busy watching him that she didn't even hear Everett ride up behind her. He reached out a long arm and suddenly jerked her off the fence and into the saddle in front of him.

"Sorry to steal your audience, Eddie," he yelled toward the older man, "but she's needed!"

Eddie waved. Everett's hard arm tightened around her waist, tugging her stiff body back into the curve of his, as he urged the horse into a canter.

"Where am I needed?" she asked, peeking over her shoulder at his hard face.

"I've got a new calf. Thought you might like to pet it."

She laughed. "I'm too busy to pet calves."

"Sure. Sitting around on fences like a rodeo girl." His arm tightened. "Eddie doesn't need an audience to break horses."

"Well, it was interesting."

"So are calves."

She sighed and let her body slump back against his. She felt him stiffen at the contact, felt his breath quicken. She could smell him, and feel him, and her body sang at the contact. It had been such a long time since those things had disturbed her.

"Where are we going?" she murmured contentedly.

"Down to the creek. Tired?"

"Ummm," she murmured. "My arms ache."

"I've got an ache of my own, but it isn't in my arms," he mused.

She cleared her throat and sat up straight. "Uh, what kind of calf is it?"

He laughed softly. "I've got an ache in my back from lifting equipment," he said, watching her face burn. "What did you think I meant?"

"Everett," she groaned, embarrassed.

"You babe in the woods," he murmured. His fingers spread on her waist, so long that they trespassed onto her flat stomach as well. "Hold on."

He put the horse into a gallop and she caught her breath, turning in the saddle to cling to his neck and hide her face in his shoulder.

He laughed softly, coiling his arm around her. "I won't let you fall," he chided.

"Do we have to go so fast?"

"I thought you were in a hurry to get there." He slowed the horse as they reached a stand of trees beside the creek. Beyond it was a barbed-wire fence. Inside it was a cow and a calf, both Herefords.

He dismounted and lifted Jenny down. "She's gentle," he said, taking her hand to pull her along toward the horned cow. "I raised this one myself, from a calf. Her mama died of snakebite and I nursed her with a bottle. She's been a good breeder. This is her sixth calf."

The furry little thing fascinated Jenny. It had pink eyes and a pink nose and pink ears, and the rest of it was reddish-brown and white.

She laughed softly and rubbed it between the eyes. "How pretty," she murmured. "She has pink eyes!"

"He," he corrected. "It will be a steer."

She frowned. "Not a bull?"

He glowered down at her. "Don't you ever listen to me? A steer is a bull that's been converted for beef. A bull has..." He searched for the words. "A bull is still able to father calves."

She grinned up at him. "Not embarrassed, are you?" she taunted.

He cocked an eyebrow. "You're the one who gets embarrassed every time I talk straight," he said curtly.

She remembered then, and her smile faded. She touched the calf gently, concentrating on it instead of him.

His lean hands caught her waist and she gasped, stiffening. His breath came hard and fast at her back.

"There's a party in Victoria tomorrow night. One of the oil men's giving it. He asked me to come." His fingers bit into her soft flesh. "How about going with me and holding my hand? I don't know much about social events."

"You don't really want to go, do you?" she asked, looking over her shoulder at him knowingly.

He shook his head. "But it's expected. One of the penalties of being well-off. Socializing."

"Yes, I'll be very proud to go with you."

"Need a dress? I'll buy you one, since it was my idea."

She lowered her eyes. "No, thank you. I ... I have one at my apartment, if you'll have someone drive me up there."

"Give Ted the key. He'll pick it up for you," he said, naming his chauffeur, who was also the new yardman.

"All right."

"Is it white?" he asked suddenly.

She glared at him. "No. It's black. Listen here, Everett Culhane, just because I've never ... !"

He put a finger over her lips, silencing her. "I like you in white," he said simply. "It keeps me in line," he added with a wicked, slow smile.

"You just remember the nice new wife you'll have and the kids running around the house, and that will work very well," she said with a nip in her voice. "Shouldn't we go back? The carpet-layers may have some questions for me."

"Don't you like kids, Jenny?" he asked softly.

"Well, yes."

"Could you manage to have them and a career at the same time?" he asked with apparent indifference.

Her lips pouted softly. "Lots of women do," she said. "It's not the dark ages."

He searched her eyes. "I know that. But there are men who wouldn't want a working wife."

"Cavemen," she agreed.

He chuckled. "A woman like you might make a man nervous in that respect. You're pretty. Suppose some other man snapped you up while you were decorating his house? That would be hell on your husband's nerves."

"I don't want to get married," she informed him.

His eyebrows lifted. "You'd have children out of wedlock?"

"I didn't say that!"

"Yes, you did."

"Everett!" Her hands pushed at his chest. He caught them and lifted them slowly around his neck, tugging so that her body rested against his.

"Ummmm," he murmured on a smile, looking down at the softness of her body. "That feels nice. What were you saying, about children?"

"If...if I wanted them, then I guess I'd get married. But I'd still work. I mean...Everett, don't..." she muttered when he slid his hands down to her waist and urged her closer.

"Okay. You'd still work?"

His hands weren't pushing, but they were doing something crazy to her nerves. They caressed her back lazily, moving up to her hair to untie the ribbon that held it back.

"I'd work when the children started school. That was what I meant...will you stop that?" she grumbled, reaching back to halt his fingers.

He caught her hands, arching her so that he could look down and see the vivid tautness of her breasts against the thin fabric of her blouse.

"No bra?" he murmured, and the smile got bigger. "My, my, another Freudian slip?"

"Will you stop talking about bras and slips and let go of my hands, Mr. Culhane?" she asked curtly.

"I don't think you really want me to do that, Jenny," he murmured dryly.

"Why?"

"Because if I let go of your hands, I have to put mine somewhere else." He looked down pointedly at her blouse. "And there's really only one place I want to put them right now."

Her chest rose and fell quickly, unsteadily. His closeness and the long abstinence and the sun and warmth of the day were all working on her. Her eyes met his suddenly and the contact was like an electric jolt. All the memories came rushing back, all the old hungers.

"Do you remember that day you fell off the horse?" he asked in a soft, low tone, while bees buzzed somewhere nearby. "And your blouse came open, and I looked down and you arched your back so that I could see you even better."

Her lips parted and she shook her head nervously.

"Oh, but you did," he breathed. "I'd seen you, watching my mouth, wondering... and that day, it all came to a head. I looked at you and I wanted you. So simply. So hungrily. I barely came to my senses in time, and before I did, I was hugging the life out of you. And you were letting me."

She remembered that, too. It had been so glorious, being held that way.

He let go of her hands all at once and slid his arms around her, half lifting her off her feet. "Hard, Jenny," he whispered, drawing her slowly to him, so that she could feel her breasts flattening against his warm chest. It was like being naked against him.

She caught her breath and moaned. His cheek slid against hers and he buried his face in her throat. His arms tightened convulsively. And he rocked her, and rocked her, and she clung to him while all around them the wind blew and the sun burned, and the world seemed to disappear.

His breath came roughly and his arms trembled. "I don't feel this with other women," he said after a while. "You make me hungry."

"As you keep reminding me," she whispered back, "I'm not on the menu."

"Yes, I know." He brushed his mouth against her throat and then lifted his head and slowly released her. "No more of that," he said on a rueful sigh, "unless you'd like to try making love on horseback. I've got a man coming to see me about a new bull."

Her eyes widened. "Can people really make..." She turned away, shaking her head.

"I don't know," he murmured, chuckling at her shyness. "I've never tried it. But there's always a first time."

"You just keep your hands to yourself," she cautioned as he put her into the saddle and climbed up behind her.

"I'm doing my best, honey," he said dryly. He reached around her to catch the reins and his arm moved lazily across her breasts, feeling the hardened tips. "Oh,

Jenny," he breathed shakily, "next time you'd better wear an overcoat."

She wanted to stop him, she really did. But the feel of that muscular forearm was doing terribly exciting things to her. She felt her muscles tauten in a dead giveaway.

She knew it was going to happen even as he let go of the reins and his hands slid around her to lift and cup her breasts. She let him, turning her cheek against his chest with a tiny cry.

"The sweetest torture on earth," he whispered unsteadily. His hands were so tender, so gentle. He made no move to open the blouse, although he must have known that he could, that she would have let him. His lips moved warmly at her temple. "Jenny, you shouldn't let me touch you like this."

"Yes, I know," she whispered huskily. Her hands moved over his to pull them away, but they lingered on his warm brown fingers. Her head moved against his chest weakly.

"Do you want to lie down on the grass with me and make love?" he asked softly. "We could, just for a few minutes. We could kiss and touch each other, and nothing more."

She wanted to. She wanted it more than she wanted to breathe. But it was too soon. She wasn't sure of him. She only knew that he wanted her desperately and that she didn't dare pave the way for him. It was just a game to him. It kept him from getting bored while he found himself a wife. She loved him, but love on one side would never be enough.

"No, Rett," she said, although the words were torn from her. She moved his hands gently down, to her waist, and pressed them there. "No."

He drew away in a long, steady breath. "Levelheaded Jenny," he said finally. "Did you know?"

"Know what?"

"That if I'd gotten you on the grass, nothing would have saved you?"

She smiled ruefully. "It was kind of the other way around." She felt him shudder, and she turned and pressed herself into his arms. "I want you, too. Please don't do this to me. I can't be what you want. Please, let me decorate your house and go away. Don't hurt me any more, Rett."

He lifted and turned her so that she was lying across the saddle in his arms. He held her close and took the reins in his hand. "I'm going to have to rethink my strategy, I'm afraid." He sighed. "It isn't working."

She looked up. "What do you mean?"

He searched her eyes and bent and kissed her forehead softly. "Never mind, kitten. You're safe now. Just relax. I'll take you home."

She snuggled close and closed her eyes. This was a memory she'd keep as long as she lived, of riding across the meadow in Everett's arms on a lovely autumn morning. His wife would have other memories. But this one would always be her own, in the long, lonely years ahead. Her hand touched his chest lightly, and her heart ached for him. If only he could love her back. But love wasn't a word he trusted anymore, and she couldn't really blame him. He'd been hurt too much. Even by her, when she hadn't meant to. She sighed bitterly. It was all too late. If only it had been different. Tears welled up in her eyes. If only.

11

*

Jennifer wished for the tenth time that she'd refused Everett's invitation to the exclusive party in Victoria. It seemed that every single, beautiful woman in the world had decided to converge on the spot just to cast her eyes at Everett.

He did look good, Jennifer had to admit. There just wasn't anybody around who came close to matching him. Dressed in an elegant dinner jacket, he looked dark and debonair and very sophisticated. Not to mention sexy. The way the jacket and slacks fit, every muscle in that big body was emphasized in the most masculine way. It was anguish just to look at him; it was even worse to remember how it was to be held and touched by him. Jennifer felt her body tingle from head to toe at the memory of the day before, of his hands smoothing over her body, his voice husky and deep in her ear. And now there he stood making eyes at a gorgeous brunette.

She turned away and tossed down the entire contents of her brandy glass. If she hadn't been so tired from overworking herself, the brandy might not have been as potent. But it was her second glass and, despite the filling buffet, she was feeling the alcohol to a frightening degree. She kept telling herself that she didn't look bad herself, with her blond hair hanging long and loose around the shoulders of her low-cut clinging black dress. She was popular enough. So why didn't Everett dance one dance with her?

By the time she was danced around the room a couple of times by left-footed oilmen and dashing middle-aged married men, she felt like leaping over the balcony. How odd that at any party there were never any handsome, available bachelors.

"Sorry to cut in, but I have to take Jenny home," Everett said suddenly, cutting out a balding man in his fifties who was going over and over the latest political crisis with maddening intricacy.

Jennifer almost threw herself on Everett in gratitude. She mumbled something polite and completely untrue to the stranger, smiled, and stumbled into Everett's arms.

"Careful, honey, or we'll both wind up on the floor." He laughed softly. "Are you all right?"

"I'm just fine." She sighed, snuggling close. Her arms slid around him. "Everett, can I go to sleep now?"

He frowned and pulled her head up. "How much have you had to drink?"

"I lost count." She grinned. Her eyes searched his face blearily. "Gosh, Rett, you're so sexy."

A red stain highlighted his cheekbones. "You're drunk, all right. Come on."

"Where are we going?" she protested. "I want to dance."

"We'll dance in the car."

She frowned. "We can't stand up in there," she said reasonably.

He held her hand, tugging her along. They said good night to a couple she vaguely recognized as their hosts; then he got their coats from the maid and hustled her out into the night.

"Cold out here," she muttered. She nudged herself under his arm and pressed against his side with a sigh. "Better."

"For whom?" he ground out. His chest rose and fell heavily. "I wish I'd let Ted drive us."

"Why?" she murmured, giggling. "Are you afraid to be alone with me? You can trust me, honey," she said, nudging him. "I wouldn't seduce you, honest."

A couple passed them going down the steps, and the elderly woman gave Jennifer a curious look.

"He's afraid of me," Jennifer whispered. "He isn't on the pill, you see . . ."

"Jenny!" he growled, jerking her close.

"Not here, Rett!" she exclaimed. "My goodness, talk about impatience . . . !"

He was muttering something about a gag as he half-led, half-dragged her to the car.

"You old stick-in-the-mud, you." She laughed after he'd put her inside and climbed in next to her. "Did I embarrass you?"

He only glanced at her as he started the Lincoln. "You're going to hate yourself in the morning when I remind you what you've been saying. And I will," he promised darkly. "Ten times a day."

"You look gorgeous when you're mad," she observed. She moved across the seat and nuzzled close again. "I'll sleep with you tonight, if you like," she said gaily.

He stiffened and muttered something under his breath.

"Well, you've been trying to get me into bed with you, haven't you?" she asked. "Propositioning me that last day at the ranch, and then coming after me, and making all sorts of improper remarks . . . so now I agree, and what do you do? You get all red in the face and start cussing. Just like a man. The minute you catch a girl, you're already in pursuit of someone else, like that brunette you were dancing with," she added, glaring up at him. "Well, just don't expect that what you see is what you get, because I was in the ladies' room with her, and it's padded! I saw!"

He was wavering between anger and laughter. Laughter won. He started, and couldn't seem to stop.

"You won't think it's very funny if you take her out," she kept on, digging her own grave. Everything was fuzzy and pink and very pleasant. She felt so relaxed! "She's even smaller than I am," she muttered. "And her legs are just awful. She pulled up her skirt to fix her stockings . . . she hardly has any legs, they're so skinny!"

"Meow," he taunted.

She tossed back her long hair, and leaned her head back against the seat. Her coat had come open, revealing the deep neckline of the black dress. "Why won't you make love to me?"

"Because if I did, you'd scream your head off," he said reasonably. "Here, put your tired little head on my shoulder and close your eyes. You're soaked, honey."

She blinked. "I am not. It isn't raining."

He reached out an arm and pulled her against him. "Close your eyes, sweet," he said in a soft, tender tone. "I'll take good care of you."

"Will you sleep with me?" she murmured, resting her head on his shoulder.

"If you want me to."

She smiled and closed her eyes with a long sigh. "That would be lovely," she whispered. And it was the last thing she said.

Morning came with a blinding light and some confounded bird twittering his feathered head off outside the window.

"Oh, go away!" she whispered, and held her head. "An axe," she groaned. "There's an axe between my eyes. Bird, shut up!"

Soft laughter rustled her hair. She opened her eyes. Laughter?

Her head turned on the pillow and Everett's eyes looked back into her own. She gasped and tried to sit up, then groaned with the pain and fell back down again.

"Head hurt? Poor baby."

"You slept with me?" she burst out. She turned her head slowly to look at him. He was fully dressed, except for his shoes and jacket. He even had his shirt on. He was lying on top of the coverlet, and she was under it.

Slowly, carefully, she lifted the cover and looked. Her face flamed scarlet. She was dressed in nothing but a tiny pair of briefs. The rest of her was pink and tingling.

"Rett!" she burst out, horrified.

"I only undressed you," he said, leaning on an elbow to watch her. "Be reasonable, honey. You couldn't sleep in your evening gown. And," he added with a faint grin, "it wasn't my fault that you didn't have anything on under it. You can't imagine how shocked I was."

"That's right, I can't," she agreed, and her eyes accused him.

"I confess I did stare a little," he murmured. His hand brushed the unruly blond hair out of her eyes. "A lot," he corrected. "My God, Jenny," he said on a slow breath, "you are the most glorious sight undressed that I ever saw in my life. I nearly fainted."

"Shame on you!" she said, trying to feel outraged. It was difficult, because she was still tingling from the compliment.

"For what? For appreciating something beautiful?" He touched her nose with a long, lean finger. "Shame on you, for being embarrassed. I was a perfect gentleman. I didn't even touch you, except to put you under the covers."

"Oh."

"I thought I'd wait until you woke up, and do it then," he added with a grin.

Her fingers grabbed the covers tightly. "Oh, no, you don't!"

He moved closer, his fingers tangling in her blond hair as he loomed above her. "You had a lot to say about that brunette. Or don't you remember?"

She blinked. Brunette? Vaguely she remembered saying something insulting about the woman's body. Then she remembered vividly. Her face flamed.

"Something about how little she was, if I recall," he murmured dryly.

She bit her lower lip and her eyes met his uneasily. "Did I? How strange. Was she short?"

"That wasn't what you meant," he said. One lean hand moved down her shoulder and over the covers below her collarbone. "You meant, here, she was small."

If she looked up, she'd be finished. But she couldn't help it. Her eyes met his and the world seemed to narrow down to the two of them. She loved him so. Would it be wrong to kiss him just once more, to feel that hard, wonderful mouth on her own?

He seemed to read that thought, because his jaw tautened and his breathing became suddenly ragged. "The hell with being patient," he growled, reaching for the covers. "Come here."

He stripped them away and jerked her into his arms, rolling over with her, so that she was lying on him. Where his shirt was undone, her body pressed nakedly into his hairy chest.

His eyes were blazing as they looked up into hers. He deliberately reached down to yank his shirt away, his eyes on the point where her soft breasts were crushed against his body. Dark and light, she thought shakily, looking at the contrast between his dark skin and her pale flesh.

But still he didn't touch her. His hands moved up into her hair, oddly tender, at variance with the tension she could feel in his body.

"Don't you want...to touch me?" she whispered nervously.

"More than my own life," he confessed. "But I'm not going to. Come down here and kiss me."

"Why not?" she whispered, bending to give him her mouth.

"Because Consuelo's on her way up the stairs with coffee and toast," he breathed. "And she never knocks."

She sat up with a gasp. "Why didn't you say so!"

He laughed softly, triumphantly, his eyes eating her soft body as she climbed out of the bed and searched wildly for a robe.

"Here," he murmured, throwing his long legs over the bed. He reached under her pillow and got her nightgown. "Come here and I'll stuff you in it."

She didn't even question the impulse that made her obey him instantly. She lifted her arms as he held the nightgown over her head and gasped as he bent first and kissed her rosy breasts briefly, but with a tangible hunger. While she was getting over the shock, he tugged the long cotton gown over her head, lifted her, tossed her into the bed, and pulled the covers over her with a knowing smile.

And Consuelo opened the door before she could get out a word.

"Good morning!" The older woman laughed, handing the tray to Everett. "Also is hair of the dog, in the glass," she added with a wry glance at Jennifer. "To make the senorita's head a little better."

And she was gone as quickly as she'd come. Everett put the tray down beside Jennifer on the bed and poured cream into her coffee.

"Why did you do that?" she whispered, still shaking from the wild little caress.

"I couldn't help myself," he murmured, smiling at her. "I've wanted to, for a long time."

She took the coffee in trembling hands. He steadied them, watching her shaken features.

"It's part of lovemaking," he said softly. "Nothing sordid or shameful. When we make love, that's how I'll rouse you before I take you."

She shuddered, and the coffee cup began to rock again. Her eyes, meeting his, were wild with mingled fear and hunger.

"Except," he added quietly, "that I won't stop at the waist."

Coffee went everywhere. She cursed and muttered and grumbled and moped. But when she raised her glittering eyes to his the pupils dilated until they were almost black.

He laughed softly, menacingly. "Almost," he said enigmatically. "Almost there." He got up. "I'll get Consuelo to come and help you mop up." He turned with one hand on the doorknob, impossibly attractive, wildly sensuous with his hair ruffled and his shirt open and his bare, muscular chest showing. "The brunette was Jeb Doyle's daughter," he added. "She's looking for a husband. She rides like a man, she loves cattle and kids, she's twenty-eight and she lives about five miles south of here. She may be small, but she's got nice, full hips. Just right for having children. Her name's Sandy."

She was getting madder by the second. He was baiting her! She picked up the coffee cup and, without even thinking, threw it at him.

It shattered against the closed door. He went down the hall laughing like a banshee and she screamed after him.

By the time Consuelo got to her, the rest of the coffee and the headache remedy had turned the bedspread a strange shade of tan.

For the next week, she gave Everett the coldest shoulder she could manage. He was gone from the ranch frequently, and she noticed it and remembered what he'd said about the brunette, and wanted desperately to kill him. No, not just kill him. Torture him. Slowly. Over an open fire.

It got worse. He started having supper with Jennifer every night, and the whole time he'd sit there and watch her and make infrequent but agonizing remarks about the brunette.

"Sandy's getting a new colt tomorrow," he mentioned one evening, smiling wistfully. "She asked if I'd come over and look at it for her."

"Can't she see it by herself?" she asked sweetly.

"Conformation is very important in a horse," he said. "I used to breed them years ago, before I got interested in cattle."

"Oh." She concentrated on her food.

"How's the decorating coming?"

"Fine," she said through her teeth. "We're getting the paper up in your bedroom tomorrow. Then there'll only be the other bedrooms to go. You never said how you liked the way the living room and the study came out."

"They're okay," he said. He lifted a forkful of dessert to his mouth and she wanted to jump up and stab him in the lip. Okay! And she'd spent days on the projects, working well into the night alongside the men!

He glanced up at her flushed face. "Wasn't that enthusiastic enough?" He took a sip of coffee. "Damn, Jenny, what a hell of a great job you're doing on the house!" he said with a big, artificial smile. "I'm pleased as punch!"

"I'd like to punch you," she muttered. She slammed down her napkin, slid out of the chair, and stomped out of the room.

Watching her, Everett's eyes narrowed and a faint, predatory smile curved his lips.

The next day, she concentrated on his bedroom. It was difficult to work in there, thinking about whose territory it was. Her eyes kept drifting to the bed where he slept, to the pillow where he laid his dark head. Once she paused beside it and ran her hand lovingly over the cover. Besotted, she told herself curtly. She was besotted, and it was no use. He was going to marry that skinny, flat-chested brunette!

She didn't even stop for lunch, much less supper. The workmen had left long before, and she was working on the last wall, when Everett came into the room and stood watching her with a cup of coffee in his hand.

"Have you given up eating?" he asked.

"Yep."

He cocked an eyebrow. "Want some coffee?"

"Nope."

He chuckled softly. "Bad imitation. You don't even look like Gary Cooper. You're too short."

She glared down at him. Her jeans were covered with glue. So were her fingers, her bare arms, and the front of her white T-shirt. "Did you want something?"

"Yes. To go to bed. I've got to get an early start in the morning. I'm taking Sandy fishing."

She stared into the bucket of glue and wondered how he'd look plastered to the wall. It was tempting, but dangerous.

"I'd like to finish this one wall," she murmured quietly.

"Go ahead. I'm going to have a shower." He stripped off his shirt. She glanced at him, fascinated by the dark perfection of him, by the ripple of muscle, the way the light played on his skin as he started to take off his . . . *trousers!*

Her eyes jerked back to the glue and her hands trembled. "Everett?" she said in a squeaky voice.

"Well, don't look," he said reasonably. "I can't very well take a bath in my clothes."

"I could have left the room," she said.

"Why? Aren't you curious?" he taunted.

She gritted her teeth. "No!"

"Coward."

She put glue and more glue on a strip of wallpaper until the glue was three times as thick as the paper it was spread on. Not until she heard the shower running did she relax. She put the wallpaper in place and started scrambling down the ladder.

Unfortunately, just because the shower was running, it didn't mean that Everett was in it. She got down and started for the door, and there he stood, with a towel wrapped around his narrow hips and not another stitch on.

"Going somewhere?" he asked.

"Yes. Out of here!" she exclaimed, starting past him.

She never knew exactly how it happened. One minute she was walking toward the door, and the next she was lying flat on the bed with Everett's hard body crushing her into the mattress.

His chest rose and fell slowly, his eyes burned down into hers. Holding her gaze, he eased the towel away and bent to her mouth.

She trembled with kindling passion. It was so incredibly sweet to let her hands run over his hard, warm body, to feel the muscles of his back and arms and shoulders and hips. To let him kiss her softly, with growing intimacy. To know the crush of his body, the blatant force of his hunger for her. To love him with her hands and her mouth.

He lifted his head a minute later and looked into her awed eyes. "You're not so squeaky clean yourself," he said softly. "Why don't you come and take a bath with me?"

Her hands touched his hard arms gently, lovingly. "Because we'd do more than bathe, and you know it," she replied on a soft sigh. "All you have to do is touch me, and you can have anything you want. It's always been like that. The only reason I'm still a virgin is that you haven't insisted."

"Why do you think I haven't?" he prodded.

She shifted. "I don't know. Conscience, maybe?"

He bent and brushed his mouth softly over hers. "Go and put on something soft and pretty. Have a shower. Then come downstairs to the living room and we'll talk."

She swallowed. "I thought you had to get to bed early. To take Sandy fishing," she murmured resentfully.

"Did it ever occur to you that you might be formidable competition for her, if you cared to make the effort?" he asked, watching her. "Or didn't you know how easy it would be to seduce me? And once you did that," he murmured, touching her soft mouth, "I'd probably feel obliged to marry you. Not being on the pill and all," his eyes went back to her with blazing intensity, "you could get pregnant."

Her breath caught in her throat. She never knew when he was teasing, when he was serious. And now, her mind was whirling.

While she worried over his intentions, he moved away from her and got to his feet, and she stared at him in helpless fascination.

"You see?" he said, his voice deep and full of secrets, "it isn't so shocking, is it?"

She lifted her eyes to his. "You're...very..." She tried to find words.

"So are you, honey," he said. "Take your bath and I'll see you downstairs."

And he walked off, oblivious to her intent stare.

Minutes later, she went nervously down the staircase in a white dress, her hair freshly washed and dried, loose around her shoulders. Something that had been brewing between them for a long time was coming abruptly to a head, and she wasn't quite sure how to face it. She had a terrible feeling that he was going to proposition her again, and that she was going to be stupid enough to accept. She loved him madly, wanted him madly. That Sandy person was after him, and Jennifer was afraid. She couldn't quite accept the idea that he might marry someone else. Despite the pain he'd caused her, she dwelled on the fear of losing him.

He was waiting for her. In beige trousers and a patterned beige shirt, he looked larger than life. All man.

Sensual and incredibly attractive, especially when she got close enough to catch the scent of his big body.

"Here," he said, offering her a small brandy.

"Thank you," she said politely. She took it, touching his fingers, looking up into dark, quiet eyes. Her lips parted helplessly.

"Now sit down. I want to ask you something."

She sat on the edge of the sofa, but instead of taking the seat beside her, he knelt on the carpet just in front of her. Because of his height, that put her on an unnerving level with his eyes.

"Afraid of me, even now?" he asked softly.

"Especially now," she whispered, trembling. She put the snifter to one side and her trembling fingers reached out and touched the hard lines of his face. "Everett, I'm...so very much in love with you," she said, her voice breaking. "If you want me to be your mistress...oh!"

She was on the carpet, in his arms, being kissed so hungrily that she couldn't even respond to him. His mouth devoured hers, hurting, bruising, and he trembled all over as if with a fever. His hands trembled as they touched, with expert sureness, every line and curve of her body.

"Say it again," he said roughly, lifting his head just enough to look at her.

Her body ached for his. She leaned toward him helplessly. "I love you," she whispered, pride gone to ashes. "I love you, I love you!"

His head moved down to her bodice, his mouth nudged at the buttons, his hands bit into her back. She reached down blindly to get the fabric out of his way, to give him anything, everything he wanted. There were no more secrets. She belonged to him.

His mouth taught her sensations she'd never dreamed her body would feel. She breathed in gasps as his lips and teeth explored her like some precious delicacy. Her hands held him there, caressed his dark head, loved what he was doing to her.

He raised his head to look at her, smiling faintly at her rapt face, her wide, dark green eyes, her flushed face, the glorious disarray of her hair and her dress.

"I'll remember you like this for the rest of our lives," he said, "the way you look right now, in the first sweet seconds of passion. Do you want me badly?"

"Yes," she confessed. She brought his hand to her body and held it against her taut flesh, brushing his knuckles lazily across it. "Feel?"

His nostrils flared and there was something reckless and unbridled in the eyes that held hers. "For a virgin," he murmured, "you're pretty damned exciting to make love to."

She smiled wild, hotly. "Teach me."

"Not yet."

"Please."

He shook his head. He sat up, leaning back against the sofa with his long legs stretched out, and looked down at her with a wicked smile. "Fasten your dress. You make me crazy like that."

"I thought that was the whole point of the thing?" she asked unsteadily.

"It was, until you started making declarations of love. I was going to seduce you on the sofa. But now I suppose we'd better do it right."

Her eyes widened in confusion. "I don't understand."

He pulled her up and across his lap. "Oh, the hell with it," he murmured, and opened the top button of her bodice again. "God, I love to look at you!"

She swallowed hard. "Don't you want me?"

"Jenny." He laughed. He turned and brought her hips very gently against his. "See?" he whispered.

She buried her face in his throat and he rocked her softly, tenderly.

"Then, why?" she asked on a moan.

"Because we have to do things in the right order, honey. First we get married, then we have sex, then we make babies."

She stiffened. "What?"

"Didn't you hear me?" He eased her head down on his arm so that he could see her face.

"But, Sandy..." she faltered.

"Sandy is a nice girl," he murmured. "I danced one dance with her, and she went back to her fiancé. He's a nice boy. You'll like him."

"Fiancé!"

He jerked her close and held her hard, roughly. "I love you," he said in a voice that paralyzed her. His eyes blazed with it, burned with it. "Oh, God, I love you, Jenny. Love you, want you, need you, in every single damned way there is! If you want me to get on my knees, I'll do it, I'll do anything to make you forget what I said and did to you that last day you were here." He bent and kissed her hungrily, softly, and lifted his head again, breathing hard. "I knew I loved you then," he said, "when you handed me that check to pay for my bull, and told me the truth. And all I could think of was that I loved you, and that you were out of my reach forever. A career woman, a woman with some money of her own, and I had nothing to offer you, no way to keep you. And I chased you away, because it was torture to look at you and feel that way and have no hope at all."

"Rett!" she burst out. Tears welled up in her eyes and she clung to him. "Oh, Rett, why didn't you tell me? I loved you so much!"

"I didn't know that," he said. His voice shook a little. His arms contracted. "I thought you were playing me along. It wasn't until you left that I realized that you must have cared one hell of a lot, to have done what you did for me." He shifted restlessly, and ground her against him. "Don't you know? Haven't you worked it out yet, why I sold the oil rights? I did it so that I'd have enough money to bring you back."

She caught her breath, and the tears overflowed onto his shirt, his throat.

"I didn't even have the price of a bus ticket." He laughed huskily, his voice tormented with memory. "And I knew that without you, the land wouldn't matter, because I couldn't live. I couldn't stay alive. So I sold the oil rights and I bought a car and I called Sally Wade. And then, I parked across the street to watch for you. And you came out," he said roughly, "laughing and looking so beautiful . . . holding onto that redheaded ass's arm! I could have broken your neck!"

"He was my friend. Nothing more." She nuzzled her face against him. "I thought you wanted revenge. I didn't realize . . . !"

"I wouldn't let Consuelo touch your room, did she tell you?" he whispered. "I left it the way it was. For the first week or so . . . I could still catch the scent of you on the pillow . . ." His voice broke, and she searched blindly for his mouth, and gave him comfort in the only way she could.

Her fingers touched his face, loved it; her lips told him things, secrets, that even words wouldn't. Gently, tenderly, she drew him up onto the sofa with her, and eased down beside him on it. And with her mouth and her hands and her body, she told him in the sweetest possible way that he'd never be alone as long as she lived.

"We can't," he whispered, trembling.

"Why?" she moaned softly.

"Because I want you in church, Jenny Wren," he whispered, easing her onto her side, soothing her with his hands and his mouth. "I want it all to be just right. I want to hear the words and watch your face when you say them, and tell the whole world that you're my woman. And then," he breathed softly, "then we'll make love and celebrate in the sweetest, most complete way there is. But not like this, darling. Not on a sofa, without the rings or the words or the beauty of taking our vows together." He drew back and looked into her damp eyes. "You'll want that, when you look back on our first time. You'll want it when the children are old enough to be told how we met, how we married. You won't want a tarnished memory to put in your scrapbook."

She kissed him softly. "Thank you."

"I love you," he said, smiling. "I can wait. If," he added with a lift of his eyebrow, "you'll put your clothes back on and stop trying to lead me into a life of sin."

"I haven't taken them off," she protested.

"You have." He got up and looked down at her, with the dress around her waist.

"Well, look at you," she grumbled. His shirt was off and out of his trousers, and his belt was unbuckled.

"You did it," he accused.

She burst out laughing as she buttoned buttons. "I suppose I did. Imagine me, actually trying to seduce you. And after all the times I accused you of it!"

"I don't remember complaining," he remarked.

She got to her feet and went into his arms with a warm sigh. "Me, either. How soon can we get married?"

"How about Friday?"

"Three days?" she groaned.

"You can take cold showers," he promised her. "And finish decorating the house. You're not going to have a lot of time for decorating after we're married."

"I'm not, huh?" she murmured. "What will I be doing?"

"I hoped you might ask," he returned with a smile. He bent his head, lifting her gently in his arms. "This is what you'll be doing." And he kissed her with such tenderness that she felt tears running down her warm cheeks. Since it seemed like such a lovely occupation, she didn't even protest. After all, she'd have plenty of time for decorating when the children started school. Meanwhile, Everett showed promise of being a full-time job.

AFTER THE MUSIC

To Hope and Lamar

1

*

It was sad to see a tour end, Sabina Cane thought as she watched the electricians strike the lights at the auditorium where she and the band had performed the night before. It had been a sellout performance here in Savannah, and thank God for road tours. Times had been hard lately, and as it was, they'd make only a small profit after all the hands were paid. Sabina often wondered if there would ever come a time when she'd have financial security. Then she threw back her head and laughed at her own silly fears. She was doing what she loved best, after all. Without singing, she'd have no life at all, so she ought to be grateful that she had work. Besides, she and The Bricks and Sand Band were already booked for two weeks back home in New Orleans at one of the best clubs in town. And this month on the road had netted them some invaluable publicity.

She stared down the deserted, littered aisles, and spared a sympathetic smile for the tired men taking down equipment at this hour of the night. They had to be in New Orleans tomorrow for rehearsals, so there was no time to waste.

Sabina stretched lazily. Her slender body in its satin shorts and sequined camisole top and thigh-high cuffed pirate's boots was deliciously outlined by the fabric that was her trademark. The Satin Girl had wavy dark hair, which she wore down to her waist, and eyes almost like silver. Her complexion had been likened to pure pearl, and she had eyelashes no photographer believed were actually real.

Albert Thorndon grinned at her from the front of the auditorium, where he was passing the time with her road manager, Dennis Hart, who was also doubling as their booking agent. Dennis had done well so far for a young publicist seeking new directions. She smiled at both of them, waving at Al.

He was one of her best friends. She'd met him through her childhood pal, Jessica, who was hopelessly in love with Al. He was Jess's boss at Thorn Oil. Al didn't know about that infatuation, and Sabina had never betrayed Jess by telling him. The three of them went around together infrequently, and maybe at the very beginning Al had been mildly attracted to her. But Sabina wanted nothing from a man in any emotional or physical sense, and she let him know it right off the bat. After that, he'd accepted her as a friend. It was Al who'd managed to get them the club engagement in New Orleans, and he'd flown here all the way from Louisiana to tell her so. Thorn Oil had many subsidiaries. One of them was that nightclub in New Orleans. She wondered if his older brother knew what Al had done.

She'd heard plenty about Hamilton Regan Thorndon the Third, and most of it was unfavorable. The elder brother was the head honcho of Thorn Oil, which was headquartered in New Orleans, and he had a reputation for more than a shrewd business head. Rumor had it that he went through women relentlessly, leaving a trail of broken hearts behind him. He was the kind of man Sabina hated on sight, and she was glad Al had never tried to introduce her to his family. There wasn't much family, apparently. Only the two brothers and their widowed mother, who was on the stage somehow or other and spent most of her time in Europe. Al didn't talk about his family much.

At times, it all seemed odd to her. Al was always avoiding his family. He never even invited Jessica to those big company barbecues out at the family ranch in Beaumont, Texas, and Jess had been his secretary for two years. Sabina found his behavior fascinating, but she never questioned him about it. She'd thought at first that her background might have been the reason that he didn't introduce her, and she'd felt murderous. But when she realized that he'd left Jessica off the guest list, too, she calmed down. Anyway, Al didn't know about her past. Only Jess did, and Jess was a clam.

Al murmured something else to Dennis, and with a wave of his hand, went to join Sabina. His green eyes frankly approved of the baby-blue and silver-satin shorts that displayed her long, tanned legs to advantage. She laughed at the stage leer, knowing it was only an old joke between them.

"Well, aren't you the picture, Satin Girl?" he said with a laugh. He had dark hair and was just her height.

"I don't know. Am I?" She struck a pose.

"My kingdom for a camera," he sighed. "Where do you get those sexy costumes, anyway?"

"I make them," she confided, and laughed at his astonished reassessment of her garments. "Well, I did take a sewing course, and it relaxes me when I'm not singing."

"Little Miss Domestic," he teased.

"Not me, mister," she drawled. "I know all I care to about housework."

"In that tiny apartment," he sighed. "Don't make me laugh. You could mop the floor with a paper towel."

"It's home," she said defensively.

"It could be better stocked if you wouldn't give away everything you earn," he said, glaring at her. "Second-hand furniture, secondhand TV, secondhand everything, just because you're the softest touch going. No wonder you never have any money!"

"A lot of my neighbors are worse off than I am," she reminded him. "If you don't believe in poverty, let me introduce you around my neighborhood. You'll get an education in the desperation of inescapable struggle."

"I know, you don't have to rub it in." He stuck his hands in his pockets. "I just wish you'd save a bit."

"I save some." She shrugged.

"End of conversation," he murmured dryly. "I know when I'm beaten. Are you coming to my party tomorrow night?"

"What party?"

"The one I'm giving at my apartment."

She'd never known Al to give a party. She stared at him suspiciously. "Who's going to be there?"

"A lot of people you don't know, including Thorn."

Just the sound of his nickname threw her. "Hamilton Regan Thorndon the Third in the flesh?" she taunted.

"If you call him that, do it from the other side of a door, will you?" he cautioned, smiling. "He hates it. I've called him Thorn since we were kids."

"I suppose he's a stuffy old businessman with a thick paunch and a bald head?"

"He's thirty-four," he told her. His eyes were calculating. "Why do you react that way every time I mention him? You clam up."

She stared down at her black boots. "He uses women."

"Well, of course he does," he burst out. "For God's sake, they use him, too! He's rich and he doesn't mind spending money on them. He's a bachelor."

Her mind drifted to the past. Rich men with money. Bait. Using it like bait. Catching desperate women. She winced at the memory. "Mama," she whispered and tears welled up. She turned away, shaking with subdued rage.

"Odd that he isn't married."

Al was watching her with open curiosity. "My God, no one could live with Thorn." He laughed bitterly. "Why do you think our mother stays in Europe, and I have an apartment in the city?"

"You said he loves women," she reminded him.

"Nobody is allowed that close," he said flatly. "Thorn was betrayed once, and he's never cared about a woman since, except in the obvious ways. Thorn is like his nickname. He's prickly and passionate and rock stubborn. His executives bring jugs of Maalox to board meetings."

"I'd bring a battle-ax," she commented dryly. "Or maybe a bazooka. I don't like arrogant ladies' men."

"Yes, I know. You two would hit it off like thunder," he returned, "because Thorn doesn't like aggressive women. He prefers the curling kitten type."

She'd have bet he'd been hoping all his life for someone to match him. She was almost sorry because the pattern of her own life had made it impossible for her to be interested. It would have been fascinating to take him on. But she was as cold as the leather of the boots she wore onstage. Ironic. She was a rock star with a sensuous reputation, and her experience of men had been limited to a chaste kiss here and there. She found men unsatisfying and unreliable. Her heart was whole. She'd never given it. She never would.

She got up from her perch and flexed her shoulders wearily. It had been a long night.

"I could use a few hours' sleep," she said on a sigh. "Thanks for coming all this way to give us the news."

"My pleasure," he said. "The vocalist who had been hired by the club manager was involved in a car crash. She'll be okay, but she won't perform for a while. They were relieved that you and the band didn't mind rushing home to fill the spot."

Sabina smiled. "We're always rushing somewhere. We're grateful to get the work."

"About tomorrow night." He seemed oddly hesitant.

"The party?" She studied him and sensed something. "You're up to something. What is it?"

He shook his head ruefully. "You read me too well. There's this benefit."

"Aha!"

"I'll tell you more about it tomorrow night when I pick you up. I need some help. It's for underprivileged kids," he added.

"Then count me in, whatever it is." She stifled a yawn. "Who's the hostess for you?"

"Jessica." He looked sad and lost. His eyes met hers and fell. "I wish... nothing."

"You've never invited Jess to a party before," she remarked gently.

"Thorn would eat her alive if he thought I was interested in her," he said, grinding his teeth. "I told him I couldn't get anyone else to hostess... Oh, hell, I've got to run. My pilot's waiting at the airport. I didn't have anything better to do, so I thought I'd catch your last performance and tell you about the club date. Pick you up tomorrow night at six, okay?''

"Okay," she said, reluctant to let the matter drop. What a horror his brother sounded! "See you. And thanks for the club date, pal."

"My pleasure. Night." He turned and walked away, and her eyes followed him with open speculation. Could he be getting interested in Jessica? What a wonderful thing that would be. Her two best friends. She smiled to herself.

It was late afternoon when Sabina finally got to her own apartment. She walked up the steps, gazing fondly down at the block of row houses. She'd lived here all her adult life, ever since she'd left the orphanage at the age of eighteen. It wasn't a socially acceptable neighborhood. It was a poor one. But she had good neighbors and good friends here, and she loved the children who played on the cracked sidewalk. It was close to the bay, so she could hear the ships as they came into port, and she could smell the sea breezes. From her room on the fourth floor, she sometimes watched them as they passed, the heaving old freighters moving with an odd grace. But the very best thing about her apartment was the rent. She could afford it.

"Back home, I see, Miss Cane," Mr. Rafferty said at the foot of the staircase. He was about seventy and bald and always wore an undershirt and trousers around the building. He lived on his Social Security checks and had no family—unless you counted the other tenants.

"Yes, sir." Sabina grinned. "Got something for you," she murmured. She dug into her bag and produced a small sack of pralines she'd bought on the way home. "For your sweet tooth," she said, handing them over.

"Pralines." Mr. Rafferty sighed. He took a bite, savoring the taste. "My favorite! Miss Cane, you're always bringing me things." He shook his head, staring with sad eyes. "And I have nothing to give you."

"You're my friend," she said. "And besides, I've already got everything I need."

"You give it all away," he uttered darkly. "How will you heat your place with winter coming on?"

"I'll burn the furniture," she said in a stage whisper, and was rewarded with a faint smile from the pugnacious, proud old man who never smiled for any of the other tenants. He was disliked by everyone, except Sabina, who saw through the gruff exterior to the frightened, lonely man underneath. "See you!" Laughing, she bounded upstairs in her jeans and tank top, and Mr. Rafferty clutched his precious pralines and ambled back into his room.

Billy and Bess, the blond twins who lived next door, laughed when they saw her coming. "Miss Dean said you'd be back today!" they chattered, naming the landlady. "Did you have a big crowd?"

"Just right," she told them, extracting two of the huge lollipops she'd bought along with the pralines. "Here. Don't eat them before your dinner or your mama'll skin me!"

"Thanks!" they said in unison, eyeing the candy with adoration.

"Now I really have to get some sleep," she told them. "We've got a gig downtown!"

"Really?" Billy asked, wide-eyed. He and his sister were ten, and Sabina's profession awed them. Imagine, a rock star in their own building! The other kids down the block were green with envy.

"Really. So keep the noise down, huh?" she added in a conspiratorial whisper.

"You bet! We'll be your lookouts," Bess seconded.

She blew them a kiss and went inside. The twins' only parent was an alcoholic mother who loved them, but was hardly reliable. Sabina tried to look out for them at night, taking them into her apartment to sleep if Matilda stayed out, as she often did. Social workers came and went, but they couldn't produce any antidote for the hopeless poverty Matilda lived in, and threats to take the children away only produced tears and promises of immediate sobriety. Unfortunately, Matilda's promise lasted about an hour or two, or until the social worker left, which-ever came first.

Sabina knew that kind of hopelessness firsthand. Until her mother died and she was put in the orphanage, she'd often gone hungry and cold herself. Losing her mother in the brutal way she did hadn't helped. But the struggle had given her a fixation about rich men and hard living. She hated both. With the voice that God had given her, she was determined to claw her way out of poverty and make something of her life. She was doing it, too. If only it had been in time to save her mother...

She lay down on the bed with a sigh and closed her eyes. She was so tired. She put everything she had, eve-rything she was, into her performances. When they were over, she collapsed. Dead tired. Sometimes she felt alive only in front of an audience, feeding on their adrena-line, the loud clapping and the cheers as she belted out the songs in her clear, haunting voice. Her own feet would echo the rhythms, and her body would sway. Her long, dark hair would fly and her silver-blue eyes would snap and sparkle with the electricity of her performances. She withheld nothing, but it was telling on her. All the long nights were wearing her down, and she was losing weight. But she had to keep going. She couldn't afford to slow down now, when she and the band were so close to the golden ring. They were drawing bigger crowds all the time wherever they appeared, and getting great coverage in the local press. Someday they'd get a recording contract, and then, look out!

Smiling as she daydreamed about that, she closed her eyes and felt the lumpy mattress under her with a wistful sigh. Just a few minutes rest would do it. Just a few min-utes...

The loud pounding on the door woke her up. Drowsily, she got to her feet and opened it, to find Al on the other side.

"I fell asleep," Sabina explained. "What time is it?"

"Six o'clock. Hurry and throw something on. You'll feel better when you've eaten."

"What are you feeding me?" she asked on a yawn, preceding him into the apartment.

"Chicken Kiev," he told her. "Pommes de terre, and broccoli in hollandaise sauce—with cherries jubilee for dessert."

"You must have kept Susi in the kitchen all day!" she exclaimed with a laugh, picturing Al's cook, a stooped little Cajun woman cursing a blue streak as she prepared that luscious repast.

"I did," he said, green eyes gleaming. "I had to promise her a bonus, too."

"Well, she certainly deserves it. Make yourself comfortable. I'll be out in a jiffy." She took a quick shower and pulled on an elegant electric-blue satin dress with spaghetti straps, a square neckline, and a drop waist with a semifull skirt. It suited her slenderness and gave her gray eyes a blue look. Normally she'd never have been able to afford it on her budget, but she'd found it at an elegant used dress shop and paid only a fraction of its original price. Bargain hunting was one of her specialties. It had to be, on her erratic salary. She wore black sling pumps with it, and carried a dainty little black evening bag, and put on the long cashmere coat, because nights were getting cold in late autumn. She left her hair long instead of putting it into a high French twist, as she usually did in the evening. When she went back out into the living room, Al got to his feet and sighed.

"You dish," he murmured. "What an eye-catcher!"

"Why does that make you look so smug?" she asked suspiciously.

"I told you I had a project in mind," he said after a minute. "You remember hearing me talk about the children's hospital I'm trying to get funds to build?"

"Yes," she said, waiting.

"I'm trying to put together a benefit for it. On local television. If I had a couple of sponsors, and you for a drawing card, I could get some local talent and present it to the local stations." He grinned. "I guarantee we'd raise more than enough."

"You know I'd do it for you, without pay," she said. "But we're not big enough..."

"Yes, you are," he said stubbornly. "A television appearance here would give you some great publicity. Look, I'm not asking you to do it for that reason and you know it, so don't ruffle up at me. The kids will benefit most, and I've got some other talent lined up as well," he told her. "But I can't sell the idea to the television stations until I've got the sponsors. I want to wheedle Thorn into being one of them."

"Will he?"

"If he's persuaded," he said, with a sly glance at her.

"Now, wait a minute," she said curtly. "I am not playing up to your poisonous brother, for any reason."

"You don't have to play up to him. Just be friendly. Be yourself."

She frowned. "You aren't going to paint me into a corner, are you?"

"Scout's honor," he promised with a flash of white teeth. "Trust me."

"I don't trust anybody, even you," she said with a smile.

"I'm working on that. Let's go."

He led her down the long flight of stairs.

"Couldn't you ask him yourself?" she murmured. "After all, blood is thicker..."

"Thorn's kind of miffed with me."

"Why?"

Al stuck his hands in his pockets with a sigh and glanced at her ruefully. "He brought a girl home for me last night."

Her eyes widened. "He what?"

"Brought a girl home for me. A very nice girl, with excellent connections, whose father owns an oil refinery. He was giving a dinner party, you see."

"My God!" she burst out.

"I called my mother after it was over, and she called up and chewed on his ear for a while. That made him mad. He doesn't like her very much most of the time, and he needs that refinery damned bad." He shrugged. "If I could get him a refinery, he'd sure rush over to sponsor my benefit."

"You could buy him one," she suggested.

"With what? I'm broke. Not totally, but I don't have the kind of capital I'd need for business on that scale. I'm a partner on paper only, until I come into my share of Dad's estate next year."

"I'm beginning to get a very interesting picture of Hamilton Regan Thorndon the Third," she said stiffly. "A matchmaker, is he?"

"That's about the size of it," Al confessed. He gestured toward his car when they reached the street. "I'm parked over there."

She followed him, scowling. "Does he do this to you often?"

"Only when he needs something he can't buy." He sighed. "You'd never guess how many businessmen have eligible daughters they want to marry off. Especially businessmen with refineries and blocks of oil stock and..."

"But that's inhuman!"

"So is Thorn, from time to time." He unlocked the car and helped her inside. "Haven't you wondered why I usually keep you and Jessica away from company parties?"

"I'm beginning to realize," she said to herself. She waited until he got inside the green Mercedes-Benz and started the engine before she added, "He doesn't want you associating with the peons, I gather?"

He stiffened, started to deny it, and then huffed miserably. "He's not marriage-minded himself. Thorn Oil is worth millions, with all its subsidiaries. He wants an heir for it. But with just the right girl, you see. Jessica has been married before, and her family isn't socially prominent," he said, biting it out. "Thorn would savage her."

It all became crystal clear. Everything... how he felt about Jessica, why he'd been so secretive. "Oh, Al," she breathed piteously. "Oh, Al, how horrible for you!"

"Next year I can fight him," he said. "When I've got money of my own. But for now I have to lie low and bide my time."

"I'd punch him out," she growled softly, gray eyes throwing off silver sparks, her long hair swirling like silk as her head jerked.

He glanced at her as he drove toward his apartment down the brightly lit streets. "Yes, I believe you would. You're like him. Fire and high temper and impulsive actions." He smiled. "You'd be a match, even for my brother."

"With all due respect, I don't want your brother."

"Yes, I know. But please don't take a swing at him tonight. I need you."

"Now, wait a minute..."

"Just to help present my case, nothing else," he promised. His smile faded as he studied her. "I wouldn't strand you with him. Thorn isn't much good with innocents. You'll know what I mean when you see the woman he's got with him tonight. She's as much a barracuda as he is. I only want you to help me convince him to sponsor the benefit. I'll get an accompanist and you can do the aria from Madama Butterfly for him."

"He likes opera?" she asked.

"He loves it."

She eyed him closely. "How does he feel about rock singers?"

He shifted restlessly, and looked worried. "Well..."

"How?"

His jaw clenched. "Actually, he's never said. Don't worry, we'll find out together."

She had grave misgivings, but she didn't say anything. After all, his older brother would probably be nothing like she imagined. He might like women, but she pictured him as a retiring sort of man like the pictures of businessmen she'd seen in magazines. She knew all too well that a rich man didn't have to be good-looking to get women.

Al's house overlooked the bay, and Sabina dearly loved it. It was white and stately, and had once belonged to his grandmother. She could picture the huge living room being the scene of elegant balls in the early days of New Orleans. There were shrubs all around it, assorted camellias and gardenia and jasmine. Now, of course, everything was dormant, but Sabina could imagine the grounds bursting with color, as they would in the spring.

Jessica came darting out of the big living room, where several people were socializing over drinks, and her face was as red as her hair. She was small and sweet, and Sabina loved her. She and Jess went back a long way. They'd shared some good times when Sabina was at the orphanage just around the corner from where Jessica lived. They'd met by accident, but a firm friendship had developed, and lasted all these years.

"Hi, Sabina!" Jessica said quickly, then turned immediately to Al. "We're in trouble. You invited Beck Henton."

"Yes. So?" Al asked blankly.

"Well, he and Thorn are competing for that oil refinery in Houston. Had you forgotten?"

Al slapped his forehead. "Damn!"

"Anyway, they just went out the back door together, and Thorn was squinting one eye. You know what that means."

"Damn!" Al repeated. "I was going to ask Beck to help sponsor my benefit," he growled. "Well, that's blown it. I'd better go and try to save him."

Sabina stared after him with wide, curious eyes. She was getting a strange picture of the sedate older brother.

"I'd better get Beck's chauffeur," Jessica said miserably. "He'll be needed."

"Before you go, is there any ginger ale in there?" she asked, nodding toward the bar in the living room.

"Not a drop. But I left you a bottle in the kitchen. I'll see you in a minute."

"Thanks!" Sabina darted quickly into the kitchen and filled a glass with ice. She was just reaching for the bottle of ginger ale when the back door suddenly flung open and, just as quickly, slammed again.

She turned, and froze in place when she saw him. He was tall and slender, with the kind of body that reminded Sabina of the men who appear in television commercials. He was powerful for all that slenderness, and the darkness of his tuxedo emphasized his jet black hair and the deep tan of his face and hands. His eyes were surrounded by thick, black lashes, and they glittered at her.

"Hand me a cup of that," he said in a crisp voice, holding out a lean, long-fingered hand. There was no jewelry on it, but she got a glimpse of crisp black hair on his wrist surrounding a Rolex watch.

She handed him the ice automatically, noting a faint scar on his cheek, near his eye. His nose was arrow-straight and gave him a look of arrogance. He had a jutting jaw that hinted of stubbornness, and his mouth was perfect, the most masculine mouth she'd ever seen. He was fascinating, and she couldn't take her eyes off him.

"What's so fascinating, honey?" he drawled. "Haven't you ever seen a man with a black eye before?"

This, she thought, must be the Beck Henton they'd discussed, because he certainly didn't fit the long, pretentious name Al's brother had.

"Not many walking around in tuxedos." She grinned. He did fascinate her, not only with the way he looked, but with that air of authority that embodied him.

She seemed to fascinate him, too, because a smile played at the corners of his mouth as he wrapped the ice in a tea towel and held it just under his bruised eye. He moved closer, and she saw that the glittering eyes under the jutting brow were a pale, icy-blue. The color was shocking in so dark a face.

He let his gaze fall to her smooth, faintly tanned shoulders and down the bodice of the trendy dress to her long, slender legs encased in blue-patterned stockings. They moved back up slowly, past her long neck and over the delicate planes of her face to her soft mouth, her high cheekbones, her dark, wavy hair and to the incredibly long lashes over her silver eyes.

"Why are you hiding in here?" he asked, breaking the silence.

"I came for some ginger ale," she confessed, showing the bottle. "I don't drink, you see. Jessica hides some soft drinks for me, so I don't have to look repressed in front of Al's guests."

He cocked his head. "You don't look repressed." That faint smile was still playing on his firm mouth. "Al's secretary must be a friend of yours?"

"A very good one."

"Jessica's all right. Al said he couldn't get anyone else to hostess for him, and she's doing a pretty good job."

Faint praise, she thought, and a bit condescending, but he had a right to his opinion. "You're going to have a gorgeous shiner, there," she remarked.

"You ought to see the other guy," he mused.

She sighed. "Poor Hamilton Regan Thorndon the Third. I hope you didn't hit him too hard."

His dark eyebrows arched, and his eyes widened. "Poor Hamilton...?"

"Al said the two of you were competing for an oil refinery," she volunteered, grinning impishly. "Why don't you just leave the oil in the ground and pump out what you need a little at a time?"

He chuckled softly. "You're impertinent, miss."

"Why thank you, Mr. Henton. You are Beck Henton, aren't you?" she persisted. "You certainly couldn't be Al's brother. You don't look like a man with a mile long name."

"I don't? And what do you imagine Al's brother looks like?"

"Dark and chubby and slightly graying," she said, fascinated by his faint smile.

"My God, I never knew Al to lie."

"But he didn't. I mean, he didn't ever describe his brother." She poured ginger ale into her glass, lifted it up and peeked at him over its rim. "You really shouldn't have hit Al's brother. Now he'll leave and I won't get a shot at him."

One eye narrowed. "Why did you want to?"

"Well, he's got an oil company," she said. "And there's a project..."

Before she could tell him why, his expression grew stern and he laughed unpleasantly. "There's always a project." He moved closer. "Why don't you have a shot at me, honey? I've got an oil company myself."

"Aren't you... with someone?" she asked nervously. He was so close that she could feel the vibrant energy of him, smell his expensive cologne. He towered over her.

"I'm always with someone," he murmured, letting his fingers toy with strands of her soft hair. "Not that it matters. They all look alike, eventually."

"Mr. Henton..." she began, trying to move away.

He backed her against the counter and pinned her there with the formidable, controlled weight of his body. He was almost touching her, but not quite. Her hands shook as he took the glass from her and set it aside on the counter.

"Shhh," he said softly, touching her mouth with one long finger. He wasn't smiling now. His eyes were darkening, intense. He tossed the towel and ice aside, and framed her oval face in his big, warm hands. They felt callused, as if he used them in hard work, and she felt threatened.

"You mustn't..."

"We're cutting a corner or two, that's all," he whispered, bending. "You're very lovely."

She should move, she should push away! But her hands flattened helplessly on his shirtfront, and she felt hard muscle and warmth against her cold fingers. His breath teased her lips as he poised his mouth over hers.

"No," she protested weakly and tried to move away.

His hips pressed her into the counter, and the twisting motion of her body provoked a shocking reaction. He drew in a sharp breath, and his fingers tightened on her face. "My God, it's been years since that's happened so quickly with a woman," he said curtly and then his mouth was on hers.

She stiffened, feeling the shock from her head to her toes, which tried to curl up in her high heels as his lips relented. He seemed to feel her uneasiness, her reticence. He drew away and searched her face with odd, puzzled eyes. Then, slowly he lowered his head again and traced her bottom lip with his teeth, slowly, gently in a masterful exploration that was years beyond her experience of men. Her fingers clung to the lapels of his jacket and her breath came quickly. She could taste him, the smoky and minty warmth of his mouth doing wild things to her pulse.

"Yes, like that," he whispered into her slowly parting lips. "A little more, honey...yes. Kiss me back this time. Kiss me..."

He incited her in wild, reckless ways. It was like some wild fantasy, that she could be standing in an intimate embrace, kissing a man whom she'd only just met in a deserted kitchen. He was no ordinary man, either; he was an expert at this; he knew ways of using his mouth that she'd never even imagined.

She gasped as his tongue probed and his mouth demanded. All at once the hunger broke through her natural reserve and she felt warmth spread through her body. A tiny, surprised moan broke from her lips as she went on tiptoe and gave him her mouth hungrily. Her hands reached up to the thick, cool waves of his hair and she held his head to hers.

"God!" he groaned. His arms lifted her and the room seemed to whirl away. It was the wildest, deepest, hungriest kiss she'd ever shared with a man, and it didn't seem as if he had any intention of stopping. She should be fighting him. Why couldn't she fight?

A long minute later, he set her back on her feet and looked down into her wide gray eyes with curiosity and caution. One of his blue eyes narrowed, and a warning bell rang somewhere in her mind, but her body was throbbing wildly and she hardly connected the telltale sign.

"You're gifted, lady," he breathed, studying her. "Not very experienced yet, but I can take care of that. Come home with me."

Her face burned and her lips trembled. "I can't," she whispered shakily.

"Why not?" His eyes blazed down at her body.

"I . . . what about Al?" she began.

He made a rough sound under his breath. "What about him, for God's sake? Have you got some wild crush on him? You won't get to first base, I promise you. Al's bringing that damned rock singer he's courting. I came because of her, but I can deal with her later." He touched her cheek gently and seemed oddly hesitant, mistaking her frozen posture for fear instead of the shock it really was. "I won't hurt you," he said mildly. "I won't rush you, either. We can discuss . . . projects."

The words began to take effect on her numb brain, and she stared up at him with dawning comprehension.

"Rock singer?"

He looked utterly dangerous, the tender lover suddenly growing cold and businesslike and threatening. "Al's got himself a new girl. But not for long," he added on a short laugh. "That's got nothing to do with you and me. You said you need money; let's go talk about it."

"You're . . . Hamilton Regan Thorndon the Third," she said.

He cocked an eyebrow. "Smart lady. Does it make a difference? I told you I had an oil company. Come on, honey, let's get away from this crowd." He touched her shoulder, lazily, caressingly. "You won't go away empty-handed, I promise."

She felt sick all over—sick that she'd let him kiss her, that she'd responded. She felt as her mother must have years ago, but with one major difference: she wasn't desperate. She'd never be desperate enough, and her kindling eyes told him so. She began to tremble with the force of her anger, her disgust.

"Hey, what is it?" he asked suddenly, frowning.

"You have such a line, Mr. Thorndon the Third," she said with a voice as cold as ice. Her fists were clenched at her sides as she backed sharply away from him. " 'You won't go away empty-handed,' " she mimicked.

"How suddenly principled you are, lady," he said bitterly. "You're the one who started talking terms right off the bat. Okay, I'm willing. How much?"

Oh, Lord, what a mess she'd made of things. Why hadn't she said something about the project? Now he thought she was a prostitute! But what a monumental ego he had, she thought, glaring up at him. "You couldn't afford me," she told him.

His eyes ran over her body again and this time there was no appreciation in his stare. "You overestimate yourself. I'd say twenty dollars would do it."

She slapped him. It was completely unpremeditated, without thought, but she wasn't taking any more insults from this creature, even if he was Al's brother.

He didn't even flinch. His cheek turned red, but he simply stared at her with those icy eyes.

"You'll pay for that," he said quietly.

"Make me," she challenged, backing away. "Come on, oil baron, hit me back." She was beautiful in her fury, silver eyes flashing, black hair flying, body taut and poised and elegant. "I'm not afraid of you."

His face gave nothing away; his gaze was unblinking and hard. "Who are you?" he asked sternly.

"I'm the tooth fairy," she said with a mocking smile. "Too bad you didn't lose any to Mr. Henton; I've got a pocket full of quarters."

She turned, forgetting her ginger ale, and strode out the door and through the house. She was livid by the time she reached the crowded living room.

Al spotted her, moving forward with a glass in his hand. He looked worried and nervous, but when he saw Sabina's face he looked shocked.

"What happened?"

"Never mind." She would hate to tell him. "Where's Mr. Henton?"

"Gone home in a snit, with a broken nose," he grumbled. "So much for that potential sponsor." He sighed. "Well, we'll just have to work on Thorn."

"Al, about working on your brother..."

A door slammed, and even amid the noise of the guests, she knew who it was and why. She stiffened as Al looked over her shoulder and grinned.

"Well, Beck sure left you a present, didn't he?" Al chuckled. "Why didn't you duck?"

"I did," came a familiar, cold drawl from behind her. "Are you going to introduce me?" he asked, pretending ignorance.

"Sure." Al placed a casual arm across Sabina's shoulder and turned her to face the man with the black eye. Al sounded casual, but his arm was tense and trembling a little. "This is Sabina Cane."

The tall man looked suddenly murderous. "The rock singer?"

"Yes," Al said defensively.

The man who'd kissed her so passionately not five minutes before glared at Sabina as if he'd like to cut her throat.

"I should have known," he said with a harsh laugh, ramming one lean hand into his pants pocket. "You look the part."

She curtsied sweetly. "Thank you, Mr. Thorndon the Third."

Al glanced from one to the other with open curiosity. "Thorn, there's something I want to talk to you about," he said.

"Forget it," Thorn told him. He gave Sabina a long, insulting appraisal. "Your taste in women stinks." He turned and walked straight toward an elegant blonde in a gold lamé bodysuit. The woman slipped into his arms, clinging to him like glue.

Sabina glared at him with eyes that burned when she saw him bend to kiss the blonde warmly on the mouth. She averted her gaze. "Al, I can't stay here. I can't possibly."

"Sabina, I'm sorry . . ."

She spotted Jessica and motioned to her. "Can you run me home?"

"Sure, what's wrong?"

"I just have a bad headache, Al." Sabina lied smoothly. She couldn't go into it now. "I'm sorry, I thought it would get better."

"If it's because of Thorn," he began, glaring at his brother, "I apologize for his bad manners."

"I'd like to tell him what to do with them, too," she told Al. "But my head's splitting. Jessica?"

"I'm ready. Come on. See you later, boss," she told Al with a shy smile.

"I'll talk to Thorn," Al said brusquely.

"Don't waste your breath on him," Sabina added. "Good night."

She walked out the door with a breathless Jessica right behind, grateful for the nippy autumn air and the dark.

"What happened in the kitchen?" Jessica demanded as they were driving back toward Sabina's apartment.

"I antagonized him," Sabina said stiffly. "Al will never forgive me, but I couldn't stand that man another minute!"

"Al says that Thorn is used to expecting the worst and he usually finds it. He's a sad kind of man, really. He doesn't let anybody get close; he spends most of his time all alone."

"Alone?" Sabina said gruffly. "That's not what I saw . . ."

"Window dressing," Jessica replied as she sped down the street where her friend lived. "His women come and go. Mostly they go."

"How do you know so much about him?" Sabina asked.

"He comes in and out of our office. His own offices are in the new building, the addition. But he and Al have business dealings they have to discuss now and then. He's always polite. Once, he even brought me coffee when I was hurrying to get some correspondence out for him and Al," she added with a smile.

He could afford to be polite to Al's secretary, Sabina thought angrily. But if Al got serious about Jessica, he knew Thorn would wage a desperate battle. He had said as much with that offhand remark at the party. And Al did feel something for Jess, Sabina was sure of it. She wanted so much to tell Jessica what she suspected.

"Thorn probably bribes people when he can't get them any other way," Sabina grumbled.

Jessica pulled into a parking space outside the apartment building and glanced at her friend. "I'll bet he's never needed a bribe," she sighed. "But Al's terrified of him, you know? So am I, really. If I ever looked twice at Al, I'll bet Thorn would have me transferred to Saudi Arabia or somewhere."

Yes, Sabina thought miserably, being nice to Al's secretary was one thing. But Hamilton Regan Thorndon the Third would cut Jess up like sausage for merely smiling at his brother.

"Just remember one thing. Al isn't blind about you," Sabina said softly. "And if he cared enough, he'd even take on big brother."

"He'd only notice me if I died and there was nobody to make coffee," Jess groaned.

"Ha! Well, I guess I'll go up and eat some toast. Damn Hamilton Regan Thorndon the Third, anyway," she muttered. "He's cost me my supper. Imagine having to work for him!"

"His secretaries kind of come and go, like his women," Jessica confided. "He's hard on women. They say he hates them."

Sabina felt herself shudder. "Yes, I felt that. He's very cold."

"Not in bed, I'll bet," Jessica said under her breath.

Sabina's face flushed, and she got out before Jess could see it. "Thanks for the ride! Want to have lunch one day?"

"I'll call you. Are you sure you're okay?" Jess added with a worried frown.

Sabina shrugged and smiled. "Just a little battle-scarred."

"What did you say to him?"

"I hit him," she said, noticing the wary look on Jess's face. "Then I dared the oil baron to hit me back."

Jess looked uneasy. "That wasn't wise. He has the memory of an elephant."

"He tried to buy me for the night," Sabina said curtly.

Jess made a soft sound. "Oh, my. No wonder you hit him! Good for you! Will you tell Al?"

She debated about that. "I'd rather not. Al doesn't know about my background. Just tell Al I'm not sorry I did it, but I'm sorry I embarrassed him."

"Al doesn't embarrass easily." Jessica toyed with the steering wheel. "I was pretty shocked when he asked me to hostess for him." She glanced up. "He's never invited me to his apartment before."

"He's started to notice you," Sabina said cautiously.

"Well, at least Thorn didn't toss me out tonight," Jess replied sadly. "He strikes me as a little snobbish where his family is concerned."

Sabina's temper flared again. "What he needs is someone who can put him in his place. And if he isn't careful, I may blacken his other eye for him!"

Jess laughed. "I can see it now—a TKO in the fifth round..."

"Good night," Sabina said, closing the car door behind her. She waved at Jess and went upstairs. Of all the unexpected endings to what had begun as a lovely evening. Closing the door of her apartment, she decided to skip dinner. She'd lost her appetite anyway. Sleep would be a welcome relief. But instead of losing herself to dreams, her mind replayed an image of Thorn and the way he'd kissed her. He'd touched her deeply, in ways she'd never expected to be touched.

How could she blame him for thinking she was easy, after the way she'd reacted to his unexpected ardor? He couldn't have known about her childhood, about her mother. She turned her hot face into the pillow. Now she'd made an enemy of him, and what was Al going to think? If only she'd stayed out of the kitchen, none of it would have happened.

She had a feeling she was going to be under siege shortly. The oil baron wasn't going to stand for having her in Al's life after this. She'd have bet money that he

was already brooding about ways to get her away from
Al, because she knew he had the impression that she and
Al were more than friends. And part of her was even
looking forward to the confrontation. She liked a sporting enemy.

2
*

Sabina got up the next morning with a feeling of dread. Immediately, her mind raced back to the night before, and her heart burned at the memory of a hard mouth invading hers.

It had been the first time she'd ever felt like that. How ironic that it should be with a man who was quickly becoming her worst enemy. She had no inclination whatsoever for the lighthearted alliances other women formed. She knew too much about their consequences.

How odd, that Hamilton Thorndon the Third should think that she was easy. She almost laughed. If there was one woman in the world his money couldn't get, it was Sabina.

With drooping eyelids she dragged herself into the exclusive Bourbon Street nightclub where she and the band were working. She'd never felt less like working, but the rehearsals went on regardless.

It was late afternoon, barely an hour from curtain time, and she was just finishing a tune about lost love, when Al came walking in. He looked as miserable as she felt, and his face looked sullen.

"Can you spare a minute?" Al asked.

"Sure," she said, jumping down from the stage in her satin shorts and top, and black leather boots. "Be right back!" she called to the boys.

Ricky Turner, the tall, thin band leader and pianist, waved back. "Ten minutes, no more. We've still got two numbers to go over."

"Okay," she agreed. "He worries," she told Al as they sat down at a nearby table while around them busboys put out napkins and silver and glassware. "He's terrified that the stage will fall through, or the lights will come down on our heads, or that I'll trip over a cord and bash in the drums." She laughed softly. "Concerts are hard on Ricky's nerves. He's just started to relax since we've been doing this gig."

"What happened last night?" Al asked bluntly.

She flushed and averted her eyes. "Ask your brother."

"I did. And he said the same thing. Look, if he hurt you..."

"I think I hurt him more," she said angrily. "I hit him just as hard as I could."

His eyes widened. "Thorn? You hit Thorn?"

"Just as hard as..."

"I get the message. No wonder he was so icy." He studied her. "He wants to see you."

Her mouth dropped. "Oh he does, does he? Did he say when?"

"In fifteen minutes. Now, before you go up in flames and say no, listen to me. I called my mother and told her I wanted to bring you to the ranch for a few days over Easter. She called Thorn and talked to him. Apparently he's ready to back down a little. I think all he wants is to issue you a personal invitation. But if you don't go to see him, everything's off. Including," he added gruffly, "my children's hospital benefit. I can't get another backer. Without Thorn, we'll just have to do a one-night live concert at some theater. We won't raise nearly enough money that soon. I haven't told him much about the benefit. He won't even listen to me right now."

"And you think he'll listen to *me*?" she said crisply. "And I don't think I want to spend Easter with your family."

"Sure you do. It'll be great fun. You'll like my mother."

"I'm sure I will, but I don't like your brother!"

He sighed. "The new hospital wing would cater to families who can't afford proper medical care," he said, eyeing her. "Especially children with fatal illnesses, like cancer. It would boast a research center as well."

Her eyes glittered at him. "Al..."

"Of course, it will eventually get built. In a few years. Meanwhile a lot of children will have to go to other cities, some won't be able to get treatment..."

"I'll do it, you animal," she said irritably. "You know I can't turn my back on any kind of benefit. But if your horrible brother tries to cut me up again, I'll paste him one!"

"That's the girl." He grinned. "Get over to his office and give it to him!"

She left him to explain her departure to the band. She was just going out the door, still in costume, when she heard Ricky wail. Sabina quickened her pace and tried not to grin.

Minutes later, she paused at the door of the plush New Orleans office that housed Thorn Oil's executive officer. Taking a deep breath, she forced her racing heart to slow down. She told herself not to let her apprehension show or give the enemy any weakness to attack. Anyway, there was no reason to believe that old poisonous Hamilton Regan Thorndon the Third might want anything worse than a pleasant chat.

She laughed to herself. Sure. He just loved having the youngest son of the family mixed up with a rising young rock star and wanted to tell her so.

With a resigned sigh, she opened the door and walked into a lavish but sleek office, where a lovely blond receptionist was typing at a computer keyboard.

"Yes, may I help you?" she asked politely, smiling at Sabina.

"I'm here to see Hamilton Thorndon the Third," Sabina said, returning the smile. "I believe he's expecting me?"

The blonde looked wary as her eyes examined the slender figure in thigh-high black leather cuffed boots, tight pink satin shorts with a low-cut white satin camisole and silver beaded vest under a thin jacket. Sabina almost chuckled. The outfit was so outrageous. But she had a performance in less than an hour and no time to change clothes, so the big man would just have to see her in her working garb. Her expression darkened with worry. She had grave misgivings about this. Especially after last night. But this business was best taken care of now. Thorn was the kind of man, from all description, who wouldn't mind walking up on the stage right in the middle of her nightclub performance to question her.

"Uh, I'll announce you," the blonde stammered, then buzzed the intercom. "Mr. Thorndon, there's a . . ." She put her hand over the receiver. "Your name, please?"

"Tell him it's Sabina," she replied in the clear voice that was her trademark.

" . . . Miss Sabina here. She says you're expecting her. Yes, sir." The receptionist hung up. "Mr. Thorndon will see you. Go right in."

Sabina was waved to a door beside the desk. Smiling coyly at the blonde, she opened the door and poked her head in.

Immediately she regretted the lack of time to change into something more suitable. She'd have to bluff her way through. As usual.

"Here I am, your worship," she told the man behind the desk as she closed the door breezily behind her. "Fire away, but make it fast. I've got a performance in less than forty-five minutes."

He rose from the desk like a shark slicing through water, all sleek, smooth pursuit. The tan suit he was wearing did nothing to disguise the huge muscles of his arms, chest and legs. As he moved around the desk toward her, she felt his eyes sweep over her, as if she were being brushed all over with a flammable liquid.

His disposition was as cold as she remembered it. Sabina tried to block the previous night out of her mind while his blue, unblinking eyes were riveted on her.

A finger hit the intercom button. "No calls, honey."

"Yes, sir," came the edgy reply. Then there was silence while the oil magnate did what he was best at— intimidation.

He folded his arms across his chest and his blackened eye narrowed as he studied her graceful figure. "You do advertise it, don't you?" he murmured with a faint smile.

"This is my stage costume. Al said you wanted to see me immediately, and I just dropped everything and rushed right over. Satin is my trademark," she reminded him.

"So I've heard. How much do you want? What'll it cost for you to promise to leave Al alone?"

"Characteristically blunt," she remarked, eyeing him. "Have you ever found anything your money couldn't buy? Besides that oil refinery, I mean. Obviously, it's much more important than a little thing like Al's happiness."

An eyebrow jerked and the blackened eye squinted. She remembered that telltale signal, but she ignored it. "I hear through the grapevine that Al flew to Savannah to tell you about that singing engagement in my nightclub."

"Your nightclub?" she asked. "I understood that it was jointly owned by the two of you, and your mother."

At the mention of his mother, his body went rigid. "Al caused one hell of an argument last night. I do not want you at my ranch over the holidays. That's the one place I don't have to suffer women."

Her chin lifted. "I like Al," she told him. "And if he wants me to join him for Easter, I'll be delighted to accept." As she said that, she wondered vaguely why Al had invited her when Jessica had his whole heart. Was she trying to put up a smoke screen?

"Listen to me, you half-baked adventuress," he said suddenly. "I'm not having my brother taken over by a wild-eyed rock singer with eyes for his bankbook!" Moving toward her, he reached into his vest pocket, caught her roughly by the arm, and stuffed a piece of paper into the valley between her high breasts. "You take that and get the hell out of my brother's sight. I make a bad enemy. Remember it!"

He escorted her to the door and shoved her out of his office. "I'll make your apologies to my mother," he added sarcastically. The door slammed shut behind her.

The blonde stared at Sabina who stood there trembling, her face red and hot with hurt and humiliation, her eyes brimming with tears of fury. Just like old times, she thought wildly, just like my mother. She reached blindly for the check—she knew it was a check. Her trembling fingers unfolded it. It was made out to her, $20,000 worth. She stared at it for a long minute, until her face went purple.

Without a single regard for good sense, she whirled, opened the door to Thorn's office and stormed back in. She slammed the door behind her, watching his pale blue eyes widen with shock as his head jerked up.

She had a feeling that no one had ever dared cross him before. If she hadn't been so furious, she might have backed down, but it was too late for that now. Crossing the room with exquisite poise, she crumpled the check without looking at it, and threw it at him.

"You listen to me, you blue-eyed barracuda," she said, her eyes flashing venomously over the desk at him. "Al's invited me to the ranch, and I'm coming. You can take your bribe and stuff it up your arrogant nose!"

With a fierce look, he stood up and moved around the desk like a freight train barreling down a mountain.

She actually backed away, positioning herself behind the big leather sofa, her eyes widening with mingled fury and fear as he kept coming.

"Don't you do it, Hamilton Regan Thorndon the Third," she challenged, glaring at him. "You lay one hand on me, and I'll have you in court so fast your head will swim!"

"It will be worth it," he said, walking up onto the sofa, boots and all.

"You take your hands . . . !" she cried as he bounded over the leather back and jerked her into his arms. She never finished the sentence. He had her mouth under his, and he was hurting her.

She fought him, twisting, hitting him with her clenched hands. He backed her into the wall and held her there with the controlled weight of his body. After a moment or two, the bruising mouth relented a little and stopped demanding. It grew unexpectedly gentle, and as his hips pressed deeply against hers, she felt the sudden impact of his masculinity and caught her breath. He lifted his devouring mouth a breath away, and his hands slid down her waist to her hips, holding her as his eyes met hers. His chest rose and fell roughly, brushing her sensitive breasts.

"You're hurting me," she said unsteadily.

"And frightening you?" he asked quietly as he saw the apprehension in her eyes.

"Yes," she confessed.

He let her move away a little, so that the shocking evidence of his arousal was less noticeable. Her heart stopped pounding so feverishly. "Do you make...a habit of chasing women...over sofas in your office?" she asked breathlessly, trying to keep her sense of humor.

He didn't smile, but the corner of his mouth twitched. "No. Most of them have the good sense not to challenge me." He let her go with a rueful laugh. "On the other hand, I've never had a woman arouse me the way you do."

She averted her face to the window, trying to fight down the blush that was forming there.

"So I can't buy you off, is that what you're telling me?" he asked, moving away to his desk to light a cigarette.

"Chapter and verse," she proclaimed.

"There are other ways," he said, smoking quietly as he watched her smooth the hair his hands had angrily disheveled.

"Like seducing me?" she challenged, facing him. "No way. I'll never let you that close a second time."

"A third time," he corrected, and a faint gleam touched his eyes. "If you come out to the ranch, you could find yourself in a difficult position. Ask Al how I react to a challenge."

She didn't need to. She already knew. "You just want to choose Al's wife, is that it? You want him to marry a woman who would work to your advantage, of course, not his."

That eye narrowed again. "Think what you like about my motives. But you'll have to go through me to get to Al. Give it up before anyone gets hurt."

"Threats?" she chided.

"Promises." He took a draw from the cigarette and something alien flared in his blue eyes. "I'm a reasonable man. You can still have the check if you want it. No strings. How's that for generosity?"

She stared at him, calculating. "Suppose I show up at the ranch for Easter?"

He took another draw from the cigarette. "Try it."

She pursed her lips. That check would go a long way toward Al's goal for the children's hospital wing. And it would needle the hell out of this overprotective oil magnate. She held out her hand.

He looked faintly disappointed, even as he reached for the check, yet he tossed it to her with careless accuracy. "Smart girl."

"You don't realize how smart. Yet," she added. She blew him a kiss and walked out. "Have a nice day," she called to the blonde secretary as she breezed out of the office.

An hour later, Sabina went onto the stage at the exclusive Bourbon Street nightclub feeling wildly reckless. Consequently, she gave the best performance of her short career. The band beat out the thick rhythm, and Sabina, in her satin and sequins, sang in her piercingly clear voice, every word discernible, her body throbbing with the drums. She could feel the music, actually feel it, and the overflowing audience seemed to feel it with her, clapping and keeping time with her, smiling appreciatively as she took them with her to the heady finale. She moved across the stage, bathed in colored lights, and held her audience spellbound as the last notes died. In the audience, Al watched her with a worried frown.

After the final set, she walked off the stage and sat down with him. Anger still glittering in her eyes.

"What's wrong?" he asked quietly.

"Read me pretty well, don't you, my friend?" she asked. She ordered a cup of coffee from the waiter and smiled at Al. "Your brother and I went two more rounds."

"Again? For God's sake! I should have known better," he growled, running a hand through his hair. "I never learn, never!"

She pulled the check out of her pocketbook and showed it to him. "This is how much he thinks you're worth to me. I'd be insulted if I were you. You're worth a hundred thousand, at least!"

Al's face went blood red and he started shaking. "I'll break his head," he hissed.

"I'll get you a hammer."

"You didn't turn around and throw it at him?" he asked, watching her fiddle with it.

She burst out laughing. "Of course I did." She grinned, neglecting to mention what had happened next. "Then he dared me to come to the ranch, and I told him hell itself wouldn't keep me away. How's that for friendship?"

He let out a breath. "My gosh! You got away with it?" He laughed. "Sabina, you're the greatest!" he said enthusiastically. "Are you coming with me, really?"

"Sure."

He seemed to grow an inch. "Fantastic." He eyed her. "Now, if I can just sell you on the rest of the plan. By the way, what are you going to do with that check?"

She unfolded the $20,000 check. "I'm giving this to you for your new project. In your awful brother's name, of course." She smiled at Al's expression as she endorsed it and handed it to him.

He took it, but his eyebrows arched. "But he'll think you took the bribe!"

"Let him," she said, leaning back.

He started to laugh. "He'll be out for blood. You haven't ever seen Thorn in action."

Want to bet? she thought amusedly. "I've lived dangerously all my life."

He reached across and caught her hand in his thin one. "Prodding Thorn isn't any way to get even. He could hurt you."

"Because he's rich?" she asked with a laugh.

"No. Because he's Thorn. Money doesn't make any difference whatsoever."

"I hate being made a fool of," she muttered. "I hate being humiliated. He's not getting away with that. I'd dearly love to pay him off."

His eyes wandered over her face. "Do you really want to get even with him and help me out at the same time?"

"Of course!" she said without hesitation.

"Then let me buy you an engagement ring."

Sabina all but fainted. The look on her face spoke volumes, and Al couldn't help laughing.

"No, you've got it all wrong. I'm very fond of you. I'm sure you're fond of me. But I don't have marriage in mind."

"A bogus engagement, then?"

"Exactly." He chuckled softly. "I'm so damned tired of having Thorn scare away girlfriends because he doesn't think I can manage my own love life. I'd purely enjoy setting him down hard for once. He's only ten years my senior, but he acts as if he were my father."

"How old did you say he was?" she asked curiously.

"Thirty-four."

"Are you really only twenty-four?" she asked, grinning. "I thought you were at least sixty."

"Shame on you. Attacking a man who's trying to assist you in a monumental vendetta!"

"What would I have to do?" she asked, pursing her lips.

"Be seen everywhere with me. Especially," he added with a hot grin, "at the ranch. That would kill him."

"What about your mother? I'd hate to play such a trick on her."

"Oh, she'd be no problem. She spends most of her time in Europe, especially since our father died ten years ago. Odd thing, Thorn was effortlessly running Thorn Oil at my age. And here am I fighting tooth and nail to keep from being taken over."

"You're not like him," she said quietly. "And I mean it as a compliment."

He cocked his head and smiled slightly. "Do you? Most women find him fascinating and wildly sexy."

"I don't like domineering men," she said flatly. "I can run my own life without being told what to do. I rebelled at an early age."

"I wish I had. I was too busy learning the oil business at Thorn's knee to fight being overrun." He smiled sheepishly. "Now that I want to cut the strings, I'm finding that they're pretty tough. I don't come into the trust until I'm twenty-five. That gives brother Thorn another year of absolute domination."

"And then?"

"Then I'll have a sizable share of stock and enough money to start my own damned oil company, if I feel like it." He brought her hand to his lips and kissed it gently. "Help me declare independence. Wear my ring for a few weeks and watch Thorn paw the ground."

"As long as he doesn't try to paw me," she said with a hearty laugh. "I'd rather take poison."

He studied her flushed face quietly. "He really got under your skin, didn't he?"

She shrugged. "It was bad enough at that party. But today was the biggest slap in the face I've had since I was a kid." She looked up. "I'll wear the ring for you. But make it something inexpensive, okay? And something you can return!"

"Will do!" He chuckled.

The ring he brought her the following day was an emerald, not too flashy but surrounded with diamonds in a platinum setting. She gasped.

"Remember that I'm not a poor man," he said before she could protest. "To me, this is an inexpensive ring."

She slid it onto her finger, shaking her head. "When I think of all the heating bills it would pay for my neighbors..."

"No," he said. "Absolutely not. You can't hock the ring."

She laughed delightedly, her eyes sparkling. "I wouldn't, you know. But I feel kind of guilty wearing it all the same."

"It suits you. Emeralds make your skin look creamy."
He hesitated a moment. "Thorn called me."

She felt her face draw into a scowl as her mood darkened. "Did he?"

He leaned back in his chair with a drink in hand. "I told him I'd just bought you a ring."

"What did he say?"

"I don't know. I hung up in the middle of it." He chuckled. "He was fit to be tied!"

"When do we leave for the ranch?" she asked apprehensively.

"Day after tomorrow."

"So soon?" she murmured, her eyes and voice plaintive.

"I'll protect you, don't worry," he promised. "We'll only be there a few days. Besides, Thorn doesn't spend a lot of time at the ranch, even on holidays. Especially now."

"Because of me?" She felt unwanted and nervous as she studied the ring. "Maybe this isn't such a good idea, Al."

"You can't back out now," he said merrily. "I'll sue you for breach of contract."

Sabina burst out laughing. "Oh, you," she muttered. Her breasts rose and fell with a heavy sigh. "Al, I'm afraid of him," she admitted softly.

"Yes, I know." His eyes were calculating. It was the first time he'd ever seen her afraid of any man, and he wondered why. "Sabina, he won't hurt you. Not physically."

Her lower lip trembled. Hating that tiny betrayal and fearing that Al would notice, she got up from the table. "I'll be packed and ready to go," she promised. "Now I'd better get some sleep. Walk me home?"

"I'll drive you," he said. "Don't worry. It will be all right."

She hoped he was on target with that prediction. She truly was afraid of Hamilton Regan Thorndon the Third, and he hated her. This was an insane thing to do; she needed her head examined. Of course, maybe he wouldn't be at the ranch. She comforted herself with that hope. Then she realized something else.

"Jessica!" she burst out as he pulled up in front of her apartment house.

He stared curiously. "What?"

She swallowed. "Uh, I was just wondering what people will think."

"That's not what you said. Sabina, please. What's going on?"

The painfully hopeful expression on his face made her come out with it. Jess would kill her, but maybe it would be worth it. "She'll kill me for telling you. But..." she sighed, eyeing him. "Well, you see, Jess is in love with you."

He seemed struck dumb. At a loss for words, he stared at the dashboard as if he'd never seen it. His fingers toyed with the key in the ignition. "She is?"

Sabina didn't reply. She just sat and watched him. He took a deep breath and began to smile.

"Are you sure?" he asked, glancing at her.

She nodded, smiling back.

"Damn!" He took another deep breath. "Jess..." Then the sudden exaltation faded and his face fell. "What difference does it make now? Thorn won't let me have her. She doesn't have an oil refinery."

"I'm going to be the decoy, remember?" She grinned at him, flashing the emerald. "Go tell Jess you just got engaged to me. She's home alone tonight. I was going to have a late cup of coffee with her after the show. You can go instead of me."

He frowned and then smiled. "Well—"

"Go on, for Pete's sake! Thorn won't know unless you tell him!"

He shrugged. "Well—"

"Faint heart never won, etc., etc.," she quoted.

"You're right." He glanced at her. "You aren't afraid to go through with this?"

Sabina shook her head. Inside she was trembling, but no one would ever know it. Jess was her best friend. Al was as much to her. She could do this one thing for them.

Besides, she thought angrily, it would do the oil baron good to be set on his heels for once. And she was just the girl to do it.

"Okay. Here goes nothing. See you tomorrow."

She got out of the car. "Don't blow it, Romeo," she teased.

He made a face at her and pulled back out into traffic, preoccupied and thoughtful. She thought about calling Jess to warn her. But then she reasoned that Jess was a divorcée with a sharp mind, and didn't. Jessica could take care of herself. Or, at least, that's what she thought until the next morning.

Just as she was having her first cup of coffee, there was a hard knock on her door.

She got up and opened it, shocked to find Jessica standing there, her eyes red-rimmed, her red hair disheveled.

"Jess!" she burst out. "What's wrong?"

"Everything," came the wailing reply. "Can I have some coffee, please?"

"Of course." Sabina pulled her robe closer and got a second cup from the cupboard. When she came back into the room, Jessica was sitting at the small table with her head in her hands. "What happened?"

"Doesn't it show?"

Sabina took a long, hard look at her best friend, shocked by her unruly appearance, the dark shadows under her eyes.

"Al and you . . . ?" Sabina said.

"Bingo!" Jessica poured herself a cup of coffee and sipped it nervously. She looked up with a pained expression. "What did you say to Al last night?"

Sabina blinked. "Nothing." She lied.

"You must have said something, you must have," Jessica moaned. She put the coffee cup down. "He came to the apartment. He was passing, he said, and thought I might have a spare cup of coffee. You know how I feel, how I've felt for months. Well, he said you and he had just got engaged, and I went crazy. I threw a lamp at him and swore." She smiled sheepishly. "Well, one thing led to another, and he kissed me. Then he told me the engagement was just to throw Thorn off the track. And he kissed me again.'' She drew in a short breath. ''Oh, my, oh, my, I guess it blew my mind, because when he started toward the bedroom, I followed. It was the shortest night of my whole life. Now I can't go home because he's still there, and I'm afraid to go to the office. I'm afraid he'll think I'm cheap, and I'm so much more in love with him this morning than I ever imagined I could be!''

Sabina's face lit up as she laughed and hugged her friend. ''He cares!'' she said. ''He does; he has to. You know Al, for God's sake! He'd never take you to bed on an impulse; he's too deep.''

''But he'll think I'm easy!'' Jessica wailed.

''Wanna bet?'' Sabina went to the phone, throwing herself down into the armchair beside it. She dialed Jess's number.

''No, you can't!'' Jessica screamed, diving for the phone.

Sabina struggled with her, grinning. ''No, you don't. Be quiet!''

It rang and rang until Al answered it drowsily. ''Hello?''

''Hi, Al,'' Sabina said.

''Hi.'' He moaned, then all of a sudden, there was an exclamation. ''Jess!'' he burst out. ''Sabina, is Jess with you? Oh, God, what she must have thought.... Is she there?''

''Yes,'' Sabina said, watching Jess hide her face in her hands. ''She is. And feeling pretty low.''

''Oh, God, the fat's in the fire now,'' Al groaned. ''Thorn will send her to Siberia the second he knows... Let me talk to her, please!''

''He wants to talk to you,'' Sabina said, handing the phone to her nervous friend. ''Go on. He sounds frantic.''

Jessica took it. ''Hello,'' she said unsteadily, brushing back her hair. ''Yes. Oh, yes.'' She began to calm down. She smiled. ''Yes.'' Jess sat down in the chair and Sabina left the room.

Sabina sipped her coffee in the tiny kitchen. Minutes later, Jessica came through the door, looking subdued and happy and sad, all at once.

"I'm going home to talk to him," she said. "But it seems pretty hopeless. Thorn wants him to marry the oil refinery, you see." She shrugged. "I guess a divorced nobody of a secretary wouldn't be good enough." She looked up. "Listen, you weren't sweet on Al, were you?"

"Al and I are just buddies. In the beginning he worked up this false engagement to get big brother off his back. But now it may serve a different purpose. As for being sweet on anyone... You know what it was like for me when I was growing up. You know I don't want involvement, and you know why."

"Yes," Jess sighed sadly. "I understand. It's just that I wish you could be as happy as I am, my friend." She picked up her purse. "I'd better go. Al said he wasn't going to work until we talked. I think he and Thorn got into a spat yesterday over the refinery heiress again."

"Big brother just radiates love, doesn't he?" Sabina said coldly.

"He's trouble. Watch out."

"You're the one who'd better take that advice," Sabina murmured. "I'm just the red herring. You're the fox." She grinned.

"Some fox." Jessica laughed. "Don't take any chances. You're the best friend I ever had."

"Same here." Sabina flashed the engagement ring. "I'll keep this warm for you," she added wickedly.

Jess only laughed. "It wasn't funny when he first told me. But now, I think it's just great!"

"I wish I could have seen your face."

"It was a fascinating shade of purple," Jessica grinned as she headed for the door. "Thanks for the coffee!"

"Any time," Sabina murmured dryly. "See you later."

Jessica barely nodded, and then she was gone.

But if Sabina thought that was going to be the end of it, she had a surprise waiting the next evening after her performance. Al and Jess were waiting for her, all eyes and expectations after she'd changed into her street clothes and grabbed her long secondhand cashmere coat and joined them at their table.

"Hi." Jess grinned.

"Yes, hi," Al seconded.

She studied them with pursed lips. "You look like crocodiles with your eyes on a fat chicken. What have you cooked up that's going to get me in trouble?"

"You volunteered," Al reminded her with a laugh.

She glared at the engagement ring on her finger. "Yes, but I'm only keeping it warm for Jess."

"Jess and I are going to get married next week," Al said.

Sabina perked up at that. She beamed, then almost cried at the look of happiness on their faces. "Marvelous!"

"Once we've actually done it, there's not a thing big brother can do to me," Al said. "Besides that, there's this tricky little loophole in the trust—if I get married, I inherit the trust immediately." He looked gloriously happy. "Thorn will never be able to tell me what to do again. And Jess and I can stop worrying about Thorn's matchmaking attempts."

"So I'm to divert him, is that it?" she asked.

Al nodded. "We'll be in Beaumont at the ranch for several days, but with Mother and me to run interference for you, it will be okay. He's in and out of the ranch because of his responsibilities and while he's working I'll sneak out with Jess to make the arrangements."

Sabina was thoughtful. Of course she wanted to help, but crossing Thorn this way could backfire. She hadn't forgotten the way she'd felt in his arms, and she didn't like being vulnerable. He probably knew how he affected her. She wouldn't put anything past him, especially if he thought the engagement was for real. He'd stoop pretty low to save his brother, and she was uneasy about the tactics he might use.

"We leave tomorrow morning, you know," Al reminded her.

"Yes, but what about the performances . . . ?"

"We've got a vocalist to fill in for you," Al responded quickly. "I'm sorry, I know you don't like that, but Thorn did mention that if you were going to be at the ranch, it wasn't practical for you to commute back and forth for the week."

She felt a burning sensation. "Will I have a job to go back to?" she asked.

"Of course," Al said. But he didn't look that confident. He swore softly. "Damn, Sabina, I'm sorry. I'm not up to Thorn's weight. My God, who is?"

"I'll discuss it with him while we're at the ranch," Sabina said. She even managed to laugh. She couldn't blame Al for being himself. Her protective instincts were what had drawn her to him in the first place. He was like a baby brother. And she loved Jessica too much to pull out now. She could handle the oil baron. She'd just be a decoy, after all. "I'd better go pack!" she said with a smile. "Now, Jess, don't worry about a thing. I'll make sure big brother doesn't take a single bite out of your intended."

Jess got up and hugged her warmly. "I love you," she said fervently. "Please be careful." She looked at Sabina, and her eyes said it all. "You're much more vulnerable than anyone realizes."

Sabina straightened. "Don't worry, I believe in self-preservation. See you in the morning, Al!" she called.

"You're a pal," he told her, and he meant it.

"I'm a nut case," she muttered to herself as she left. She had a feeling this was going to be the worst mistake of her life—like prodding a cobra with a straw.

3

*

The Thorndon ranch was just outside Beaumont, Texas, surrounded by white fences and huge oak and pecan trees. The house was a two-story Victorian model, gleaming white, with intricate gingerbread woodwork and a huge front porch and a lawn that was glorious in spring. The trees were bare now, because it was late autumn, but Sabina could picture it in warm weather with flowers all around. She'd seen a house like that in a storybook at the orphanage when she was a little girl, and she used to dream of living in one. Her eyes were wide and sad as she studied the sleek lines of the Rolls-Royce parked in the driveway. The oil baron's car, no doubt, she thought bitterly. He had so much, and she'd had so little all her life. Her mother's lover must have been just such a man. . . .

"This is home," Al told her, stopping his Mercedes-Benz just as a solitary rider came into view against the backdrop of the trees. Wearing a tan sheepskin coat and a creamy white-brimmed hat, the rider sat astride the most magnificent black stallion Sabina had ever seen.

The rider was coming toward them at a gallop, through a herd of white-faced, red-coated Herefords, so close to his horse that they seemed to be irrevocably joined. Sabina watched him, fascinated, and wondered if he was one of the cowhands who worked for the Thorndons. That lean, easy grace spoke of hours in the saddle.

"He rides beautifully, doesn't he?" Al murmured. "I remember watching him when we were boys and wishing I could do it half as well. He used to ride in rodeo competition, but then Dad died and he had to take over the oil company. I don't think he's really been happy since."

Sabina frowned slightly as the meaning of the words penetrated. The solitary rider had closed the gate he'd just ridden through and remounted, coming near enough that his face was recognizable. He cocked his hat over one eye and gave Sabina a slow, insolent smile. The black eye had lost some of its vividness. Now just a faint discoloration attested to its existence.

"Hello, rock singer," Hamilton Regan Thorndon the Third said mildly. "Fancy you on a ranch, cream puff."

She looked at him expressionlessly, as if he were a faintly interesting exhibit in a museum. "Yes, I know, I'll just be bored silly. But I'll muddle through somehow, oil baron," she said with a sweet smile.

He didn't like that cool appraisal or the taunting words, and his eyes narrowed as he lit a cigarette.

"How's it going?" Al asked casually.

"Feed's low," Thorn said. "We'll have to supplement the stock through the winter. I've sold off the culls already."

"That's the cattle business for you," the younger man agreed. "Is Mother here yet?"

Thorn's face grew colder. "She isn't coming."

Al stared at him. "Not coming?"

"The new boyfriend doesn't want to come all this way for a holiday," the older man said with a mirthless laugh. He drew on the cigarette. "And Mother doesn't want to leave him. Early days, you know."

"I'm sorry," Al said. "I'd hoped ... It's been over a year since she's set foot on the ranch."

"She doesn't like the smell of cattle." Thorn's eyes went to Sabina, chilling blue eyes. "You won't be able to wear satin shorts around here, honey," he added.

"Okay." She shrugged. "I'll just go naked. Al won't mind," she said with a grin.

Thorn threw his cigarette to the ground. "You'll have separate rooms here," he told them. "And no midnight wandering, or so help me God, I'll throw both of you out the door!"

He turned his horse without another word, leaving Sabina spellbound.

"Whew!" Al sighed, easing the car up the driveway. "Mother really must have upset him this time."

"Does Thorn resemble her?" Sabina asked curiously.

"He looks like our father," he said. "A mirror image. Sometimes he acts like him, too. Dad was a passionate man, but he had a core of pure steel, and he used it on everybody. He could send our mother into tears with a look and keep her that way for days if he was angry. She got even, in the most basic way."

She stared at him. "Other men?"

His face darkened. "Other men. Thorn's always hated her for it, and she knows it. I think that's why she stays away. She can't really help the way she is, I suppose, but Thorn never forgave her for betraying Dad." He glanced at her after he'd parked the car behind the Rolls. "Dad caught her with one of her lovers. He dragged her out of the hotel, threw her into his car, and was driving her home in a rage when he wrecked the car. He was killed."

Sabina bit her lower lip. "How old was Thorn?"

"Twenty-four. My age. I'll never forget the way he looked at Mother, or what he said to her. She left the ranch just after the funeral and went to live with an aunt in England."

She shivered. So he knew, too. He knew. Her eyes closed.

"What is it?" Al asked, concerned.

"Nothing," she murmured. "Just a chill." She pulled her coat closer around her. Under it, she was wearing her only pair of cowboy boots, with designer jeans and a bulky gray sweater over a white blouse. The jeans and sweater, like the coat, were from the nearly new shop, and Al just shook his head as he studied her.

"You amaze me," he said. "You always look like something out of Rodeo Drive, but you hardly pay anything for it."

"I know where to look," she said with a grin. "Let's go. I'm just getting warmed up."

"Thorn bites when he's in this mood," he cautioned her. "Don't underestimate him. Stick close to me."

"You can count on it."

The house was misleading. Judging by its front, it was a bastion of quiet elegance. But inside it was a masculine stronghold. The living room was done in earthy tones, with Indian rugs and a strong Mexican influence as well. The walls in the living room and den were pecan-paneled, and hunting trophies and rodeo awards lined the wall of the den.

"Thorn's," Al told her, quiet pride in his voice. "He always took top money. The men still gather around when he feels like a little bronc busting out in the corral. It's quite a sight."

"How big is the ranch?" she asked.

"Not very, by Texas standards. But it's a good place to relax, and Thorn likes to experiment with his purebred Herefords. He's very much into embryo transplants right now, genetic improvement."

That was Greek to Sabina. She'd spent a little time with her grandfather, her mother's father, who had a farm just outside New Orleans. But that was years ago, before the old man died. She had just a few pleasant memories of being allowed to ride horses and breathe clean, country air and gaze toward an uncluttered horizon.

Her fingers lightly touched one of the awards, feeling its cold metal surface. It chilled her, like the man who'd earned it. "He must be very proud of these," she told Al.

"He is," came a deep voice from the doorway.

She turned to find Thorn, long-legged, narrow-hipped, devastating in jeans and a half-unbuttoned blue plaid shirt. He was still wearing dusty boots and the wide-brimmed hat that emphasized his dark complexion. His blue eyes were piercing from across the room, and his chiseled lips turned up in a twisted mockery of a smile.

"The metal is an alloy; they aren't worth much," he told her, oblivious of Al's glare.

"How sad," she sighed, moving away. "You couldn't even hock them if you needed money, could you, Hamilton Regan Thorndon the Third?"

"My name is Thorn," he said in a tone laced with authority.

She looked up, tossing back her long, silky hair. "That's what your friends call you, I'm sure," she said.

"I am not, and never will be, your friend. I will call you Hamilton or Mr. Thorndon the Third or Hey, You. Take your pick."

His eyes were flashing with anger, but she didn't even flinch. He pursed his lips. "Declaring war, honey? Watch out. You're on my turf now."

"I don't have a white flag to my name," she returned with deliberate provocation. Honey. She hated that silky endearment that she'd heard so often in her youth. "And don't call me honey, your worship."

"My God, you're brave," he said tartly.

She corrected him. "I just don't like being walked on," she said, never letting her gaze waver.

His blue eyes searched her face for a long, static moment, while he seemed to be trying to read her mind.

She laughed. "Looking for weak links? I don't have any. I'm every bit as hard as you are."

"You'll need to be," he said.

Recognizing the tone, Al stiffened. "Uh, Sabina, let's see the rest of the house."

She turned her eyes away from Thorn, feeling a weakness in her knees. She had had this tingling feeling for a few seconds, but she didn't dare let him know it.

"Sure," she told Al, taking his hand quickly.

"I'm opening up a new oil field out on the western stretch of the property," Thorn told his brother. "Ride out there with me."

"Now? Like this?" Al asked, indicating his gray suit.

"Change first."

"Want to come along, Sabina?" Al asked.

"She rides?" Thorn laughed mockingly.

"*She* sure does," Sabina said with a deliberate vacant smile. "*She* even speaks all by herself, without help."

"I'll just get my suitcase out of the car. Be right back." Al told Sabina with a smile and a wink. As he walked out, she had to fight the urge to run after him.

"You make everything a challenge, don't you?" she asked Thorn after a minute.

His gaze almost knocked the breath out of her. "Honey, you're a walking challenge," he said. "And if you aren't careful, baby brother or no baby brother, I'm going to take you up on it."

"I'm not issuing an invitation. I have wonderful instincts for self-preservation," she replied as lightly as she could.

He drew a cigarette out of his pocket and lit it without taking his gaze off her. "What a hell of an irony," he said with a cold laugh. "That night in Al's kitchen, I'd never touched anything so sweet. And not five minutes later, I had to face what you actually were."

Her temperature was rising. "I'm a rock singer," she told him coldly. "Not a tramp. My profession has nothing to do with my morals."

His breath came deeply, as though he were deliberately controlling it. The cigarette fired trails of smoke between his lean fingers. "I won't let you marry Al," he said forcefully. "I'll do anything I have to do, but I'll stop you."

"Anything?" she challenged.

He nodded slowly. "Within limits," he said quietly, letting his eyes wander slowly down her body. "Don't make me hurt you, Sabina." His voice was deep and as smooth as velvet as he watched her. "You can't help what you are, I suppose. But I want Al married for something more than his bankroll."

Her face dropped. "You think I'm a gold digger?"

"I know you are," he said. "Remember the check for twenty thousand that I gave you?"

She wanted to tell him what she'd done with it. But that would lead to other questions, questions she didn't want to answer. He might get the truth out of her in a weak moment, and where would that leave Al and Jessica?

"If you do what I ask, I'll forget the check," he said. "And I'll get you all the performances you and the band can handle. All you have to do is leave Al alone."

"But, he's such a sweet little feller," she murmured with a wicked smile. "Besides, he turns me on, you know?"

He moved closer, so that she could feel the warmth of his body, and the wild longings it produced tricked her into looking up. His eyes trapped hers. His free hand moved to her face and lightly touched her mouth. The slight sensation made it tremble.

"Stop that. You're no more an experienced woman than I am a monk. I've had women. And if you're not damned careful, I'll have you."

"After I've been embalmed, maybe," she retorted. "And will you please remember that I'm engaged to Al?" she said too quickly.

His fingers were under her chin, sensually tracing the long line of her throat, and she could taste his smoky breath on her lips, feel the strength, warmth and power of his lean body and smell his cologne and faint leathery scent.

"Sure you are. For now." He traced his fingers over her soft cheek, down to the curve of her lips. He drew in a slow, heavy breath. "Skin like milk," he whispered. "Soft mouth, even if it doesn't quite know how to kiss."

Her eyelids felt heavy, her body felt weak. She looked up at him and couldn't look away.

He dropped his hand abruptly as if the contact with her skin was disturbing to him. "I'm not gentle," he said abruptly. "There's never been a woman who could make me gentle. I like it rough, and I don't hold anything back. And that's the last thing you need, cream puff. I won't seduce you. That's not my way. But I could lose my head with you, so keep a few yards away from me while you're here, okay? It would be hell living with myself if I seduced a virgin."

She couldn't even move, the words were such a shock.

"Yes, I know," he said softly, searching her eyes. "It doesn't go with your image, or even with the other things I know about you. But I'd stake my life on your innocence." His eyes fell to her mouth, lingered there. "It would have been so easy, I even had it planned. Now I'll have to find some other way."

"I don't understand."

"I'm ruthless. Didn't Al tell you? I always get my own way. Always." He sighed angrily. "Except with you. If you'd been the experienced little tart I thought you were, I could have seduced you and told Al, and that would have been the end of it."

Her eyes were lost in his. "You'd go that far?" she asked quietly.

He nodded. "He's my brother. I love him, in my way." His gaze silenced her. "He's the only thing I do love, so look out. You chose to ignore the warning I gave you. You took a bribe and welched on it."

"Did I?" she murmured, staring up at him. "Why don't you tell Al?"

"Not just yet," he replied, his eyes promising dark delights. "I'm going to bide my time. Maybe it will be worth the twenty thousand to have you off the place."

His eyes were the coldest she'd ever seen. If he was vulnerable in any way, it didn't show, but she could almost picture him as a child. She'd have bet that he was a loner from the beginning, a quiet, confident child who wouldn't be pushed by anyone. He'd probably done his share of fighting because of his mother.

"Why are you looking at me like that?" he asked, his tone jarring.

"I'm sorry we're enemies," she said with her irrepressible honesty. "I'd have liked you for a friend."

His face got even sterner. "I don't have friends. Men or women."

"Did it ever occur to you that not everybody in the world is after you for what they can get?"

He burst out with laughter that was cynical and mocking. "You're just the person to tell me about that, aren't you, honey? You, with your eyes like dollar signs!"

"Sabina?" Al called.

She turned and quickly fled from the den without looking at Thorn. "Here I am," she called. "I'll freshen up and meet you back down here, okay?" she told him, as she ran up the staircase. Al followed, frowning thoughtfully.

Remembering what Thorn had said to her made her knees go weak. The threats she understood; he was trying to protect his brother. Ironically, so was she. But in spite of it all, how had he known she was a virgin, when all his imagined evidence pointed in the opposite direction? She turned away from the mirror, forcing herself not to ask impossible questions. All she had to remember was that Thorn was the enemy. If she forgot, he could destroy any hope of Al's marriage to Jessica. She had to keep that in mind. If only it wasn't so difficult to hate him. He was a rich man, like those she'd known in her childhood, like the last one in her mother's tragic life.... She shuddered a little at the black memory, but even that couldn't get the oil baron out of her mind. Somehow, she felt a kinship with him. She understood him. She wore a mask, too, and shunned emotional involvement. What a pity they were in opposite camps.

4
*

Sabina hadn't ridden a horse in a long time, but she sat on the little mare Thorn gave her with grace. It had been a long time, but she remembered very well how to ride. Her grandfather had taken care of her for a year or two, until he died, and he'd been a good rider himself. It had been the happiest period of her life. She'd loved her grandfather dearly, and mourned terribly when she lost him.

The country around the ranch was fascinating. Not too many miles away was the Big Thicket, a fascinating junglelike area where orchids grew wild. Early in the 1800s it had been a trapping outpost. Nearby were the ruins of a French trading post. After that came lumber and rice plantations. And in the early 1900s, oil was discovered in the Spindletop Oil field. Beaumont became the birthplace of three major oil companies. Four, if Thorn Oil was included. The Sabine River, which led into Orange, east of Beaumont, was the origin of Sabina's name. Her father, she understood, had lived on its banks as a boy.

As they were coming back from a look at some land where men were setting up a drilling rig, Thorn had explained it to Sabina with unexpected patience. She had been openly fascinated by it. Al had grinned, watching them, because he'd never seen Thorn so approachable. Al himself looked different in Western gear, except that his jeans were new and had a designer label, and his gray hat was smothered in feathers. Next to Thorn, in his worn and obviously used outfit, he seemed citified. "It's great out here," Al told his brother.

"I'm glad you said that," Thorn drawled, cocking his hat over one eye. "I'll let you help us brand the replacement heifers."

"It's not that great, Thorn," came the quick reply, with a grin.

"So I figured. You need to get out here more often. Sitting behind that desk all the time isn't healthy. Neither is all the partying," he added with a pointed glance at Sabina.

"Al doesn't party." She defended Al, not looking at Thorn. "He has parties."

"Is there a difference?" he drawled.

Al interrupted. "That's all over, anyway. When Sabina and I get married, I won't have the time anymore."

That set the big man off. He reined in his horse and stared at Al until the shorter man visibly fidgeted.

"Marriage is a big step. What about her career?" he asked pointedly. "Is she going to give it all up to stay home with you?"

"So what if she wants to work? What's wrong with a woman being independent?" Al asked.

"Not a damned thing," his brother agreed, "until her independence interferes with your own. Do you like the way other men leer at her in those body stockings she wears?"

"I wouldn't call it leering," Al muttered.

"Well, I would," Thorn said flatly. He crossed his tanned forearms over the pommel and glared at Sabina. "And what are you offering him? Your spare time? I understand you're on the road most of it."

That was a question she hadn't thought about. Her music was part of her life, giving it up was impossible. But she was supposed to be engaged . . . it was time to think fast. "Well, I guess I'll just stay home and have babies," she sighed, and looked up in time to catch an odd expression in the oil baron's eyes. He let his gaze drop down her body, till he was eyeing her midriff. He frowned before he caught her eyes again. Incredibly, she blushed.

"Are we going to see the rest of the ranch now?" she asked quickly. "I'm getting hungry."

"The old timers," Al murmured with a grin, "used to butcher a cow along the way."

"Beef on the hoof," Sabina said with an evil smile in Thorn's direction. "Walking steaks..."

"Touch one of my purebred Herefords and I'll take your arm off," Thorn replied with a faint smile.

"Spoilsport," she muttered. "Some host you are."

"They're purebred, dammit!" Thorn laughed reluctantly.

"Okay. Tell you what," she said agreeably. "I'll eat the registration papers with it."

His blue eyes twinkled unexpectedly. Al had to stifle a smile of his own. It had been years since he'd seen Thorn like that. The older man was grim most of the time; he hardly ever cracked a smile. Sabina was working subtle witchcraft on Thorn.

She sighed and shrugged. "Well, if I faint from lack of food, and fall onto a rattlesnake, and get bitten and die, just remember, it's all your fault."

Thorn held back another laugh and turned his stallion. "Come on, for God's sake, and I'll feed you."

He spurred his horse and rode ahead of them to open a gate. Sabina's eyes followed him helplessly, her heart spinning in her chest, a bright new feeling making her light-headed with elation.

"He never laughs," Al said under his breath. "That's a first."

"He's just forgotten how," Sabina said, and her eyes were soft on the tall man's back. "Jess said that deep inside he was a lonely man, and I didn't believe her. Now I do."

"He's lonely from choice," he reminded her, concerned. "Don't go soft on him, Sabina. You never know with Thorn. He'll get your guard down, and then he'll strike. I've seen it happen far too often."

"I'll be careful," she promised. After all, it was just a game, wasn't it? "Don't forget to invite me to the wedding."

Al grinned. "You can give her away, if you like," he teased.

She glared at him. "How did I ever get friends like you?"

"Pure luck," he returned smugly. Sabina laughed and rode after Thorn.

They didn't dress up for dinner that night, although Sabina had halfway expected that they would. Nevertheless, she wore a gray skirt and blue-and-white checked blouse instead of jeans.

Thorn was alone in the living room, brooding over his drink. The white pullover sweater he was wearing with his dark slacks emphasized his own deep tan and black hair. As if he felt her watching him, his head turned and his icy blue eyes met hers.

"Where's your satin, rock star?" he chided.

"I didn't want to risk having your heart stop, Mr. Thorndon the Third," she said with a wicked smile as she joined him.

He caught her arm with a lean, steely hand and held her as she tried to walk past him. "I've told you that I don't like that name," he said in a tone softly laced with menace. "Don't push me. It's dangerous."

She could feel the danger, and she regretted her barb almost as she'd said it. "Mr. Thorndon, then," she said softly. "Will you let me go, please?"

"Did it hurt to ask?" he chided, abruptly releasing her arm. He turned away. "What will you drink?"

"I don't."

He whirled. "You what?"

"I told you at Al's party. I hate alcohol."

He scowled down at her. "A social drink isn't considered alcoholism."

"I'm sure it isn't, and I'm not sitting in judgment," she assured him. "I simply do not like the taste of liquor."

He shrugged. "Suit yourself, tulip."

"What?" she broke out.

"Tulip," he repeated. His pale gaze wandered over her face, down to the deep, full red of her mouth. "Maybe someday I'll tell you why I call you that."

"It must be some horrible reason," she said with resignation, sitting down.

"I'm not a bad man," he said, towering over her as he moved to the side of her chair. "I just don't like opportunists."

Her eyes searched his blue ones. "Or women."

His face hardened. As he took a long drink from the glass he studied her quietly.

For an instant the room seemed to vanish—everything seemed to stand still. She found unexpected depths in those eyes of ice blue and her heart felt jumpy and odd. His lean, dark fingers caressed the glass he was holding, and she felt as if he were touching her. There was something fierce about the way he was looking at her; an odd kind of violence lingered under his thick black lashes. She had to struggle not to remember what they'd shared in that kitchen at Al's house.

"Is Sabina your real name?" he asked quietly.

"Yes." She looked back helplessly, locked to him by a gaze she was powerless to break, while her breath became ragged in her throat.

"Do you know who the Sabines were?" he continued in a voice like velvet.

She did, but she couldn't think; she felt hypnotized.

He bent, moving one hand to her throat. His fingers were cold, and she jumped.

"I won't hurt you," he whispered, misunderstanding the involuntary reaction. His fingers traced the wildly throbbing artery at her throat, and his mouth was so close she could taste the scent of whisky on it. It should have revolted her, but it didn't. Her eyes fell to his hard lips, and she remembered with aching clarity the way they'd felt when he'd kissed her.

"The Sabines," he continued huskily, "were women taken by the Romans."

"Ra...raped by the Romans," she corrected. Her voice sounded odd.

"Sometimes men and women enjoy wild lovemaking," he whispered. "Passion in itself is violent. Like the way I feel with you, tulip, when I touch you and feel you start to tremble. The way you're trembling now. You want my mouth like hell, don't you?"

She wanted to deny it, to rail at him. But she couldn't even speak. Her lips were parted and she wanted his. Wanted his!

"I want yours, too," he whispered roughly, and the hand at her throat slid down to her collarbone, tracing exquisite patterns on her creamy skin. "I want to touch you in ways that would shock you. My skin on yours, my mouth on your body..."

"Don't," she moaned, and her gray eyes, wider than saucers, looked up into his. "I'm...I'm Al's girl."

His nose nuzzled hers and his mouth threatened to come down and take possession of her lips. She could almost feel its texture, exciting, hungry. "Then why," he whispered, "are you begging me to kiss you?"

"Damn you!" she whimpered, swatting at him.

He stood up with a mocking smile on his dark face, his eyes sparkling as they met hers. "You fascinate me, Miss Cane," he said after a minute, fingering his whiskey glass idly as he studied her flushed face. "All that delicious innocence, waiting to be taken. Why hasn't Al had you? Are you afraid of sex?"

She was hardly able to catch her breath. Why did he affect her this way? "You have...a dirty mouth," she muttered, hating that faint amusement in his eyes.

"Yours is incredibly tempting, rock star," he replied, lifting his glass to his lips. "I'd like nothing more than to seduce you, right where you're sitting."

She started to jump at him, out of sheer frustrated fury, when another voice broke the silence.

"Where is everybody?" Al called from the hall. He sauntered in, oblivious of the tense undercurrents in the room. He was wearing a casual denim suit with a patterned blue shirt. It suited his fairness. But he wasn't any match for Thorn.

"You two look so different," Sabina observed quietly, glancing from one to the other.

"Our father was dark-headed and blue-eyed," Al explained. "And our mother was brunette and green-eyed. I guess we got the best of them both."

Thorn's face hardened. "Let's go in," he said, gulping down the rest of his drink. He set the glass down roughly on the desk and strode out ahead of them.

"Ouch," Al muttered, hanging behind. "I never know which way he's going to jump. He and Mother must have really had it out over the phone the other night."

"Don't they get along at all?" Sabina asked.

"Once or twice a year." He led her into the dining room. "Let's eat. I'm famished!"

It didn't help that Thorn kept watching her at the dinner table. He had a predatory look in his eyes, and a rigid cast to his features that was disturbing.

"How did you become a rock star, Miss Cane?" he asked over dessert.

She flinched at the unexpected question. "Well," she faltered, fork poised over the delicious cake Juan had just served them, "I sort of fell into it, I suppose."

His straight nose lifted. "How?"

"I was told that I had a voice with potential," she said. "I tried out in an amateur competition, where the prize was a one-night appearance at a downtown club. I won." She shook her head and smiled wistfully. "I was delirious. I'd been waiting on tables up until then, because it was the only work I could find. I did the one-nighter, and the club management liked me enough to keep me on. From there, I got other engagements. Then I met up with The Bricks and Sand Band."

"Jessie told me about that," Al added. "It wasn't so much a meeting as a head-on collision."

"Ricky Turner and the boys were hired to play for me the first night at a rather sleazy little joint off Bourbon Street," she said, her eyes twinkling. "Somehow, they'd gotten the idea that I was a stripper instead of a singer, and the drummer made a remark that set me off the wrong way." She shrugged and took a deep breath. "Well, to make a long story short, I knocked him into his base drum five minutes before the performance."

Thorn's mouth curled up reluctantly. "But you still teamed up?"

"We didn't have a choice that night." She shook her head. "Ricky laughed himself sick. The drummer had quite a reputation. We did several numbers, and we seemed to score big with the audience. The manager suggested that we stay on for a few more nights. His business boomed. So Ricky and the guys and I decided to team up." She smothered a laugh. "To this day the drummer still avoids me, but now we've got more offers than we can accept."

She didn't tell him that she was trained to sing opera, or that she'd gone hungry a time or two to afford the lessons. Or that all the doors to the Met were closed by her dwindling finances. Or that the amateur competition she'd won had been won with an operatic aria. When the nightclub offer came, it was for quite a sum of money and she'd needed it too much to refuse. She thought about the $20,000 check Thorn had written out so carelessly and could have cried. It was nothing to him, but at one time that much money would have been her mother's salvation.

"Hey, you're a million miles away," Al teased.

"Sorry," she said, forcing a smile as she finished her dessert.

Thorn was still watching her from his kingly position at the head of the table. She couldn't look at him. The luxury of letting her hungry eyes feast on his handsome features was too tempting. It made her remember how she'd felt when he'd kissed her. She'd been shocked by her wild response to him. He appealed to her senses in delicious ways. But he was the enemy, and she'd do well to remember it.

"Our mother also performs on stage," Al volunteered, ignoring Thorn's glare. "She does character parts. Right now she's doing a play in London."

Thorn set his cup down hard. "Al, I'd like to discuss that new field we're considering."

Al's eyebrows shot up. "You couldn't possibly be asking my opinion," he chided. "You never have before; you always go ahead and do what you please."

"You're coming into your majority next year," Thorn reminded. "It's time you took part in board decisions."

"My God, I'll faint," Al said with a little sarcasm. His eyes narrowed as he studied the older man. "Are you serious?"

"Always," Thorn said, with a pointed glance at Sabina. "In every way."

He was reminding her that he'd warned her off Al. She lifted her cup in a mock salute and smiled at him challengingly.

"Let's go," Thorn told his brother, rising. "You'll excuse us, Miss Cane? I'm sure you can find something with which to amuse yourself."

She glared at his broad back as he led Al into the study and closed the door firmly.

Old Juan, the man who kept house for Thorn, came to clear the table, and she offered to help. He smiled and shook his head. "No, *señorita,* but *muchas gracias,*" he said charmingly. "Such work is not fit for such dainty hands. I will bring coffee and brandy to the living room, if you care to wait there."

"Thank you," she said, smiling at the dark little man. She'd expected Thorn to have an older woman doing the cooking and cleaning, but it seemed he didn't like any women around him. He had definite prejudices in that direction.

She wandered into the living room and stopped in the doorway to feast her eyes on the interior design. Like the den, it mirrored the personality of its owner. It was done in browns and tans with a burgundy leather couch and love seat and big sprawling armchairs in desert patterns. There was a huge Oriental rug by the ornate fireplace. Over the mantel was a portrait of a Hereford bull. On a nearby antique table stood an elegant chessboard and hand-painted wooden chess pieces. The drapes echoed the color schemes of the furniture, dark colors that gave the room a bold, masculine atmosphere.

There was a piano beyond the chessboard, a Baldwin. Sabina was drawn to it irresistibly. She sat down on the bench, her back straight, and raised the lid over the eb-

ony and ivory keys. There had been a piano at the orphanage, and one of the matrons had taught her
painstakingly how to play it, taking pity on her fascination with the instrument. Her fingers touched the keys,
trembling with wonder at its exquisite tone.

Slowly, softly, she began to play Rachmaninoff's
Second Piano Concerto, a passionate piece of music that
mirrored her own confused emotions. Her eyes closed as
her fingers caressed the cool keys, and she drifted away
in a cloud of music.

She wasn't sure exactly when she became aware of eyes
watching her. She stopped in the middle of a bar and
stared nervously toward the doorway where Thorn was
completely still, spellbound, with Al at his shoulder.

"Don't stop," Thorn said quietly. He moved into the
room and sat down on the sofa with a cigarette in his
hand, motioning Al into a chair. "Please," he added
gently.

Distracted, it took her a minute to pick up where she'd
left off. Thorn's penetrating gaze made her nervous. But,
as usual, the music swept her away, just as it did when she
sang. She finished the piece with a flourish, closed the lid
and stood up.

"You play brilliantly," Thorn said, and the words
seemed to be forced. "Where did you learn?"

"I was taught by a friend," she said, neglecting to add
whom or where. "She wasn't a professional, but she read
music quite well. She taught me to sight read."

"She did a brilliant job," he said. "You could play
professionally."

"No, thanks," she said with a nervous laugh. "It's too
wearing. At least when I sing, I don't have to worry about
where my hands are going. On the piano I'd do nothing
but make mistakes in front of an audience." She sat
down on the arm of Al's chair. "Do you play?" she
asked him.

"No. Thorn does."

Surprised, she looked at the older man.

"Shocked?" he taunted, taking a draw from the cigarette. "I enjoy music. Not, however, that noise that passes for it in your world."

It was a challenge. He didn't like her ability; it irked him that she didn't fit the mold he was trying to force her into. Now he was going to cut back; his eyes told her so.

"Noise is a matter of taste," she told him. "I like rhythm."

He lifted an eyebrow and an amused smile turned up his hard, chiseled lips.

She stood up. Well, she might as well live down to the image he had of her. "Say, what do people do for amusement out here?" she asked Al.

"We watch movies," Al told her with a chuckle. "Thorn, want to join us?"

Thorn shook his head. "I've got some paperwork to get through."

Al led Sabina out of the room and down the hall to another, smaller room. "We've got all the latest movies. Which would you like to see?" he asked, showing her the collection stowed beneath the VCR's giant screen.

"I'd really like to sit on the porch and listen to the crickets, if you want to know," she confessed. "But that would bother your brother. He likes me to run true to form."

He ruffled her hair. "Don't let him get to you. Thorn's crafty."

"So am I," she said. "Why does he dislike me so?"

"I think perhaps you remind him of our mother," he said slowly. "She's very much like you, in temperament. Though not in appearance. And there's something else... He really doesn't know how to handle his own emotions, so he pretends not to feel them. You get under his skin. I've never seen him like this."

"Maybe I ought to leave," she suggested hopefully.

"Not yet," he said with a twinkle in his eyes. "Things are just getting interesting."

"You won't leave me alone with him?" she blurted out.

He frowned. "Afraid of him?"

"Yes," she confessed.

"That's a first."

"I suppose it is," she said on a sigh. "He really gets to me, Al."

"Has he threatened you," he asked suddenly.

Not wanting to alarm him, she laughed off his question. "In a way. But I'm not worried."

"I think I am," Al said quietly. "There's a very real hunger in his eyes when he looks at you. I've never seen exactly that expression in them before. He's crafty. Don't let him too close."

"Never mind about me," she reassured him. "I like a challenge. He is a sporting enemy, you know."

"You're incorrigible."

"Not to mention stupid," she teased. "Enough of that. You said you were going to manage some time with Jess. How?" she asked with a wry smile. "He's very sharp. If you invite her here—"

"Yes, I know," he said, checking his watch. "But if he thinks that you and I are watching a movie together, he'll be busy elsewhere, won't he?" he asked with a grin.

"Genius," she said, laughing. "But won't he hear the car?"

"No. Because I won't be driving it. Jessica's going to meet me about a quarter of a mile down the road. When the movie ends," he added, putting in the videocassette, "just go straight upstairs. I don't imagine Thorn will come out of his study for hours yet."

"What if he does? Or if the phone rings for you?"

"Tell him I've gone to the bathroom, and you'll give me the message when I come out," he said, gesturing toward the bathroom in the corner.

"Have it all figured out, hmm?" she teased.

"You have to, around Thorn. Sabina, I'll never be able to pay you back for this," he said gratefully.

She stood on tiptoe and brushed his cheek with her mouth, just as the door swung open and Thorn glared at them. He was wearing a tweed jacket with a white shirt and tan slacks, and looking irritated.

"I have to go to the office for an hour or so," he told his brother impatiently.

"I'll take messages while you're gone," Al promised, struggling not to show his relief.

Thorn glanced from Al to Sabina, and closed the door with a muffled slam.

"He hates it." He chuckled. "He hates the whole idea of my not marrying the oil refinery heiress. Well, I'm off. Hold down the fort!"

"Beat him back home. Please," she pleaded.

"Just go to bed and lock your door, and yell through it if he asks where I am," he said. "Tell him I ran out for coffee or back to my house to pick up something."

"Okay. Have fun."

He lifted an eyebrow. "Never fear."

He darted out the door and she sat down, glancing with no interest whatsoever at the screen. Halfway through the movie she cut the machine off, deciding she needed some fresh air. Borrowing a jacket from the hall, she walked out onto the porch.

The ranch was quiet amid the dark, peaceful night. She sat down in one of the oversized rocking chairs and the wicker squeaked pleasantly as she lazily nudged it into motion. She almost went to sleep, drinking in the night sounds, the distant baying of dogs, the singing of crickets. The stars were out and it was a perfect night for lovers. She was glad for Jessica that Al had finally admitted his feelings. She only hoped that they could all keep Thorn in the dark. Of course, once Jessica and Al were married, it would be too late. Thorn would have to accept Jess then.

So this was the oil baron's world. Classical music and quiet nights and open country. He wasn't really the sophisticated cynic she'd first met. She wondered if he'd ever really given in to his emotions, if he'd ever been in love. But that kind of thinking was dangerous, so she let her mind wander, lulled by the sounds of the countryside.

The soft purr of an engine startled her. She peered out into the darkness, trying to see who it was. Al should be coming back any minute. But what if it wasn't Al?

She stood up just as Thorn appeared, taking the steps two at a time. He stopped at the post when he spotted her, his face scowling in the scant light from the windows.

"What are you doing out here alone?" he asked curtly. "Where's Al?"

"He had to run back to town to turn off something at his house."

"What?"

"He didn't say," she returned, fighting to keep calm.

"And he left you here all by yourself, songbird? How thoughtless. Why didn't he carry you off with him?"

She held on to the porch railing to keep from giving over to panic. "I didn't want to ruin his reputation," she said with a coy grin.

"You're engaged, for God's sake," he replied, coming closer. "Aren't you?"

"You were the one who had palpitations at the thought that we might want to share a room," she reminded him.

"I'm old-fashioned that way," he replied, his eyes glittering down at her.

"A strange attitude for a womanizer," she challenged.

He stood looking down at her, not speaking, not moving, and she realized belatedly that they were alone and he was the enemy.

"Family is different," he said after a few moments. "Family matters."

"Which is why you don't want me to belong to it."

"There's no question about your belonging to it, honey. No way am I going to let Al be hooked into marriage with a notorious..."

"Don't you dare call me foul names!" she warned. "I hit you once and I'll do it again. You really know nothing about me," she added.

His blue eyes narrowed. "What do you see in Al?" he asked bluntly.

She shrugged, dropping her eyes. She was still wearing the borrowed, oversized jacket, and her hair was blowing in the chill breeze. "He's gentle," she said finally.

Before she realized what was happening Thorn was looming over her. The dim light from the house cast a strange sheen in his eyes. "I frighten you, don't I?" he asked quietly.

"Yes." She'd never made a habit of lying. Except with that "engagement" to Al, and it was in a good cause.

"Why?" he persisted.

She smiled slowly. Ironic how safe she felt with him, even as her blood raced and her heart pounded and her legs trembled. She was afraid of everything and nothing when he was near. "I don't know," she admitted. "You wouldn't be a reincarnated ax murderer, by any chance?"

His hard mouth softened into a faint smile. "I hate it when you do that," he remarked. "I'm not used to quick-witted women."

"You aren't used to people, are you?" she asked gently. "I mean, you work with them, and you go to board meetings, and there are social obligations. But you keep to yourself, I think."

"I get the same impression about you," he said warily. He leaned against the post and studied her. "A pity you're wrapped up in ribbon and wearing a tag with Al's name on it. I might have given you a run for that money you want so badly."

"Why do you go around with women you have to buy?" she asked bluntly. This man was so different from her stereotyped impression of a rich man. He was hard and cold, but he would never have raised a hand to a woman. She knew that instinctively.

His eyes searched hers. "They don't get very close that way, Sabina," he said quietly.

Watching him light a cigarette she tugged the jacket closer. "I don't know whose this is," she said. "But I didn't want to go all the way upstairs to get my own . . ."

"It's mine," he said. "I don't mind."

She felt strange wearing it now, though, and she tingled at the thought of it lying against his hard body.

"How old are you, tulip?" he asked.

"Twenty-two," she returned. "Not quite young enough to be your daughter."

"No, not quite," he agreed with a lazy smile. "I was fourteen, my first time."

"Off with an older woman, I'll bet," she murmured demurely.

"She was an old lady of eighteen," he said, his eyes twinkling as she met his gaze. "The most sought-after girl in the school. When my father found out I got a whipping I'll never forget," he recalled. "My father had strong views on morality, and the fact that I was male didn't make one bit of difference to him."

"He didn't want his son to get a reputation for being easy," she teased. The smile faded then as she looked at him, wanting so much to ask about his parents.

"Yes, my mother loved him," he said quietly, reading the question. "But he was a hard man, Sabina. It wasn't easy for him to love. He thought of it as a weakness. In some ways, I can understand how my mother felt. She was a butterfly, always in the thick of society. He was like me. He much preferred the ranch to the city. They were basically incompatible. But that doesn't excuse her actions. He'd be alive today if she'd been faithful to him."

She was remembering her own mother, the pain of each new man, the horrible night when it all ended....

"What was your mother like?" he asked.

"Like yours," she said under her breath. She looked away, pulling the jacket closer. "I don't talk about her, to anyone."

He lit a cigarette. "Is she why you're still a virgin?"

She nodded. "I don't want that kind of life."

"Are you as passionate with Al as you were with me that night in the kitchen?"

The question startled her. She turned, searching for words. Good heavens, Al had never kissed her at all. She was still trying to come up with some kind of answer when he abruptly tossed the cigarette off the porch and moved toward her.

"No," she said, backing away. "No, Thorn, don't."

"You make my name sound like a benediction," he said in a hot breath. His hands shot out, lean, hurting hands, jerking her against his long, warm body, holding her there even as she struggled. "No, honey," he said in a voice like velvet, stilling her hips. "Don't do that."

She looked up, her hands flat against his chest, her eyes wild, her hair all over her face. "It isn't fair to Al," she said.

"Don't you think I know that?" he said in a grating voice. His eyes were glittering, his face as rigid as steel. His breath came heavily and hard. "I want you," he said huskily. He studied her breasts under the jacket, where they rose and fell with her uneasy breaths. "Are you wearing anything under that top?" he whispered.

"No," she said in a choked whisper. "I'm not."

She felt her knees go weak. Her eyes looked into his and she was lost. Drowning. Her body felt the warmth and power of his. Involuntarily, she brushed against him. Her full lips parted, wanting his mouth.

"I could touch you there," he murmured softly. His lips touched her forehead, open and moist as his hands slid around to her waist.

She trembled as his fingers pressed against her soft skin.

"Has he?" he asked curtly. "Has Al touched you there?"

She swallowed. "He... I'm old-fashioned, too. I've never..."

His mouth moved to her closed eyelids; his tongue tested the length of her lashes. "Untouched," he whispered deeply. "Soft and moon-kissed, and I want you so much, tulip. I've paid for women most of my life, in one way or another. But I've never been the first man." His breath sounded ragged, and the mouth hovering above hers was hard and warm and smoky. His hands were on her rib cage now, and she trembled as the tips of his fingers just brushed the outside edge of her taut breasts.

"This is just the beginning, this hunger. It gets worse." He breathed against her mouth. "I never gave a damn before, but I'm deliberately going to rouse you. I want to watch you. I want to hear those first sweet little gasps of passion when I touch you where no man ever has."

"Thorn..." Her voice broke. She was trembling all over; her hands were buried in his soft white shirt, crumpling it over the wall of his chest. Her eyes were lost in his, and she was more helpless than she'd ever been in her life, completely at his mercy.

He lowered his head, his open mouth touching hers, brushing it with gentle probes that made her own lips part eagerly, so that he could fit them exactly to his.

He was so slow with her, so lazily confident, that she never thought of holding back. His warm, expert mouth pressed her lips apart and his tongue eased inside her mouth, tasting her with a rhythm that built and built and built as his fingers trespassed teasingly under her arms. The smell and feel and touch of him tormented her until finally her breath caught and she moaned, deep in her throat.

He felt her body arch against his thighs and he shifted his dark head to look down at her, at the mouth his had crushed and cherished. Her eyes were wild, shocked, glazed with desire.

"If I touched you now, you'd cry out," he whispered, searching her flushed face.

"Please," she pleaded, hurting, aching for his hands.

"Is it really that bad?" he breathed deeply, fascinated by the expression in her soft eyes. "All right, baby, I'm going to give you what you want."

"So... hungry," she whispered tearfully. "Never... never before..."

"I know," he murmured. His mouth touched her eyelids, closing them. "Shhh. Be still, and I'll be so gentle with you..."

His hands were edging under her camisole top while his mouth threatened hers, poised over it. He found the hem and his warm hands slid up her rib cage, slowly, tenderly.

Her body jerked, trying to lift into his hands, but she was trembling like a leaf.

"Sweet," he whispered, shaken by her ardent response. "Oh, God, how sweet! Here, little one..."

He gave her his hands, and she did cry out, a sound that stunned him, shocked him. She threw her head back, her hands pressing against him, her body arched toward him in glorious abandon as waves of pleasure exploded in every cell of her body. His hands were warm and hard and calloused, and when they contracted, she almost fainted.

"Thorn," she moaned. "Thorn, it's like fire; it burns, it burns," she whispered.

"God," he breathed reverently, shaken. She was like rose petals in his hands, so soft, so delicate, the skin smooth and warm, the tips hard in his palms. The first time... He took her mouth under his and felt his lips tremble as he kissed her and kissed her and kissed her. He was so far gone that the distant drone of a car only barely got through to him. She smelled of gardenias and his body was in agony with its need of hers.

He lifted his head. Her eyes opened, drowsy with passion, hungry for him. Her mouth... He had to brush it with his, just once more, to savor the honey of her lips.

"It's Al," he said unsteadily. He took a deep, steadying breath and didn't let go of her right away, because she looked weak enough to fold up. "You're a miracle," he whispered. "A miracle. And you're his damn you! Damn you, Sabina!" Crushing her arms under his fingers as the car came closer, he pushed her roughly away and went into the house without another word.

She couldn't face Al, not like this. She ran into the house and down the hall and back into the VCR screening room. Hurriedly, she shoved the tape into the machine and fell into a chair. By the time Al walked in, she'd just barely gotten her nerves steady and her hair smoothed. She didn't want him asking questions. She couldn't have borne having to answer them right now. She was devastated.

"How did it go?" Al asked, sneaking in the room.

"He came back unexpectedly. I couldn't think fast enough. I told him you'd forgotten to turn off something at your house."

"Good girl! So he won't even be suspicious. That was quick thinking." He grinned. "Any problems?"

She shook her head, avoiding his eyes. "Of course not. Well, good night. See you in the morning."

"We'll go riding. At least, it will look that way," he said with a chuckle. "I'm sneaking off one more time, to get the license."

"I'll be a nervous wreck!" she exclaimed, then rushed off without elaborating.

Behind the door of her bedroom, she collapsed. How had Thorn conquered her so easily? If Al hadn't come back... She blushed wildly, hotly, at the thought of where they were headed. She'd wanted him and it had been obvious that he wanted her, too. Her body still pulsed with the pleasure his hands had taught her. Her mouth burned from his kisses. She felt an ache that wouldn't stop. Tears welled up in her eyes. Oh, Jessica, she thought. If you only knew what I'm going through for you!

She turned out the light and went to bed, hoping the days would pass quickly. She was far too vulnerable to Thorn, and she was dubious about her dwindling strength. He could put her in an impossible situation. And what then? What if he went too far and seduced her? He'd promised he wouldn't, but he'd lost control. She'd felt it. He wanted her just as fiercely as she wanted him, and it could happen. That would destroy her. It would ruin her future. Because there could never be another man after Thorn. Never.

5

*

Tugging on a pair of gray slacks with a pullover
V-necked striped top and boots, Sabina went downstairs
the next morning, expecting to find Al at the breakfast
table. Instead, she found only Thorn.

He was sitting at the head of the table, toying with a
napkin, obviously waiting for something or someone. He
was in denim today, rugged looking, a cowboy from out
of the past. His shirt was half open in front, and she
could see dark skin and a feathering of body hair. She
remembered her own voice pleading with him to touch
her. Her face flamed, her heartbeat shook her. She
wanted to run.

His blue eyes jerked up and he found her watching
him. "Sit down, songbird. Juan's just bringing breakfast."

There was no way out. She pulled out the chair next to
his and sagged into it, turning over the cup in her saucer
as Thorn poured hot coffee into it from the carafe.

"Cream or sugar?" he asked.

"I take it black," she said. "Caffeine keeps me going
on tour. But I've never had the luxury of cream and
sugar."

His eyes wandered over her shoulders, her bare arms.
"Is that how you stay so thin?"

"I'm not a heavy eater," she said. Her eyes focused on
the coffee cup, until he reached out unexpectedly and
tilted her chin up to his probing stare.

"It isn't fair to Al," he said quietly.

"What isn't?" she stammered.

"Wearing that," he said, indicating the engagement
ring flashing in the overhead light. "Not when you can
want another man the way you wanted me last night."

"I did not—" she began defensively.

"Don't." He touched her mouth with a lean forefinger, and his eyes were stern and narrow. "Don't lie. I could have taken you if he'd waited another half hour to come home."

"Leave me alone, Thorn!" she burst out.

"I won't," he promised. He leaned back in his chair and lit a cigarette. "I can't. You won't take advice. So you can take the consequences."

"What are they?" she returned. "A night in your bed?"

"I'd love that," he said with genuine feeling as his eyes wandered hungrily over her face and made her flush with embarrassment. "It's been a long time since I've wanted a woman the way I want you."

"I'm not like that," she said with quiet pride.

"Yes. That makes it worse." He sipped his coffee. "Where are you from, Sabina?"

"New Orleans. Why?"

"How did you meet Al?"

"Jessica introduced us."

He shot her a piercing look. "Nice girl, Jessica. Did you know that she's in love with my brother?"

Her cheeks burned and the cup almost overturned in her hands.

"I see that you do," he persisted, leaning forward to flick ashes in the ashtray. "Doesn't it bother you, hurting her?"

"What do you care about Jessica's feelings? I didn't think secretaries mattered in your world."

"I don't like that," he said coldly, and his icy, pale blue eyes glittered. "I'm no snob, songbird."

"Oh, but you are, Mr. Thorndon," she assured him bitterly. "You have deep prejudices."

"Only about a certain type of woman, which has nothing whatsoever to do with breeding," he returned.

"Breeding," she scoffed. Her eyes lit up. "You'd probably just as soon breed people the way you breed bulls. You keep a portrait of a Hereford bull over your living-room mantel, but I don't see any pictures of loved ones on your walls. Don't people count with you, oil baron?"

His jaw tightened as he crushed out the cigarette. "You never will, honey," he said in a voice as smooth as silk. "Physically, maybe, but no other way."

"Thank God," she replied fervently.

His temper flared, but at that moment Al chose to join them at the table.

"Morning," he said with an ear-to-ear grin. "Breakfast ready?"

"Juan!" Thorn roared, his voice deep and piercing.

"*Si, señor,* I bring it now!" came the quick reply from the kitchen.

"When Thorn growls, everybody jumps," Sabina murmured dryly, with a pointed glance in Thorn's direction.

"You may learn how, before it's over," he warned her.

"You two aren't arguing, are you?" Al asked Thorn. "Future in-laws ought to get along."

If looks could kill, Al would have dropped dead from the impact of Thorn's angry glare.

"Don't listen for wedding bells too soon, brother," he warned Al. "There's plenty of time. You're young."

"Who made you wait?" Al asked him with a calculating stare. "Remember that stacked blonde you wanted to marry, and Dad threatened to disinherit you? You ran off with her, but he followed and propositioned her, right in front of your eyes. He told her that you wouldn't inherit anything if you married her, but that he had plenty of money, and she switched loyalties on the spot. Is that why you're so worried about me making the same mistake?"

"Go to hell," Thorn said softly. He got up from the table and walked off without a backward glance.

"How horrible," Sabina said under her breath. Her heart ached when she considered the pain Thorn must have endured at such a young age.

"Yes, it was, but he's let it lock him up for life," Al said quietly. "He's hardly human these days, all because of one woman who betrayed his trust. He's got to stop living in the past."

"He'll get even," she said.

He smiled softly. "Not in time," he promised. "Not nearly in time. Let's eat and we'll hit the trail."

They rode so far the ranch was out of sight. Thorn hadn't been seen since breakfast, and Sabina felt oddly sad that he'd gone without it. He must be starving. When they reached the fork in the trail, Al waved and rode on ahead. They'd agreed that if Thorn came looking, she'd say Al had decided to give his roan a workout and didn't want to force her to ride so fast when she was out of practice. She rubbed her arms, wishing she'd borrowed a jacket. It would be cold until the sun rose higher in the sky.

She reined in at the river that cut through the property and sat quietly in the clearing, watching the water flow lazily downstream. She got down to examine a set of tracks, and grinned to herself. Deer tracks. They must have watered at the river. Her grandfather had taught her how to track deer; she'd never forgotten. She felt like one of the old pioneers.

"Are you lost, city girl?" came a sardonic drawl from behind her.

She glanced around, not even surprised to find Thorn leaning over the pommel of his own horse, watching her.

"Nope. I'm tracking deer," she informed him.

He swung down out of the saddle, tilting his wide-brimmed Stetson at a jaunty angle over his eyes, and knelt down beside her. His batwing chaps spread out and his boots made a leathery creak with the motion.

"Tracks," he exclaimed.

"Sure," she told him. "That one's a buck. It's got a pointed, cloven hoof. The other is a doe; it's rounded."

"Who taught you that?"

"My grandfather. He used to take me tracking every fall, before deer season opened," she confessed. "At least, until he died." Her eyes grew sad with the memory. "At that time he was the biggest thing in my life. I worshipped him."

"What else did he teach you?"

"Oh, little things. How to tell when rain was coming, how to make things grow. He was a farmer."

Thorn got to his feet slowly, staring down at her with a confused expression. "You worry me."

"Why?" she asked, rising gracefully. "Because I know how to track deer?"

"Because you don't fit any mold I've ever seen," he said, lifting his chin and scrutinizing her. "Because I want you. I could almost hate you for making me vulnerable, even physically."

That was a shocking admission, but it was like him. He didn't pull punches. She wouldn't have expected it. He was a hard man, and it would have been someone like him a hundred years ago who would have tamed this land where they were standing, and fought off hostile forces, and made the fields green and bountiful.

"You're staring again," he said sharply.

"You're very much a man, Mr. Thorndon," she said, spellbound enough to be honest with him. "I've never met anyone like you before. The men in my world are shallow people. You're solid and honest. I meant it when I said I'd have liked you for a friend."

"No, you wouldn't," he said with a mocking smile. "You'd have liked me for a lover, and that's what we'd be already if you hadn't tangled yourself up with my kid brother."

"I don't think so," she returned. "I'm afraid of you. You take people over, you own them. I couldn't bear to be owned."

"I could make you like it."

And probably he could, but she wouldn't let herself think about that. Her gaze drifted beyond him, toward the meadow behind the banks that stretched to a long line of trees on the horizon.

"It's so lovely here," she said. "So quiet. How can you bear New Orleans after you've lived here?"

His jaw became taut. "I cope—with most things."

She turned back to her horse, but Thorn was in front of her before she got two steps, a solid wall she couldn't bypass.

"It's not that easy," he said, and his hard, lean hands caught her by the arms and held her in front of him. "Where's my brother?"

"He gave the roan its head. He'll be right back," she insisted.

"Not for a little while, Sabina," he whispered, leaning toward her. "Kiss me. I went to bed aching for you; I woke up hurting.... Kiss me, damn you!"

His mouth pressed into hers, and none of the teasing foreplay of the night before was left between them. He lifted her against his lean, powerful body and his arms swallowed her while his mouth taught her new lessons in the art of intimacy. Suddenly, she felt his body harden against her, enticing her. Protesting, she twisted and his hand swept down to the base of her spine to hold her still, even as a groan burst from his lips.

He lifted his head, and his eyes frightened her with their wild glitter.

"Don't move against me that way," he whispered hoarsely. "It arouses me unbearably."

She blushed, but he bent his head again, and his mouth stifled the words she was about to utter.

Her fingers let go of his shirt to slide under it. She sighed as she felt the curly hair covering his muscles, and her fingers tangled in it. She felt his body tauten even more and sensed that he was reacting to the gentle movement of her hands. Her education in sensual things was sadly behind that of most people; there'd been no one to ask except girlfriends, and most of them knew as little as she did.

"Sabina, for God's sake, don't, baby," he whispered, stilling her hands. He drew away slightly, looking more formidable than ever, his eyes glazed, his face taut.

She slid her hands out from under his shirt, shaken by the fierce ardor she'd provoked, and by her headlong response to it.

She could hardly breathe and Thorn's heart was pounding like a trip-hammer. He laughed softly, strangely, and his chest rose and fell in irregular jerks.

"You burn me up," he said huskily. "The smell of you, the feel of you . . . It's been years since I felt like this."

His words were flattering, but she was getting nervous. They were in a deserted place, where no one would look for them, and Al wouldn't be back for hours. There was a wildness in Thorn that she hadn't expected at the beginning, a reckless passion that matched her own free spirit.

"Thorn," she whispered.

His mouth took the whisper and inhaled it, opening her soft lips to a deep, slow, probing kiss. His hands slid down her sides to her hips and drew them lazily against his in easy, dragging movements. She was so lost in the warm teasing of his mouth that she didn't protest this time. His body and its responses and demands were becoming familiar now. He was like a part of her already.

"I've never made love standing up," he whispered in a voice that was deep and a little unsteady. "You make me wonder how it would be."

A tiny wild sound escaped from her throat, and he smiled against her lips. "I want you," he growled softly. His hands slid to the backs of her thighs and lifted and pressed until she thought she'd go crazy with the sweet, piercing pleasure. He laughed again, roughly. "I want you. I want to lay you down in the grass and let my body melt into yours. But that would be playing right into your hands, wouldn't it, witch woman? You'd love that, making me lose my head with you. You'd hold it over me like a scimitar. . . ."

"Thorn!" she exclaimed, dragging her mouth from his. "I'm not like that, I'm not!" Her drowsy eyes sought his and she searched their cool blue depths slowly, remembering all at once what Al had said over the breakfast table about the blonde who'd betrayed Thorn. Her fingers lifted to his mouth, touching it gently, liking the hard warmth of it. "She was crazy, wanting money instead of you. . . ."

His eyes flashed. The whispered words seemed to anger him. He caught her long hair and jerked her face up to his. "She was a tease, too," he said curtly. "A woman with an eye to the main chance."

The words came out like an insult, and she knew that whatever had been growing between them had wilted.

"You're hurting me," she said quietly.

His nostrils flared and his face hardened, but slowly he released his cruel hold on her hair and let her move away from him. His gaze went down to the small fingers still pressed against his chest, and he lifted them away.

He wasn't a man at the mercy of his emotions now, she thought, watching him light a cigarette with cool, steady hands. He'd become as cold as stone.

His mouth curled slowly. "You've got one hell of a lot of spirit. Al may miss you, after all."

"He isn't going anywhere."

"No. But you are." He lifted his head, studying her insolently. "I'm working on a little surprise for you, tulip. Just another day or so, and I'll have everything I need."

"How exciting," she murmured. "I can hardly wait. Does Al know?"

The smile faded. "I don't want him hurt any more than he has to be. Not that you seem to mind playing around with me behind his back."

How could she tell him that the engagement was a bogus one, that Thorn appealed to her senses in a way that left her completely at his mercy? That she loved him, wanted him, needed him. It was a maelstrom of discovery that left her knees weak. It couldn't happen so quickly, could it? He was arrogant and ruthless and narrow-minded. But he was more man, pound for pound, than any male she'd ever run across in her life. Her eyes coveted the very sight of him. And because of that, she turned away and wouldn't let him see her face again.

"I'll leave you to your work, oil baron," she said as she mounted her horse. "I'm going to find Al."

"Enjoy his company while you can," he returned, mounting his own horse with lazy grace. "You haven't got long."

"What was your father like, Thorn?" she asked suddenly, curious.

"Like me," he said shortly.

"No wonder your mother is the way she is," she said sadly. "She must have been devastated when he died."

He frowned. "What a hell of a way she has of showing it!"

"Al showed me a picture of your father; he's told me things about him." Her hand lifted to shade her eyes from the sun. "He must have been a strong man. There aren't a lot of strong men in the world. I imagine she's been looking all this time for someone who halfway measured up to him, without the least success. She's relatively young, Al said. What a pitiful way to live."

He glared at her, but he was listening. "She might have showed him she cared while he was still alive. He'd be alive, but for her."

Her soft eyes wandered all over him, loving every rippling muscle, even the stubborn set of his jaw. He'd changed her whole life so quickly. "Perhaps he made it impossible for her to show it. Perhaps she only wanted to capture his attention. And afterward, after it happened, the guilt would have been terrible. Some men take a lot of forgetting," she said.

"How the hell would you know?" he challenged.

He was back to his old impossible self. She shrugged delicately and rode away without answering. If she'd said anything else, she might as well be talking to the wind. She rode back to the path where she'd left Al, dismounted, and sat on a stump waiting for him to return.

She could hardly believe how fast it had happened. She hardly knew Thorn, for heaven's sake! But he'd worn on her nerves and her emotions and her heart more in the past few days than most men had in months, even years. She wanted him, and it was oddly comforting to realize that he felt the same hunger for her. It was a dead-end street, of course. There was no possible future in it. But while she could see him and be near him, she took a terrible pleasure in her growing love for him. There was a lot of man under that cruel, cynical exterior. She was only sorry he was her enemy, that he'd never let her see behind his mask. It would be sheer heaven to be loved by such a man.

Al appeared a few minutes later, grinning. "We got the license," he said, giddy with excitement. "And we decided to set the date. We're getting married the day after Easter."

"That's Monday!" Sabina exclaimed.

"Yes! Oh, God, I'm so happy," he burst out, and danced her around the clearing in a mad little waltz.

Sabina laughed and danced, and tried not to think of how soon her bubble was going to burst. When Al broke the news to Thorn, it would all be over, and she'd never see the oil baron again.

"How about the ring?" she exclaimed.

"You can give it back when we drive to New Orleans Monday morning," he explained. "We want you to come along and stand up with us at the service. Okay?"

"I'd love to! Jessica and you. It's been my fondest dream."

"Mine, too, but it wouldn't have been possible without your help," Al said solemnly. "Thorn would have stopped us. This is the only way it could have worked. Has he been at you again?"

"Not really. We just talked," she lied, crossing her fingers behind her back.

"Good." Al let her go and mounted his horse, watching her mount beside him.

"But I've made him mad again, I'm afraid."

"How?"

"I told him your mother must miss your father terribly and be looking for someone who measures up to him," she murmured.

"That's what I've always thought," he replied. "Dad was one of a kind."

"Like Thorn," she said involuntarily.

He studied her, frowning. "Sabina, don't lose your heart to him. He hasn't got one of his own."

"I know that already," she said. "Don't worry about me, I'll be fine. Besides, a few days from now, it will all be a memory." That was a sobering thought. "Hey, I'll race you back!"

"You're on!"

And they galloped back to the house.

Thorn went out that evening, resplendent in his evening wear, and Sabina felt a surge of mad jealousy as she imagined him with some slinky blonde like the one he'd brought to Al's party.

"He does draw women," Al muttered later as they watched television. "He always has. But not one of them touches him emotionally. He says he'll never let any woman have a hold on him."

"I imagine he must have reason, don't you?" she said. "Can I play the piano?"

"What? Sure!" He turned off the television. "If you don't mind, I'm going to take advantage of Thorn's absence and go call Jessica."

"Mind? Get out of here and do it! I'm delighted to have some time to myself. Not that you aren't good company," she added.

He chuckled. "Don't wear out the keys."

"Not me."

He left and she played late into the night, her fingers touching the keys that Thorn's fingers had touched. It was a wildly exhilarating thought, and made her hungrier than ever just for the sight of him. But when she finished and went to bed, he still hadn't come home.

He wasn't at breakfast, either, but Al looked disgruntled as they dug into the hearty egg and bacon platter that Juan had prepared.

"Thorn's having a party Saturday night," he muttered. "And he's invited Jessica."

"Uh, oh. Think he's suspicious?" she asked quickly.

"I don't know. He says the party is being held to announce our engagement. But it's all a rushed-up job, with telephoned invitations. And it's not like Thorn to give in so easily. I think we've been discreet enough, but he's made some long-distance calls, and I overheard something that worries me." Al lifted his head, and his eyes were narrow with concern. "Listen, what could he find out about you if he dug really deep?"

She stared at him blankly. Her mind whirled, grasping. No, she thought wildly, no he couldn't find out anything after all these years. "Well...not much," she faltered. "Why?"

"Because he's in a good mood this morning. And that makes me suspicious."

She glowered at her toast. "Maybe it was just good humor left over from his night out," she said.

Al looked at her long and hard, but he didn't say a word.

A visiting cattleman stopped by after lunch, and Al went to show him around the ranch while Thorn took care of business in his study. Sabina sneaked out the door and went around the back of the house into the woods, beyond the little gazebo that so beautifully matched the house and faced the distant pastures. It was an unseasonably warm day. In her jeans with a green knit top, she looked younger than ever, with her long and soft hair blowing in the wind.

Her mind drifted as she watched a bird circle and soar toward the top of a huge live oak near the small stream. She wished it was warm enough to paddle in the creek.

"You look like a wood nymph."

She whirled to find Thorn standing behind her. He was clad in a white shirt and dark blue slacks with a suede blazer, all sleek muscle and dark tan. A feathering of crisp, curling black hair peeked out of his shirt. He was wearing his wide-brimmed creamy Stetson, and he looked suave and very Western.

"I'm just getting some air," she said defensively.

"Why aren't you with your intended?" he asked, leaning back against a tall oak, his boot propped behind him, his arms folded.

"Al was talking business; I didn't think I'd be welcome."

"Al doesn't know anything about the cattle business," he said. "He's buying time with Bellamy until I get there." He smiled faintly as he studied her. "The longer I take, the more Bellamy will worry. By the time I get there, he'll sell at my price. That's business, tulip."

"You said you'd tell me why you called me tulip," she reminded him. He was almost approachable today. She even smiled at him.

"There's a song about a yellow tulip and a big red rose," he murmured.

The song was one her mother used to sing, and she knew the words quite well. It was an old song—and one of the lines was something about it being heaven "when you caressed me" and "your lips were sweeter than julep...." She stared at him and went as red as the rose in the song.

"I see you know the song," he remarked, smiling insolently.

"I'm engaged to Al," she told him.

"Give him back the ring."

"I can't," she growled.

"That's the last chance you'll get from me," he said, his face grim. "You'd better take it, while you still can."

"Is that a threat?" she asked with a laugh.

"It's much more than a threat." He was looking at her as if he'd never seen her before, an odd expression in his blue eyes. "You're unique, Sabina," he said. "And if you hadn't proven to me already that you're just after Al's money, I might be tempted to forget everything else. But I can't stand by and let Al make this kind of mistake."

"Are you going to spend your life running interference for him?" she asked quietly, not making a challenge of it. "He's twenty-four. Eventually he'll have to stand on his own. And what if you aren't there to prop him up?"

"You're missing the point," he said flatly. Tugging a cigarette out of his pocket, he lit it, inhaling deeply. "I've spent the past ten years of my life building up the company. I've made sacrifices...." He took a draw from the cigarette and let the smoke out roughly. "I'm not going to let him throw away his inheritance. It was hard bought."

She looked at him openly, seeing the lines of age in his face, the wear and tear on him. "Al was fourteen when your father died," she recalled. "You had all the responsibility then, didn't you?"

For an instant he looked vulnerable. Then as if the shutters came down, his expression was masked. "I didn't break under it."

"I don't think you can be broken," she said, searching his eyes. "I even understand."

"Oh, yes, I'm sure you do," he said, eyes narrowing as he held her gaze. "Your own life hasn't been easy street until now, has it?"

He couldn't know, she assured herself. She shrugged. "What do you mean, until now?"

"Designer jeans," he remarked. "Designer gowns. Expensive coats. You live well for a struggling singer."

If only he knew! She smiled inwardly. "I do okay," she said.

"How many boyfriends have you had in your young life?" he asked.

Her shoulders rose and fell. "None, really," she admitted, letting her eyes fall to his shiny boots, oblivious of the momentary softening in his face. "Guess I never had much time for all that. I've worked all my life."

His jaw clenched. "Yes. So have I."

"Not like I have, rich man." She laughed, throwing back her dark head. All her tiny triumphs glittered in her eyes. "I've waited tables and scrubbed floors. I've worked double shifts and fended off roaming hands and smiled over the nastiest kinds of propositions. I've worked in clubs so rough they had two bouncers. And I've done it without any help at all, from anybody!"

He didn't speak. His firm lips closed around the butt of the cigarette as he took another draw and then crushed it under his boot. "Did you get tired of the climb up? Is that why you've decided to marry Al when you're not in love with him?" he asked bluntly.

"Why do you say that?" she stammered.

"You never touch each other." He moved away from the tree and loomed over her, tall and threatening and unbearably masculine. "You smile at him, but not with love. You don't even kiss him."

She shifted backward restlessly, and he followed, too close. "I'm not demonstrative in public," she insisted.

"You're not demonstrative in private either, are you?" he demanded. His hands shot out and suddenly drew her close, so that his breath was on her forehead and his body threatened hers from head to toe. Her heart seemed to stop beating at the unexpected proximity. "You even freeze up with me, until I start kissing you, tulip."

"Thorn, don't," she whispered.

"I can't help myself," he said on a hard, contemptuous laugh. "I can't stand within five feet of you without losing my head. Haven't you noticed? My God, I hate what you do to me!"

She looked up into his deepening blue eyes and shivered with apprehension. Could he sense the secret, dark pleasures that she felt from the tautening of his body against hers, from the crushing strength of the hands gripping her arms?

Around them came the sound of birds, and the faraway rippling of water in the creek. The wind was stirring the limbs of the trees, and leaves crunched underfoot as she shifted in his embrace. But she was more aware of her own heartbeat, of the fleeting nature of her time with him. Just a few more days... after that she'd never see him again, she knew it. Once Al was safely married, the oil baron would put her out of his mind. This, all of this, was just a means to an end, an attempt to make her break the engagement. But she was getting involved in ways she'd never meant to. She looked at him and loved him, bad temper, ruthlessness and all.

"It will all be over soon," she said softly.

"Sooner than you realize," he replied sharply. "Break off the engagement, while you can. Don't make me hurt you. I don't really have any taste for it now. But I have to protect Al."

Involuntarily, her fingers reached up, hesitated, and then touched his thick, dark eyebrows. Incredibly, his eyes closed, he stood very still, not moving at all. And that response made her bold. She traced all the hard lines of his bronzed face, learning its patrician contours, touching high cheekbones, his straight nose, his broad forehead, the indentations in his cheeks, the firm, warm line of his lips, his jutting, stubborn chin. His breath stirred as her fingers lingered beside his mouth.

She felt an answering hunger. Was it so much to ask, just one more kiss? One more passing of lips against hers? One kiss to remember, to live on? She rose on tiptoe, her hands behind his strong neck, and touched her mouth to his chin. It was as high as she could reach, but not nearly enough.

"Thorn," she breathed huskily. "Thorn, please..."

He was breathing as roughly as she was. "What do you want from me, Sabina?" he whispered back.

"Memories," she managed to get out.

His eyes opened, dark and very soft. He reached down and picked her up in his arms, holding her while he searched her hungry eyes. "Memories," he said gently, in a tone he'd never used with her before. "Yes, I can give you those. In another time, another place—I could have given you a child as well."

She trembled, her eyes filling with tears, and he buried his face against her throat as he carried her deeper into the woods.

"I want you," she told him, whispering it, her voice torn with hunger and pain.

"Me, and not Al?" he asked.

She drew in a breath and looked up into his eyes, wanting only to explain, to tell him everything. But she didn't dare.

His face hardened, even as his eyes blazed with open desire. He laid her down under a big oak tree, on a pallet of leaves, and slid alongside her. "I'm richer than Al is," he said under his breath. "If money is the big draw, why not set your sights on me, tulip?"

"It isn't money," she said hesitantly.

"Well, it damned sure isn't love," he shot at her. His eyes kindled as they wandered the length of her body and back again, hungry on her breasts, her lips, her face. "Beautiful," he whispered. "You're so beautiful you take my breath, my will, my mind. I hold you and want nothing more from life than the taste of your mouth on mine."

"We're enemies," she whispered sadly.

"If it weren't for Al, and your innocence, we'd be lovers," he said. He ran his hand slowly over her shoulder, her collarbone, holding her eyes as he slid it onto her breasts and traced the hard tips.

Her lips parted with the unexpected movement, and he bent and took the sound from them with his own. She closed her eyes and the kiss got harder, deeper, hungrier. She moaned. His breath came heavily. He moved a hand to his suede jacket, unbuttoned it, and tossed it aside. He opened his shirt and tugged it free of his trousers, and drew her hands against his hard, hair-feathered chest. His mouth became more demanding, and she felt herself getting weaker by the second, done in by her own consuming love for him, by the pleasure she'd never known before. She sighed, nuzzling her face against him while his warm, deft fingers made quick work of buttons and hooks, and suddenly smoothed over her with exquisite delicacy, petal-smooth, feather-warm.

She gave a high-pitched little cry and tried to curl up, but he eased her onto her back and smoothed the fabric completely away from her body.

The breath he took was audible as he stared down at cream and mauve contrasts, lifting gracefully with her sighs. "Oh, God," he whispered reverently, poised over her.

Her wide, gray eyes searched the hardness of his face, looking for vulnerability, but it only grew harder as he looked at her. She could feel a sudden, helpless reaction as he stared blatantly at her breasts, and it embarrassed her. She tried to cover them, but he brought her hands to his mouth, shaking his head.

"Don't be shy," he said gently. "I'm just as aroused as you are."

His eyes glittered as he suddenly moved down, shifting so that his whole body covered hers, with his elbows taking the brunt of his formidable weight. "See?" he murmured as his hips moved in a slow rotation against hers, and she felt the blatant proof of the statement. "My God, I want to take you," he said huskily. "I want to strip you and grind your body into the leaves under mine, and make you cry out when the moment comes...."

Her face felt hot. She pressed her fingertips against his hard mouth as the pictures flashing in her mind embarrassed her. "You...mustn't."

"Watch," he whispered, drawing her eyes down to his chest. He moved, shifting so the thick hair over it teased her breasts. The abrasive contact shocked her with pleasure, and her body suddenly jerked, arching helplessly against his, while her eyes told him how helpless she was to stop it.

"Your mind may want to stop, but your body can't. You want me. It must be pure instinct, because we both know you've never known the full intimacy of a man's body."

"I want to," she moaned, touching his chest helplessly. "I don't care if it hurts, I want you..."

"Sabina," he whispered. His mouth opened on hers and he gave her the full weight of his body, holding her, devouring her eager lips. She whimpered, and the sound made him shudder. Her body trembled as the warmth and strength of his burned into it, his chest pinning her soft breasts, his legs tangling in hers.

His hand edged between her breasts, his thumb stroking her, his fingers tracing her. His breath quickened, and he suddenly shifted, his mouth moving from hers down to one creamy breast.

She cried out, arching, her body shuddering with unbelievable pleasure, and her glazed eyes met his as he lifted his head. His hand stroked her, warm and confident and soothing.

"This is what passion is all about," he said softly, holding her gaze. "Total, absolute loss of control. Sensual oblivion. A few minutes of this and you'd kill to have me end the torment."

Her eyes stared up into his, through a fog of hunger and need and love.

He sat up, holding her down by the waist, studying the visible tremor of her body. He was none too calm himself, but he fought for self-control. He sighed heavily then, smiling ruefully at the expression on her face.

His lean hands shook her gently. "Virgins are hell on the nervous system," he murmured.

Her mind was only beginning to focus. "I would have begged you," she said numbly.

"Yes. But even then I wouldn't have gone any further." He drew the front of her bra together and fastened it, then her blouse, with slow, steady hands. "A casual relationship isn't for you. I don't think it ever would be, despite the offer."

"Thank you," she whispered.

He studied her quietly. "Now tell me you're not really marrying Al."

Was that why he'd made love to her? she wondered miserably. To make her break the engagement? Her eyes closed. "I still am."

He glared down at her with pure hatred. "You have until tomorrow night to give him back the ring. If you don't..."

She fumbled for words. "I'm sorry," she said. "I can't."

He got to his feet angrily, buttoning his shirt and snatching up his jacket and hat while she sat and watched him curiously.

"My God, you're something," he said. It was no compliment. He glared at her openly. "I've never known a woman to be so damned mercenary!"

That hurt, but she didn't let him see how much. "And you're as unprincipled yourself, oil baron," she shouted back. "You made love to me just to make me break the engagement, didn't you?"

His face went rock hard. "Sure," he said coldly. "I'm ruthless, remember? I thought you might be persuaded to settle for me."

"For how long?" she asked with a bitter laugh. "A few weeks, until you sated yourself?"

"That would depend on how much you wanted," he said with deliberate cruelty, as if he knew! "Most women will sell themselves for the right price or the right reason."

Her face paled, and she could have sworn there were traces of regret in his expression. She turned away. "Thanks for the lessons."

"You're an apt pupil. But school's out now."

"Just as well," she said. "The tuition is too high."

"You're paying for experience," he said tauntingly.

Her head jerked around, her eyes revealing hatred for all the other women he'd had before her. "Did you pay them?" she asked.

His eyes narrowed. "Sure. A diamond here, a mink there. Trinkets."

Trinkets. The price of survival. Her eyes grew wild, her face blanched as she saw her mother's face at the end of life, heard the pitiful words come torturously out of that frail throat.

"Oh, damn you!" Sabina cried, hating him for being that kind of man, hating him for what others had done to her mother, for what they had made of her. "Damn you, damn you . . . !" She sobbed.

"Sabina, wait!" There was an odd hesitation in his deep voice when she turned and began to run. But she didn't stop. Instead she let the wind cut into her face, let the tears cloud her vision as she ran on, lost in her own hell of memories.

6

_____ * _____

After she washed her tear-stained face and calmed down, Sabina changed into a soft, clinging brown-and-cream dress that suited her dark hair and eyes. Gathering her courage, she smoothed her hair and went back downstairs. She'd purposefully taken her time, so that the Thorndon brothers and the visiting cattlemen were just coming back into the house when she reappeared. She wouldn't look straight at Thorn; she couldn't. Instead she went to Al, who immediately gathered her to his side—a movement that Thorn watched with cynical eyes and a mocking smile.

"Want to ride over to Houston with us?" Al asked her. "I'm going to show Mr. Bellamy the city on the way to the airport." He indicated the heavyset, smiling man nearby.

Sabina nodded.

"Take your time," Thorn told the two men, but his brooding gaze never left Sabina. "I've got a business meeting in New Orleans in an hour. I'll go alone."

Relieved, Sabina was glad of the opportunity to escape from Thorn's sensual pull, even for a little while. She went with Al and the cattleman and was delighted when the outing kept them away from the ranch until late that evening. By the time they got home, it was bedtime, and Sabina was only too glad to have avoided another confrontation. _Oh, Thorn,_ she thought miserably, _why did it have to be this way?_ Why couldn't they have met under different circumstances? He wanted her so much, there had to be a glimmer of feeling for her under all that ice. Perhaps he might even have loved her, if she'd had a chance to be herself with him. The one time they'd really talked, there had been a rare rapport between them.

And in the woods, he'd whispered, "Another time and place, I might have given you a child...."

It reminded her of the taunt she'd made the first day at the ranch, about having babies, and Thorn's eyes had gone to her stomach with a wild kind of hunger. Her eyes closed as a soft moan rose in her throat. How could he be thinking of children with her if there was no emotion in him? A man interested in a body would certainly be thinking of ways to prevent that from happening, wouldn't he? She almost groaned aloud. If only she knew more about men. But Thorn hated what he felt for her, and made no secret of it. As far as he was concerned, she was only the gold digger his brother wanted to marry, a heartless flirt, a woman with her eye to the main chance. She sighed bitterly. None of that was true, but he'd never know. Because in two days, she'd be out of his life for good, and only the memories would remain. At least, she told herself, she had those, as bittersweet as they were.

The next day at breakfast, Thorn reminded them about the engagement party, which was being held that night. The way he said it sent chills up Sabina's spine.

"It will be formal," he told Sabina, his blue eyes challenging.

"I have a gown," she replied. "I won't disgrace you." She didn't look straight at him. She hadn't been able to since their confrontation in the woods, and she'd avoided him every minute she could—a fact of which he seemed angrily aware.

"Of course you won't," Al replied, studying his brother. "You look smug. Any particular reason?"

"I'm holding some good cards," the older man replied with a narrow glance in Sabina's direction. "What are the two of you planning to do today?"

"We're going down to New Orleans to get me a new dinner jacket," Al said smoothly. "My old one is getting a bit tight."

"Don't stay there too long," Thorn cautioned.

"Wouldn't dream of it," Al promised him.

They did go into New Orleans, but while they were there, they held a council of war with Jessica.

"I'm scared," the redhead confessed as they lunched in a small outdoor cafe. "What if Thorn sees through the act? We don't get married until the day after tomorrow!"

"He doesn't suspect anything," Sabina assured her, patting her hand. "Trust us. We'll handle it."

"It's just that it's so risky, even now," Jessica bit her lip, her eyes worshipping Al. "I'm afraid of Thorn."

"He does inspire those feelings," Al said with a chuckle. "But not for much longer. Once we're actually married, there isn't a thing he can do."

"And I'm taking good care of your ring," Sabina told her, grinning as she held it out. "How fortunate that we wear the same size!"

"There's no one I'd trust with it more," Jessica said warmly. "I feel that we're imposing on you, though. You're the one taking all the risks. And all the contempt. I can imagine what Thorn's put you through."

"He hasn't bothered her," Al said with blessed ignorance.

But Jessica, watching the expressions that crossed her friend's face, wasn't fooled. A minute later, when Al went to the men's room, Jessica urgently leaned forward.

"Don't let Thorn hurt you," she pleaded. "Not even for our sakes. I don't want you to suffer."

Sabina searched her friend's eyes. "Jess, I'm in love with him."

Jess's eyes widened. "In love?"

"What do I do now?" Sabina whispered miserably. "It's the first time, and it hurts. And he thinks I'm nothing but a gold digger." She hid her face in her hands. "Oh, Jess, if he found out the truth about me, he wouldn't even soil his feet by walking on me."

"Stop talking like that," Jessica said with genuine concern. "You're every bit as good as he is."

"No," Sabina said. "Not in his mind. For all my small bit of fame, if he knew my background he wouldn't let me through the front door, and you know it."

"Oh, Sabina, what can I say? I feel so guilty!" Jessica said, frowning.

"I'll get over it," Sabina said. "All I have to do is live through the next couple of days. I'll grit my teeth. And then I'll be on the road. Maybe then, when I'm away from him, it won't bother me so much."

"And Thorn?" Jessica said probingly. "How does he feel?"

"He wants me."

Jessica sighed. "Oh, I see."

"Here's Al back. Don't give me away, please. I couldn't bear to have him know how I feel about his brother," Sabina pleaded. "Thorn would chew me up like candy if he knew!"

"I won't say a word." Jessica smiled as Al came back. "Hi, pal," she said, leaning over to give him a peck on the cheek.

"Hi, yourself," he said lovingly.

Watching them, Sabina felt like crying. If only Thorn could look at her that way, talk to her that way, just once. But that was a pipe dream. She'd learned to her sorrow that reality was painful. Thorn would never be hers. The most she could hope for was that she might linger in his memory as the one woman who got away.

That night, the house was filled with guests enjoying a catered buffet supper and dancing to a live band. It was the Saturday night before Easter Sunday, and Sabina thought she'd never seen such elegant clothes before. Her own strappy gown looked simple by comparison, which was probably what Thorn had intended. She might buy one expensive used dress, but her budget didn't allow her to buy several. This was the one she'd worn to Al's party, and she wondered if Thorn recognized it. He gave her a mock toast from across the room, and she turned away, hurt.

"He did that deliberately, didn't he?" Jessica asked. They escaped for a minute alone in the ladies' room.

"Baiting me," Sabina said with a sigh. "You can't imagine what it's been like. If I didn't like you so much..."

"I love you," Jessica said fervently, and hugged her. "Someday, somehow, I'll make it up to you."

"Are you happy, my friend?" Sabina asked with a tiny smile.

In her black satin dress, with her flaming red hair cascading over her shoulders, Jess was a vision. "Deliriously. I only hope it happens for you, too, one of these days."

"It would be a pity if it did," she replied carelessly. "I don't want marriage, and an affair is out of the question."

"But, Sabina, one day you'll want a family."

She winced. "No."

"With the right man, it would be different," Jessica assured her. "Your children would be wanted, loved."

Sabina's soft gray eyes widened as she thought about having a little boy with dark, waving hair and ice-blue eyes. Her heart skipped wildly. It was pure unadulterated stupidity. She had to stop thinking about Thorn that way.

"Are you all right? You're very pale," Jessica said softly.

"All right?" She was remembering the way it felt to kiss Thorn and she burned all over. "Yes. I'm all right. Let's go back."

Al came up to them, fighting the urge to stare at Jessica. "Well, let's see if we can throw the wolf off the track, shall we?" he asked Sabina. "Jess, I wish there was some other way."

"We could leave the country," Jess murmured. "There wouldn't be an easier way, with Thorn."

"Miss Cane?"

Thorn's deep, slow voice rang out and all at once Sabina noticed that the crowd had stopped dancing and everyone was looking at her. She felt like a criminal being fingered, not like an up and coming celebrity in the entertainment world. But despite her modest dress, she held her head high and moved toward him gracefully. His eyes followed her movements with a tangible hunger and something oddly like pride.

"I've told our guests that you have quite a talent with music. How about doing something for us?"

"I'd be delighted," she said, approaching the small combo, which boasted two guitarists, a drummer and a pianist. They were much younger than The Bricks and Sand Band, but the pianist had style. She went straight toward him.

Thorn was expecting some raucous tune, so that he could embarrass her in front of his elegant guests. But the joke was going to be on him. She smiled secretively as she told the pianist what she wanted. And, fortunately, his training enabled him to provide the accompaniment she needed. Otherwise, she'd have had to sing a capella.

She turned to face the group. "I don't think I have to introduce this piece," she said with a faint smile in Thorn's direction. "I'm sure most of you will recognize it immediately." She nodded toward the pianist.

Thorn settled back against the door with a brandy snifter in his lean hand, his face mocking, challenging. *Conceited little girl,* he was saying without words, *you expect these very elite people to know your pitiful rock songs?*

She nodded toward Thorn then smiled at Jess and Al, who were almost jumping up and down with glee.

The pianist began, and she drew in a deep breath and suddenly burst into the exquisite aria from Puccini's "Madama Butterfly." The crowd stood completely still in the large room, as if every breath was suddenly held. Eyes widened as the piercingly clear voice rang out, as the sweep and flow and dramatic intensity of her voice told the well-known story in classic operatic style. When the melody broke into the high, achingly sweet notes near the end, tears were rolling down the cheeks of two of the women listening. And as she held the final note there was a shattering as if of glass. She finished. As she was bowing, she looked toward the back of the room, where

Thorn had been standing. Only a tiny pile of broken crystal attested to the fact that he'd even been there at all.

"Bravo!" came the cries from the guests. *"Bravo, bravo!"*

"My dear," one tall matron said as she rushed toward Sabina. "I understood Thorn to say that you were a rock singer!"

"Yes," Sabina said with a smile. "You see, I couldn't afford to go to New York to study. It was my dream, but I'm finding a niche for myself in pop music. At least I can still sing the arias."

"And beautifully," the matron said, tears still in her eyes. "So beautifully. It was a privilege to listen to you."

"Thank you." With a final smile for the older woman, Sabina joined Al and Jessica as the band started up again.

"He broke the glass," Al said quietly, nodding toward the crystal on the floor.

"Did he hurt himself?" Sabina asked, concerned.

"I don't know."

Without thinking she rushed out the door and down the hall toward his study. The door was ajar. She pushed it open and walked in, her eyes searching for Thorn. He was at the window, smoking a cigarette.

"Thorn?"

He turned, his eyes dark and threatening, his face hard.

"Your hand . . ."

"Hand?" He lifted the free one and stared at it. He seemed not to have noticed that it was cut.

"I'll dress it for you," she said quietly. She went ahead into the half bath beyond the desk and riffled through the cabinet for antiseptic and a bandage.

He joined her, filling the small room, glaring down at her. His presence overwhelmed her, but she didn't speak. She bathed his hand, loving the calloused feel of it, the dark beauty of its leanness, its flat nails. She washed away the smear of blood and checked the cut for slivers of glass.

"I've never heard anything so beautiful," he said absently. "Your voice is a gift."

She laughed. "Yes, I suppose it is. I wanted a career in opera, you see. But I never had that kind of money. Training is expensive. I scrimped and saved to get what I could, but…circumstances made it impossible for me to continue."

"I knew you were penniless. I didn't know about the operatic aspirations, though," he said blankly.

"Don't try to cut me up, please," she said quietly. "I'm not nearly the threat you seem to think I am." She looked up as she put the bandage in place. "My life hasn't been easy. Don't make it any harder for me."

He reached out and gently touched her cheek, and his eyes narrowed. "Then get out, while you can. I've got a trump card. Don't make me play it in front of Al."

She smiled gently. "Trump card? You make me sound like a public enemy."

"You are," he said under his breath. His jaw tautened. "You're the most dangerous woman I've ever known."

She sighed as she put away the bandages and antiseptic. "Well, I'm glad to know that."

"Give Al back the ring, now, and we'll call it quits."

"Why?" she asked, her eyes searching his.

"Because you'll be cheating him. And me." He tossed the cigarette into the sink, where it hissed going out in the residue of water. "Sabina, we can't live under the same roof without sleeping together. Al's my brother. I love him. But I want you. And, God help me, wanting you is a fever I can't put out. One day, one night, it will be the way it was in the woods," he said huskily, watching her blush. "Except that I won't be able to stop in time. You know that, damn you!"

She searched his eyes. "You really care about Al, don't you?" she asked.

"Yes, I care," he said harshly. His eyes were devouring her face. He started to touch her and then drew back. "Sometimes I almost forget what kind of woman you really are, for all that soft innocence that drives me mad." He drew in a sharp breath and turned away from her. "Forget it. I must be going soft in my old age. Let's rejoin the rest. I'll even announce the engagement for you."

He strode ahead of her with his face set in rigid lines, his long legs making short work of the hall. Cutting straight through the crowd, he poured himself a glass of whiskey. When he turned, with a reckless, do-it-or-die look on his face, Sabina knew immediately that the war wasn't over. It was just beginning.

"Ladies and gentlemen, I'd like to make an announcement," he said, lifting his glass to get everyone's attention. "My brother, Al, has chosen a fiancée. May I introduce to you his choice, Miss Sabina Cane," he said, toasting her, his smile deliberately cruel as he concluded. "Sabina Cane, the illegitimate daughter of a New Orleans lady of the evening and one of her many paying admirers."

Sabina felt the blood drain from her face, but she didn't falter. She merely stared straight into Thorn's eyes. She didn't glance over her shoulder, where Al's expression was murderous, or to her side, where Jessica's face was contorted with pity.

The crowd split, clearing a path for her as she walked toward Thorn. She didn't miss a step. Her face was white, her eyes dark with pain and hurt, but she faced him bravely.

She didn't know where the courage was coming from, because inside part of her had died. All the long years she'd kept her secret, held it back, forbidden Jessica even to mention it aloud. And here the oil baron was, producing it like an incubus, taunting her with it in front of his elegant guests.

"Congratulations," she said unsteadily. "You've found me out. But let me tell you all of it, oil baron. My mother was in love with a boy who went away to Vietnam and didn't come back. He left her pregnant and her family threw her out into the streets. She wasn't eligible for welfare because she made a few dollars too much in tips from a waitressing job. Her earnings were just enough to pay the rent, but not much more. When I was born, she took on a night job as well, to support us. But after a few years of that, her health gave out.'' She straightened, aware of the hush around them, aware of the frozen expression on Thorn's dark face.

''The one thing she had in abundance was beauty. So when she couldn't get any other kind of job, she accepted a date with a wealthy merchant. He was the first. He bought my first pair of shoes, and other trinkets,'' she added, watching the word register in his narrow eyes. ''The second was a shipping tycoon, a friend of the merchant. He paid off the overdue rent and bought us a whole week's worth of groceries as well. We'd been getting scraps from the butcher to make soup until then, because we didn't have enough money for anything more.'' Thorn's face was so drawn by now that it looked pasty. ''There were other men after that. She'd discovered the luxury of having enough to eat and warm clothes and necessities for her little girl. Then she met Harry. Harry was rich, but he had this one little idiosyncrasy. He liked to beat her until she couldn't stand up....'' Her voice was beginning to tremble now, as it all came back. She swallowed and straightened again. ''She loved him desperately, and when he was sober, he seemed to love her, too. But one night, he had too much to drink. And he beat her to death. Right in front of me.''

''Oh, God,'' Thorn whispered, his voice tormented, his eyes wild.

She drew in a slow breath. ''So I was sent to the local orphanage, where I learned how to work for a living. I've been doing it ever since. And trying to live down the past. Ironically, until tonight, there was only one other person in the whole world who knew it. Now,'' she turned to the guests, who were staring helplessly at her, ''I suppose I'll be dragging it behind me like a chain as long as I live. There's just one other little thing. This is what you wanted, I believe, Hamilton Regan Thorndon the Third.''

And she tugged off her ring and turned to hand it to Al.

"Just a minute," Al said, coming forward. He faced his taller, older brother with venom in his eyes. "That was unwarranted, and unworthy of you. And if you don't apologize, I'll knock you down, big brother."

Thorn gave him a considering look and nodded. "Yes, it was unworthy," he said in a subdued tone. "And damned cruel. Miss Cane, I apologize for my lack of manners," he added, looking straight at Sabina.

Her eyes were so clouded with unshed tears, she was unable to see the lancing pain in his icy blue eyes. She only nodded, turned and left the room.

Thorn hadn't apologized for his insolence, only for his lack of manners, she thought hysterically. She packed quickly, dragging clothes from drawers and stuffing them into her carryall. She felt poleaxed. Devastated. Apparently, he'd done some checking into her past and come up with this—what had he called it—his trump card.

She laughed through tears as she finished packing. It was so cruel to throw that in her face, in front of all those people. So cruel!

The door opened and he was standing there. His eyes were dark, his face unsmiling, his posture stiff and strange.

"Did you bring a knife?" she asked. "I can only assume you intend to finish me off in private."

"I shouldn't have done that to you," he said in a tone she'd never heard him use. He had one hand deep in his pocket, the other holding a cigarette. "It was like tearing the wings from a butterfly, and about as satisfying. I had no right."

"Why bother about rights?" she asked, smiling bitterly. "Nobody else ever did. I wasn't even a person when I was little. I was that love child down the street, Bessie's yard child. At the orphanage it was a little better. At least I didn't have to watch her with men." Her eyes clouded at the memory and Thorn actually flinched. "I knew she was doing it for me—I even understood—but that didn't make it any easier." She ground her teeth in an agony of remembrance. "I hated her for a long time. Until he killed her.'' Her eyes closed and she shuddered, trying to blot out the memory. "It took years to get over that, and I was so alone. I missed her then,'' she whispered. "But I hated what she had to become, and I hated rich men dangling expensive gifts to lure her in, to tempt her. If her health had held out, maybe it would have been different. But she had to support us, and that was the only way she could find. Still I'll hate what she became until the day I die, and I'll hate rich men who made her that way. I won't be like her, I won't, I won't!''

She was crying openly, and Thorn's face had gone white. Absolutely white.

Her lower lip trembled and she fought for control. "This isn't much, is it?'' She nodded toward the dress. "You wanted to show me up in front of your wealthy guests down there, and you did it, too. I don't have money to throw away on designer gowns. The clothes I wear are all secondhand, but I need to have them to perform in. Al says I'm the best bargain hunter around.''

His eyes were fierce and the cigarette had to be burning his fingers, but he didn't even seem aware of it. He looked tormented. "I gave you that check . . .''

"I gave it to Al,'' she said wearily. "He's building a new wing for the hospital, a wing for disadvantaged children. The project we wanted your support for was a benefit to help build it. I endorsed the check and signed it over to him, to be donated in your name.''

She turned away from his white face, which was drained of emotion, and life, and picked up her carryall. "As for the engagement, you'll find out soon enough that it was a sham, and why. Now go away, Mr. Thorndon the Third. Get out of my sight, before I get sick.''

He stared at her, trying to find words. "I'll drive you home.''

"No, you won't,'' she said sharply. "After what you did to me downstairs, you won't drive me anyplace. I'll walk.''

"Sabina,'' he whispered in anguish.

"Congratulations, you won," she said, her hot eyes glaring at him. "Aren't you proud of yourself, oil baron?"

"No," he growled. "I'm ashamed." His eyes searched her face one last time before he turned and went out the door, closing it gently behind him. Sabina glanced around the room slowly and went out behind him.

She met Al and Jessica as she started down the staircase.

"We'll drive you home," Al insisted. "I'm sorry. God, I'm so sorry!"

"Regrets don't accomplish anything, dear friend," she said with a wan smile. "Just get me out of here, please."

"I'll stay with you tonight," Jessica said firmly. "And no arguments. I won't leave you alone. Al, he may be your brother, but he's a monster."

"He's going to be a lonely one from now on," Al promised her. "We're getting married. All out in the open. And I'm forming my own company. We'll talk tomorrow. Thorn's really fixed things tonight."

Sabina didn't say a word. She was in love with Thorn, and he'd shown her graphically that he didn't give a damn about her. She wondered if the pain would ever stop. She felt eyes watching as she went out the door, but she didn't turn. She couldn't have borne the sight of him. She still cared. Damn him, she still loved him.

7

*

Jessica's pale eyes narrowed with concern as Sabina sat huddled in her gown and robe drinking the coffee they'd brewed.

"Are you going to be all right?" Jess asked, breaking Sabina's trance.

"Of course I am," Sabina said coldly.

Jess saw right through the mask behind the stiff lip and the determined rigidity. "You really love that man, don't you?"

Sabina took a slow breath and a sip of the hot black coffee. "He doesn't deserve to be loved."

"I'm tempted to agree," Jessica said, watching the taller girl. "But I got a look at his face as we were going out the door. If I were old Juan, I'd hide all the guns tonight."

"Did he look as if he might follow me home and shoot me as well?" Sabina laughed hollowly, but there was curiosity in the question, too. She looked up, searching Jessica's face. "Did he?"

"He looked as if he might blow his own brains out, if you want to know," she replied quietly. She wondered if she ought to tell her anguished friend the rest as well, that there had been a kind of loving anguish in Thorn's blue eyes.

"He'll get over it," Sabina said, leaning back in her chair wearily. "When he's had time to reason it out, he'll decide that it was all my fault and he'll pat himself on the back for his brilliance. He saved Al from me, you know."

"Al told him the truth." Jessica bit her lip. She hadn't meant to let that slip.

Sabina's face went stark white, her eyes as big as saucers. "And what did Thorn say?"

Jess shifted restlessly. "He didn't say anything, but Al had to call his dentist. Thorn knocked two teeth out."

"Then what?" Sabina asked.

"Thorn stormed off to his study and locked the door." Jessica sighed. "Al figured he deserved the punch, and I think I deserve one, too, for what we've done to you and Thorn with this stupid deception," she added tearfully. "If we'd had any idea . . ."

"Thorn and I live in different worlds," Sabina said quietly. "You mustn't blame yourselves. It would never have amounted to anything. I would have been just another notch on his belt."

Jessica shook her head. "I'm afraid not. If it had only been that, Sabina, he wouldn't have minded hurting you. Al said he was like a wounded bear. Even the ranch foreman wouldn't go near him. He went to Al, and that was a first."

"All those people," Sabina said under her breath, closing her eyes. "All those exclusive people, knowing everything about me." She shuddered. "I don't know how I stood there and said those things to him."

"I was so proud of you," Jessica said. "So proud! You were every inch a lady, and it was Thorn who was getting the killing glances, darling, not you. No one's ever beaten him before."

Perhaps she'd beaten him, but at what cost? "Everyone will know now," she said dully. "We'll never get another job. I'll have to leave the band—"

"Stop that!" Jessica said firmly. "I won't let you feel sorry for yourself. You're just not the type."

"I could turn into the type right now," Sabina laughed bitterly.

"Can I fix you something to eat?"

"I'd like Thorn's heart, fried," she said with pure malice.

"Yes, I imagine so. How about some steamed liver, instead?"

Sabina laughed in spite of herself. "No. I don't want anything." She huddled closer in her robe. "Al was terrific, wasn't he?"

"Absolutely." Jessica's eyes warmed. "That was the first time he's ever stood up to Thorn, you know. I don't think it will be the last, despite the loss of his teeth. He didn't duck. He said he figured Thorn had the right."

Sabina hardly heard her. Her mind was drifting in and out of the past, shivering with the force of the memories. For years she'd fought to suppress them. Now they wouldn't be suppressed anymore.

The phone rang and Sabina stiffened.

Jessica soothed her. "It's probably Al." She got up and answered it. "Hello?" Her face went rigid, and she started to speak, but whoever was on the other end apparently said something that got her attention. She paused, glancing warily at Sabina. "Yes. Yes, I think so." She bit her lip. "I don't know if she'll listen, but I'll tell her. Yes. Yes. Good night."

She put down the receiver and turned. "Thorn," she said quietly.

Sabina's eyes grew as hard as diamonds. She averted her face.

"He wanted to make sure you had someone with you tonight," Jessica said, feeling the way. "He..." She hesitated. "He sounded odd."

"I don't care," Sabina said brutally. "I'll never care again. Let's get some sleep."

Jessica watched her friend walk out of the room. Sabina was too hurt right now to listen, but if his voice was any indication, Thorn was hurting, too. That concern had been real. Perhaps he hadn't quite realized it himself, yet, but he'd destroyed the one thing of value in his life. Sabina had gotten closer to him than anyone else, and he'd lashed out at her with a fury. Al had said that. But the cruelty had backfired. It had cost him dearly. Jessica felt like a traitor to admit it, but she felt sorry for her future brother-in-law. Sabina and Thorn were so alike, both trapped in shells of their own making, keeping the world at bay so that it couldn't hurt them. She shook her head sadly and went to bed. Long after she had lain down, she heard Sabina's sobs.

* * *

Al and Jessica were married early Monday morning. It turned out to be more of an ordeal than Sabina had expected. She'd thought that, under the circumstances, Al would get one of his employees to stand up with him, but when she got to the small church, Thorn was there.

Sabina, in a neat beige suit, hesitated at the back pew. Jessica, in an oyster-colored street-length dress, came to meet her.

"He won't bother you," Jessica said gently. "Al made him promise."

Tears threatened to overflow Sabina's eyes. She was still vulnerable, afraid of what he could do to her right now. She hesitated. "I almost didn't come," she confessed softly. "I... Dennis, our road manager, got an offer this morning for a gig at a fabulously well-known club in New York City. Right out of the blue, at a fantastic salary. We jumped at it, of course. We needed the job really bad, and I'm...not known in New York." She choked on the words.

"Nobody will know!" Jessica said firmly. "For heaven's sake, those people aren't going to run to the nearest newspaper and have it all dragged out on the front page! Even Thorn wouldn't do that to you!"

"Wouldn't he?" Sabina asked unsteadily. She stared at his back in the dark business suit he was wearing, at the dark hair that her fingers had stroked. So they'd dulled his fangs, had they? She still felt savaged, and her pride was in tatters. The humiliation he'd heaped on her was fresh enough to burn. She'd stood up to him before, and she wasn't going to run. But her heart pounded wildly with every step she took with Jessica to the front of the small church, where the minister, Al and Thorn waited.

Thorn turned as she came down the aisle. He watched her with an intensity that almost tripped her up. His face was pale and drawn. There were deep, harsh shadows under his haunted blue eyes. So you can't sleep either, she thought coldly. Good! I'm glad you can't sleep!

She edged around him without actually meeting his searching gaze and stood on the other side of Jessica for the brief ceremony. All through it, as the minister spoke the age-old words, she felt her heart aching for what she might have had with Thorn in another time, another place. Tears blurred her vision of the minister and she bit her lip to keep the tears at bay. As he spoke the words "with my body, I thee worship," her eyes went helplessly, involuntarily to Thorn, and found him staring at her. She quickly dropped her gaze to the carpeted floor.

Thorn, she whispered silently. Thorn! How much he must have hated her, to be so cruel. His conscience was bothering him. He was guilt-ridden, but she had to remember that it was only that. He'd never cared. He'd only wanted her. And now he pitied her. Her eyes closed. That hurt the most, that all he felt was pity. She'd rather have his contempt.

It was all over in minutes. Al kissed Jessica with gusto, and then turned to be congratulated by the minister and Thorn. Sabina brushed Jessica's flushed cheek with cool lips and grinned at her.

"Be happy," she said softly.

"We'll see you soon, when we're back from Nassau."

"Not unless you don't go at all," Sabina said with a forced laugh, aware of Thorn's deep, slow voice behind her. "The band and I have to leave for New York tonight. We'll be at the club for two weeks, and Dennis said something about a video we may film there. Some agent heard us in Savannah and thinks we may have video appeal, how about that?"

"Things are looking up," Jessica grinned. "I'm so glad for you."

Sabina nodded. "Yes, I'm looking forward to it."

Jessica stared at her uneasily. Sabina was as pale as Thorn, and she seemed subdued, haunted. Of course, Thorn's presence here was enough to do that to her.

"I thought you still had a week to go at the club here," Jessica said under her breath.

Sabina shifted from one foot to the other. "Al let us out of it, with no argument from the other partner," she said, refusing even to say Thorn's name.

"Where can I write to you?" Jessica asked.

"Send it to the apartment house, in care of Mr. Rafferty," Sabina said,.her voice dull and lackluster. "He said he'd hold my mail for me until I got back. I packed this morning."

The two women embraced warmly and Sabina turned to kiss Al, gently and with genuine affection. "Congratulations, pal," she said with a hint of her old brightness. "Take good care of my best friend, will you?"

"You bet," Al said. He looked radiant, but his green eyes were narrow with concern. "Take care of yourself, you hear?"

"Of course."

He kissed her cheek. "Thanks. I'm only beginning to realize just how much Jess and I really owe you for today," he added quietly.

"Just be happy. See you," she said with a forced grin. She turned, trying to get past Thorn without speaking, but he wouldn't move. Al and Jessica discreetly moved off with the minister, deserting her. She clutched her purse convulsively and stared at his striped tie.

"Well?" she asked tightly.

His quiet, darkened eyes studied her, memorized her. His hands slid into his pockets. "I'd like an hour with you."

"I don't have an hour. I don't have five seconds for you, oil baron," she said curtly.

"I expected that you'd react that way. Maybe I can condense it. I didn't know the truth. Does that count for anything?"

She finally lifted her eyes and had to fight not to throw herself into his arms. He looked and sounded genuinely sorry. But if she'd hoped for more than a surface regret, it wasn't there. Or he was hiding it well.

"Should it?" she asked. "You savaged me!" Her lower lip trembled, and he looked violent for an instant. "I never told anyone about my past, not a soul, except Jessica!"

His face hardened. "Didn't anyone ever tell you it's dangerous to keep secrets? I tried to make you give the ring back without going that far, but you wouldn't do it."

"I couldn't," she returned hotly. "I'd promised to divert you until they could get married."

He ran a rough hand through his dark hair. "Al could have leveled with me at the outset! I like Jessica, I always have. I wouldn't have fought him if I'd known he was that much in love with her."

"He was afraid of you," she said, her voice short. "He said you'd put an end to it. They're the only friends I've ever had, so I agreed to help them. I wanted to pay you back for the way you'd treated me...." She had to stop as the rage threatened to choke her. She could barely see the shadow that darkened his eyes. "And you... trying to buy me for the night—" She laughed shakily. "My whole childhood was one long procession of men with money. You can't imagine how I hate rich men and desperate women who let themselves be bought!"

"Maybe I understand better than you think," he said. "We talked occasionally. You might have told me. It would have saved a lot of grief."

"And give you the perfect weapon to use against me?" she burst out. "Wouldn't you have loved that! An illegitimate orphan with a tramp for a mother, from the back streets of New Orleans."

"Stop it," he said roughly. "I never would have hurt you—"

"What would you call stripping my soul naked in front of Beaumont's finest?"

He looked around the church uncomfortably. "I've apologized," he said tersely.

"Some apology," she returned. "I told Jessica that you'd find some way to put the onus on me. You don't make mistakes, do you, oil baron?"

His eyes darkened as they looked down into hers, and his jaw clenched. His chest rose and fell heavily with each breath. "You don't know me."

"Oh, yes, I do," she said fervently. "I know you inside out. You're so warm and safe in that shell you wear that you'll never let anyone else in it with you. You'll keep the whole world away, and tell yourself you're satisfied. You'll grow old, with no one to love or be loved by. You'll have that fortune you've made, and you'll have all the women you can buy. But you'll be alone until you die."

His breathing was audible now, his eyes cutting. "Are you through?" he asked.

"Almost." She searched his face, feeling her will cave in, her body tremble with remembered pleasure, with the bittersweet agony of loving him. "I came too close, didn't I?" she asked quietly. "You didn't just attack me to save Al. You hated me because I saw too much. I saw beneath that mask you wear."

His eyes flashed anger, his tall body tensed. "Get out of my life," he said in a harsh whisper.

"I thought I'd already done that," she said lifting her chin. "You win. You always win. You even told me so. I should have listened. Goodbye, Hamilton Regan Thorndon the Third," she said with a forced, broken laugh. "I hope you and your money will be very happy together."

"If you're going, go!" he said icily.

She knew she'd never forget that hard face, not as long as she lived. She turned away, turning her eyes down. Her steps quickened as she started back down the aisle.

"Al... Jessica... see you!" she called. And Thorn watched her every step as she ran blindly from the church.

The next few weeks seemed to pass like slow motion. Sabina wasn't even aware of being tired, of pushing herself as she and the band gave one performance after another. But she did, exhausting her body and soul, as if to purge herself of the painful memories.

They filmed the video their first week in New York. It was exciting, and Sabina's head reeled when she heard about the thousands of dollars it had cost. All Dennis told her was that they had a backer, but he kept changing the subject when she asked who. Not that it mattered, she supposed. It was the newest way to break into the recording field, anyway. One video on the music channel could make or break a new group, and she was almost sure that theirs was going to be a sensation.

The young production crew that filmed it for them was wildly supportive, impressed with the quality of Sabina's voice and the throbbing rhythm and harmony of the song Ricky had written. It was titled "Ashes and Wind," and they decided on a rooftop fantasy, with Sabina wearing black tattered chiffon and being chased across rooftops with smoking chimneys by a man in a top hat carrying a white cane. It was funky and wild, and a lot of fun.

Ricky Turner was overwhelmed with the finished product. It was in the can days later, and in a month it would be released on the cable music channel.

The group was getting advance publicity, too, with ads on television and radio and in the print media, and their opening at the New York club netted them some flattering reviews. The advertising would surely boost sales of "Ashes and Wind," Ricky told them smugly. And if Sabina hadn't been so involved in performing and trying to get over Thorn all at once, she might have wondered about the amount of money all this was costing. And where it was coming from.

"The advertising is drawing big crowds," Dennis mentioned one afternoon, excited about the fact that the club had already booked them for two additional weeks. "And next week, the video will be out. We're going great, people. Just great."

"Yes, we sure are," Ricky murmured. "I just hope nothing goes wrong."

"Worrywart," Sabina said accusingly. "You just sit and brood on things to worry about, and nothing ever goes wrong."

"That's what worries me."

She threw up her hands and walked away.

The New York club was an exclusive one, over fifty floors up near Rockefeller Center, and the city spread out below in a jeweled fantasy at night. Couples held hands at their tables while the band performed the soft rock music it was growing famous for, and Sabina felt a twinge of envy. It had never bothered her before. But then, she'd never known what love was until Thorn walked into her life.

The memory of him made her sad, bruised her heart.
It had been a tragic thing all the way around. If she'd had
good sense, she'd never have agreed to run interference
for Al. But then, he and Jessica wouldn't be married now
and looking forward to any kind of life together.

Her eyes misted over as she thought what it might have
been like if she and Hamilton Regan Thorndon the Third
had met under normal circumstances. If, that first night
at Al's party, they'd been strangers altogether and could
have started from scratch.

But just as quickly, she remembered his harsh accusation that last night, about her illegitimacy, her mother,
and she went hot all over with rage. She wasn't good
enough for him. Eventually, he'd have found it out even
if they'd started dating and Al hadn't been in the picture. He'd have found out about her past, and he'd have
walked away. When Hamilton Thorndon married, it
would be a society ingenue, a Houston oil heiress or a
New Orleans society woman. It certainly wouldn't be an
illegitimate child and orphan.

As long as she lived, she'd remember his face at the
church. If only it had been something deeper than a
guilty conscience, she might have been tempted to throw
herself into his powerful arms and take up residence. But,
of course, it hadn't been anything deeper. Because he
wasn't capable of it. Especially with a woman like her.

Bitterness replaced her frustration and she pushed
harder, rehearsed longer, put her whole heart into her
performances. She'd show him. Her past wasn't going to
hold her back. She'd make a name for herself, have the
whole world at her feet. And then he'd see what he'd
passed up; he'd be sorry.

She looked at herself in the mirror, sighing. Sure. Look
what Thorn passed up, she thought miserably, seeing
dark eyes dominating a white, drawn face. Even her hair
was lackluster, and she was losing weight rapidly. She
turned away from her reflection, demoralized.

When she got back to the club, Ricky was glaring as the
technicians finished the set and adjusted the heavy lighting.

"I don't like the way that light's hanging," he muttered, pointing to one of the small, low-hanging spotlights.

"You're just overanxious, as usual," she said accusingly. "Come and have some coffee with me. I want to ask you about that new number we did in the video."

He shrugged philosophically as she dragged him away. "Okay," he said. "Maybe it won't come crashing down on your pretty head."

"If it does, I'll remember that I told you to leave it alone," she promised.

The words were prophetic. That night, as they started into their routine, the small spotlight swiveled and came loose. It crashed down onto the stage to the hysterical screams of the packed audience, hitting the side of Sabina's head.

She was knocked out as the hardware still attached to it cut into her shoulder. It wasn't a big light, fortunately, but it was heavy enough to do some damage.

Sabina regained consciousness in the hospital, her eyes unfocusing, her body hurting. The last thing she'd remembered was singing a song and hearing a yell from the door of the club, a tormented yell in a voice she'd thought she recognized. But then the spotlight made impact. She'd thrown up an arm and felt shattering pain in her head and shoulder. And then, darkness.

"Come on, come on," came a harsh, commanding voice. Her hand was being restrained, gripped in something rough and warm that wouldn't let go. "You're tough, tulip. You even beat me. Now come on and fight your way back. I'm not letting go until you do. Come on!"

Her eyes blinked. It had been warm and comfortable in her oblivion and now she was hurting like hell. She moaned.

"That's it," the voice continued, softer now, coaxing. "That's better. Open your eyes, honey, let me see your eyes."

Weren't they open already? How odd they felt. She struggled and her heavy eyelids slowly lifted. There was

someone bending over her. She blinked and her eyes
opened a little wider. A man. An older man, with a
stethoscope. She glanced around numbly and saw the
maze of machines connected to her body, in a tiny room
whose window faced a nursing desk. She tried to move,
but there were wires everywhere. She blinked again.

"Miss Cane, do you feel any discomfort?" the elderly
man asked.

She had to lick her dry lips before she could answer.
"Hurts," she managed. "Head. And...my...my
shoulder." She tried to move, but the pain was too great.
She was gently pressed back into the pillows.

"You've been in a coma, but you're going to be all
right now. We're going to give you something for the
pain," he said. "You'll be fine."

Her eyes closed again. It was too much of an effort to
keep them open.

The next time she opened them, it was to find herself
in a hospital room. Her mind still felt foggy, but the pain
had lessened considerably. She glanced toward her right
shoulder and found it bandaged. It felt odd when she
moved, stiff and sore. There was something tugging uncomfortably at her temple, too. She reached up slowly
with her left hand and found something like thread there,
and raw skin. Stitches!

"Hello."

That voice.... She frowned drowsily, turning her head.
Even half unconscious and full of painkillers, she reacted to the sight of him. She lay there helpless, looking,
staring, loving.

"Thorn," she whispered.

He leaned over her, his face looking tired, his blue eyes
soft. Sabina couldn't believe her eyes. She had to be
dreaming.

He was wearing a dark suit and he looked rumpled.
The white shirt had blood on it. She frowned. Blood?
Where had he gotten that? And it was a dinner jacket,
not a suit. Her eyes went back up to his.

"Are you in pain, darling?" he asked softly.

She was delirious. He wouldn't call her darling. Anyway, he wasn't there. She closed her eyes. "Sleepy," she mumbled, and it was the last thing she remembered.

Daylight streamed in through the blinds, disturbing her sleep. She brushed at it, as if it were a fly she could shoo away.

"No," she muttered. "Go away. Too bright...."

"I'll close the blinds."

Had somebody spoken? She heard a chair creak and hard, heavy footsteps. She turned her head on the cool pillow and saw him again. The pain had returned so this time she knew she wasn't dreaming. It really was Thorn.

8

_____ * _____

Sabina stared at him with eyes that wouldn't quite focus. Painkillers and weariness had made them foggy.

"How do you feel?" he repeated, his voice deeply textured and slow.

Her eyes searched his face blankly as she tried to fit the pieces together. He hated her. He wanted her out of his life. He'd shamed her and humiliated her and told her to go. Why was he here?

"Terrible," she said, her voice thin and weak. Restlessly, she turned her disheveled head against the soft white pillowcase. She felt numb discomfort. "That light...." She tried to get up.

"Settle down. You'll tear something loose," he said curtly. Firm but gentle hands nestled her back down into the pillows.

"My shoulder...." She tried to move it, but there were bandages. And the other arm had a Styrofoam pad under the forearm and a tube leading to a needle in the wrist. "What—"

"An IV," Thorn said. He sat down in the chair beside the bed and leaned back. "You've got a nasty concussion," he said quietly. "And a bruised shoulder, and some cuts and bruises. But your doctor says that if you keep improving, you'll be out of here within five days, and back at work in about a month."

She blinked. None of this was making sense. And why was he here? Her eyes went to his stained shirt. He was still wearing the dinner jacket, and the same shirt.

"You've got blood on your shirt," she faltered.

"So what?" he asked. His eyes were anything but soothing.

"How long have I been here?"

"Three days," he said, and there was a world of meaning in his tone.

"Were you...at the club when it happened?" she persisted.

He sighed roughly, grabbed an ashtray already half full of stubs, and lit another cigarette. "No," he said a moment later. "I was at a dinner party in Manhattan. I'd planned to stop by later. Dennis phoned me as soon as he'd called for an ambulance." He laughed shortly. "The ambulance and I got there at the same time. I rode in with you."

She didn't understand any of it. "Why are you here?" she asked, confused. "You hate me."

His angry glare seemed to underline her statement. "Who else have you got?" he asked bluntly. "Al's in Saudi Arabia, with Jessica, on a business trip for me. Dennis and Ricky and the guys were willing to stay with you, of course, but they had to finish off the club engagement with another vocalist."

"Another singer? Who?" she asked, her ears perking up.

"Does it matter?"

She sighed, feeling uncomfortable and confused and thoroughly miserable. Her big chance and someone else was taking her place, while Thorn sat there glaring at her as if he despised her. Her eyes closed. Tears welled up and spilled out.

"Oh, for God's sake, not that!" Thorn growled.

Her lower lip trembled, too, and she bit it to keep it still. "I'm being taken care of, obviously," she said, forcing her eyes open. "Thank you for all your concern, but why don't you go home? I can take care of myself now. I'm good at it. I've had years of practice."

He got up, looming over her, with one hand in his pocket and the other holding the cigarette. The blue eyes that glittered down at her were impossible to read.

"What do I have to go home to?" he asked bluntly.

That threw her. She dropped her gaze to the sheet. She wanted to tug it up and wipe her wet eyes, but both hands were immobilized. "You've got your women, oil baron." She laughed coldly.

"I'm alone," he said. His eyes studied her up and down and returned to her face, where a stark white bandage was taped around her temple and her neck. "I have no one."

Unable to meet his gaze, she stared blankly at the needle in the back of her hand. "Join the club."

He drew in a slow breath. "You're going to be out of commission for a while."

The implications were just beginning to get through to her. She looked up at him in a daze. Yes, she'd need looking after, and a place to rest. Since Jessica wasn't around now, what would she do?

"There's no need to panic," Thorn said, lifting the cigarette to his mouth. "You're coming home with me. I'll take care of you until you're back on your feet."

"Like hell you will!" she burst out, horrified at the thought of being completely at his mercy for weeks.

He lifted his shoulders and let them fall. "I expected that," he said absently, studying her. "But what else can we do, tulip? God knows, you can't be left alone."

"Get me back to New Orleans," she said. "I can stay in my own apartment. Mr. Rafferty will look after me."

His face hardened. He turned away. "Rafferty thinks you're a cross between a saint and the good fairy."

She stared at him nervously. "How do you know?"

His broad shoulders shifted as he stared out through the window blinds. "I wanted to see where you lived."

She shuddered. "Why?"

When he turned, his face was expressionless. "It's a hovel," he said coldly.

Her eyes blazed. "It is not! It's a decent, economical place to live, and I have good neighbors! They'll take care of me!"

He took a final draw from his cigarette and crushed it out angrily. "Mr. Rafferty is hardly able to take care of himself. How do you think he'd manage those stairs to your apartment several times a day?"

Tears threatened to come again, as she realized how right he was, how helpless she was.

"Yes, I know, you're proud and you hate being obligated to me in any way," he said quietly. "But you don't have much choice."

But being near him, living with him . . . how would she bear it? Especially knowing how he felt about her, how he hated her.

"You said that I was afraid to let anyone come close to me. That I was afraid of involvement. Aren't you the same way?"

She felt trapped. "Yes, but . . ."

He reached down, drawing his fingers softly against her cheek, her mouth, holding her eyes with his. "I've hurt you more than I ever meant to, Sabina," he said gently. "For God's sake, let me make amends in the only way I can."

"To salve your conscience?" she asked unsteadily.

He stared at her mouth, running his lean finger sensuously around its perfect bow shape. "If that's what you want to believe."

"It was only desire. You said so."

"I did, didn't I?" he murmured.

"Thorn—"

"I'll take care of you."

"But, the band—" she moaned.

"They can live without you for a few weeks," he said. "Once that video hits the market next week, you'll be a legend in your own time, anyway."

That hardly registered. Between her foggy mind and his devastating nearness, she wasn't thinking straight. "How did you know about the video?"

He tilted her chin up a little more. "Never mind how I knew." His voice sounded oddly strained. "Listen, I need to go back to my hotel and change. Will you be all right now?"

She blinked, suddenly realizing that if she'd been here for three days, he had, too. She knew because he was wearing the same clothes he had on when she was brought in.

"You've been here all this time?" she burst out, aghast.

He brushed the unruly hair away from her pale face. "Yes."

"But why?"

"I like hospitals," he growled. "I love sitting in emergency rooms and watching people in green uniforms pass by, and sitting in waiting rooms in the intensive-care unit begging to see you for five damned minutes three times a day! And there's nothing quite as comfortable as a straight chair in a waiting room."

"You didn't have to—" she began.

"How could I leave you, for God's sake?" he said, and his eyes wandered hungrily over her face. "You were in a coma when we got you here!"

"Coma?" she parroted.

"Until you opened your eyes and started grumbling at me early this morning, I wasn't sure you'd come out of it at all, despite what the doctor said."

"You can't pretend you cared whether I did or not," she said coldly.

"You can't imagine how I felt," he said in a rough undertone.

"That's right," she replied abruptly, giving him a burning look. "Remember me? The illegitimate kid from the wrong side of the—"

She suddenly stopped as a lean, hard finger settled over her mouth.

"Don't," he said, regret forming a mask of strain over his handsome face. "I tried to tell you at Al's wedding how deeply I regretted that. You might not believe it, but I hurt myself as much as I hurt you."

Her face turned into the pillow as it all came back, a bitterly vivid memory.

"I disgraced myself, you know," he said after a long pause, sounding ironic and self-mocking. Her eyes came up to meet his and he smiled. "That's right. None of the people who came to that dinner party will even speak to me now. And the matron who cried when you sang even went so far as to sell her stock in my company. How's that for revenge?''

She showed a hint of a smile. He seemed to be more amused than angered by the reaction. "You don't mind?"

"Of course I mind," he murmured. "I'm never invited to luncheons or formal dinners these days. I'm having to survive on old Juan's cooking, and he's mad at me, too. He burns everything he sets before me. Juan is another of your instant conquests," he added ruefully.

She flushed, lowering her eyes to his stained shirt. Odd where that stain was, just about where her bleeding head would have rested if he'd held her.

"If you'll come home with me," he said, "Juan will have to cook good meals, and I'll gain back some of the weight I've lost. So will you. You've lost a bit yourself."

"I've been working hard," she said.

"Yes. Dennis told me." He stuck both hands in his pockets. "Come on. I dare you."

Dare. The old word from her childhood brought her eyes up. She stared at him, taking in the mocking smile, the challenge in his blue eyes. "All right," she said. "I'll go with you."

He smiled slowly. "Think of it as a crash course in human relations. You can teach me to be human, and I'll teach you how to be a woman."

Her body tingled. "I don't want to become a ..."

"Hush." He bent and kissed her mouth tenderly, barely touching her. "I won't seduce you, even if you beg. Okay?"

She could hardly catch her breath. "You could make me beg," she whispered with painful honesty.

"I know. Is that what frightens you?" he asked gently.

She nodded. Her eyes were so close to his that she could see their dark blue outline, the wrinkles beside his eyes.

After a pause, he said, "You aren't the only one who's vulnerable. I'd better let someone know you're awake." He said it as if the weakness irritated him. He pressed the call button and before she could get her mind together enough to question him, he was out the door and the nurse was inside making a condition check.

"How lucky you are," the young nurse said with a smile as she took Sabina's temperature. "The ICU staff bent the rules a little for Mr. Thorndon when they saw what his presence was doing for you. He sat and held your hand and talked to you all the time. You kept having seizures and he sat there like a man possessed, watching us work on you." She shook her head with a sigh. "We were all afraid you wouldn't come out of it. Comas are so unpredictable, and we're helpless to do anything about them in circumstances like these. We just have to sit and wait."

The thermometer came out and Sabina stared at the nurse. "Thorn stayed with me all that time?"

"He sure did," She sighed. "What a heavenly male. Lucky, lucky you." She grinned, finished her tasks, and breezed out again.

Thorn was back less than an hour later, still worn but a little more relaxed. He had an attaché case with him, and after sitting down in a chair beside the bed, he opened it and took out a sheaf of papers.

"Go to sleep," he told her. "I'll sit here and work."

From his pocket, he pulled out a pair of reading glasses, tinted ones that looked more like pilot's sunglasses. She smiled faintly at the way he looked in them as he bent over reams of paper. He was wearing a white turtleneck sweater with a blue blazer and dark blue slacks, highly polished boots and a cream-white Stetson. She looked at him with adoration.

He looked up, smiling warmly at her. "Go to sleep," he repeated gently.

"Aren't you tired?" she said drowsily. "You need some rest, too."

"I can't rest away from you," he said quietly.

If only she wasn't so sleepy. But her head had been throbbing and she'd asked for something to kill the pain. The injection of Demerol was just beginning to work.

"Don't . . . leave me," she whispered sleepily.

"Never again," came the soft reply, but she was past hearing.

A week from the day she'd entered the hospital, Thorn took her back to Texas. She was weak, and she'd suffered some vertigo and nausea those first days out of intensive care. But now she was on the way to recovery, and it felt wonderful to be outside again, even in the bitter cold.

Christmas was barely a week away. So was the band's new video. She smiled, remembering the brief visits the guys had made to her room, when they could get past Thorn. He was determined that she should rest, and ran interference like a professional. Ricky and Dennis managed a few minutes, long enough to tell her how well the club engagement was going, despite the fact that their stand-in vocalist was male. Anyway, they said, the video was going to be the big thing, and it would be on the music channel within days. She was to look for it. Thorn's ranch was beyond the limits of the cable company, but he had a satellite dish, so they'd be able to get it anyway.

She was surprised to find the ranch fully decorated for Christmas, all brightly lit and an enormous fir tree loaded with decorations, and a kitchen full of baked delights. Under the tree were dozens of presents. Sabina had a downstairs room, so that she wouldn't have to risk climbing stairs.

"Is your mother coming for Christmas?" she asked Thorn once she'd settled in. She was sitting in the living room with him during their first evening at home.

"No," he said quietly, filling a glass with whiskey. "Maybe after the New Year, though, when Al and Jessica get back."

"There are only the two of us for Christmas?" she asked hesitantly.

He turned, watching her in the blue velour robe he'd brought her. "Just the two of us," he agreed quietly.

"But, all those presents—!"

He looked uncomfortable. He sat down beside her, putting his glass to one side while he lit a cigarette. "I invited a few people over on Christmas day."

Her face went white, and his jaw tautened. "No," he said quickly. "Not anybody from that damned crowd!"

She swallowed, and clutched at her robe. She still felt vulnerable. "Sorry."

"You'll learn to trust me," he said putting the cigarette to his mouth. "I don't make promises that I don't keep. I'll never hurt you again."

She forced a smile. "Okay."

"I invited your Mr. Rafferty and a couple of twins and their mother, and that elderly woman who lives on the first floor in your building..." he began.

Her face froze in mid-smile. "You what?"

"They're your friends, aren't they?" he said.

"Yes! But, I never dreamed—"

"I told you I wasn't a snob," he reminded her. "I thought it was about time I proved it to you."

"But, what about your friends?" she asked, concerned.

He took the whiskey glass in his lean hand and sipped at it, laughing mirthlessly. "I don't have any," he said, and sounded so alone that she felt tears sting her eyes.

9
*

She stared at him hungrily. "You met my friends when you picked up my things at the apartment?" she asked, after a minute.

"That's right," he said, turning. His eyes swept over her thin body in the deep blue velour robe. The robe was one of hers, old and worn, and his face hardened as he saw the worn places. "I looked for nightclothes, but that robe and a couple of cotton gowns were all I could find," he added.

She lowered her eyes, embarrassed. "They're all I have," she confessed. "I had to spend most of my money on stage costumes."

"You mean 'what was left.' After all, you gave away most of what you had to your neighbors," he said.

She looked up and saw a surprising look on his face, which she was helpless to decipher. "You saw how they live," she faltered.

"Yes." He lifted the whiskey glass to his mouth and took a sip. His broad shoulders rose and fell with a heavy breath. "I suppose I've had money myself for so long that I'd forgotten what it was like to be without it." He dropped down beside her. "Not that I ever lived the way your neighbors do. My father always made good money."

She curled her feet up under her and leaned her head back against the sofa, watching him. He was good to look at, she mused. So handsome and big and vibrantly male. She smiled softly. All the bad memories faded as her heart fed on him.

He glanced at her and saw that searching look, and smiled back gently. "Feeling better?"

She nodded. "Will I have to go all the way to New York to have the stitches out?" she asked, voicing a question that had worried her for two days.

"Of course not," he said. "I've had my doctor call yours, and I've made an appointment for you on Friday. I'll drive you in to Beaumont."

"What will they do to me, do you know?" she asked, frowning.

He reached out and touched her hair lightly, tracing its sheen to her shoulder. "Just an office checkup, that's all. They'd never have let you out of the hospital if they'd had any doubts about your recovery."

"Of course." She lifted her shoulders and winced as the bruised one protested.

"How does it feel?" he asked, nodding toward her arm.

"Sore." She laughed.

He put down his whiskey glass and moved closer, opening her robe with such deft assurance that she didn't think to protest the intimacy. The gown underneath covered her of course, but it was old and worn thin. When he drew the robe away from her body, he smiled wickedly at the flush on her cheeks.

"You can't possibly be self-conscious with me?" he teased. "Not after that day in the woods."

Her eyes widened, as they looked into his, and the smile on his face began to fade. His long fingers drew a pattern down her throat, tracing the madly throbbing pulse, lingering just below her collarbone where the loose gown had sagged.

"I wanted you," he breathed. "Never more than that day, when you let me open your blouse and look at you, and touch you, and taste you." His jaw tautened as he sighed wearily. "I was so wrong about you, Sabina. I knew it then, but things had gone too far. I was afraid of what was happening to me. I hated you for leading me on, when you belonged to Al, for keeping us both on a string. I couldn't be sure you weren't the gold digger I thought you were. I didn't trust my instincts. It never occurred to me that you could have been pretending. But it should have. Everything was wrong about that engagement. A blind man could have seen through it.''

''You were trying to protect Al. I realized that, although it didn't help a lot at the time,'' she said quietly. ''I've been so ashamed of my past, you see.''

''Why?'' He brushed the dark hair away from her face. ''None of it was any of your doing. Your mother did what she could for you. I can see that it would have left scars, but it was never your fault.''

Her eyes fell to his chest. ''I was there the night my mother died—'' she closed her eyes ''—that last night, when he hit her...'' Her voice broke.

''Darling, don't.'' He pulled her gently into his arms and held her and rocked her, his hand smoothing her long hair, his deep voice soothing her. ''It all happened a long time ago. It's over.''

She dabbed at the tears, shifting and moaning as her shoulder began to ache again.

''Did I hurt you?'' he asked softly. His hand moved to her face and touched it hesitantly, learning every soft contour, as hers had once done to his, delighting in its vulnerability.

''Thorn,'' she whispered.

His breath became audible. His mouth was poised just above hers and his eyes looked deep into her own as his fingers passed slowly down her throat to her collarbone and still further. She tensed, but he shook his head.

''No,'' he whispered. ''Let me touch you.''

She bit her lower lip as his lean hand eased under the fabric, and he watched her as the tips of his fingers teased softly around the edges of one perfect, creamy breast.

He moved, easing her down onto the couch, and she heard the springs shift under them. But what he was doing was so delicious that she didn't even protest. She trembled with sweet anticipation, wanting him so much that it was almost painful. His arm made a pillow behind her head, and he smiled softly as her body jerked toward his fingers.

''Wicked, wicked...man,'' she whispered brokenly, watching his face.

"Indulge me," he whispered back. "You can't know how it was, seeing you in that hospital bed."

It was hard to think. "The nurse said...that you talked to me and...held my hand...oh!" she gasped as one lean finger brushed the hard tip of her breast.

"Did she tell you that I sat by you when they told me you might not come out of the coma, and that I cried like a boy?" He put his hard mouth slowly, warmly on hers. "Because I did. Open your mouth."

"Cried...?" She couldn't think. His tongue was working sorcery on her parted lips, and his hand had eased down completely over her bare breast, so that she could feel not only his slightly calloused fingers, but also the wrinkly moist warmth of his palm. "Thorn," she moaned, and her body arched.

"Open my shirt, and do that to me," he whispered into her mouth. "Let me teach you how to arouse me."

Her breathing became short. Her hands shook so much she could hardly fumble the buttons of his shirt open. To be allowed free license with his body was overwhelming.

She eased her fingers down against the thick mass of hair and over the warm muscles. She searched for his skin, finding taut peaks that might have been the mirror image of her own. Her eyes found his.

"Do men...too?" she whispered.

"Yes." He held her head gently in his hands. "Open your mouth, and put it against me, there," he whispered, guiding her down his chest. She did as he told her, and he groaned harshly, a sound that made her head lift so that she could see his face.

"Don't you moan when I put my lips on you?" he whispered, smiling.

Her eyes were full of wonder. "Oh, Thorn, I never knew—!"

"Thank God." He moved, peeling the gown to her waist, and she let him, lying pliant in his arms, watching his face as he saw what his stroking had accomplished. "I like knowing that you're a virgin," he said unexpectedly, touching her lightly. "You aren't afraid of the first time with me, are you?" he asked quietly.

Her face reddened. "I can't . . ."

"Not now, little tulip," he said with a laugh. He bent and eased his bare chest down over hers, and smiled at the way she trembled. "Yes, I like that, too. I like the way it feels to have you half nude against me. You're a sexy woman."

"Thorn, I won't be—" she tried again.

"Where would you like to be married?" he asked.

She stared at him as if he'd gone crazy. "What?"

"Where would you like to be married?" he murmured against her mouth. "Beaumont or New Orleans? Mr. Rafferty can give you away, and Jessica can be matron of honor."

Her palms flattened against his chest. "I can't marry you," she said.

His face went expressionless. "Why not?" he said.

She drew a breath and tried to get up. Surprisingly, he let her, watching as she drew her gown back up and shouldered gingerly into her robe again. "I just can't, that's all."

"Is it your career?" he persisted. "Because I'll compromise."

She shook her head. She wrapped her arms around her waist, dying inside because he'd just said the one thing she wanted most in the world to hear. She loved him, would have died for him. But she couldn't marry him.

"Then why?"

"How would you announce it?" she asked with a bitter laugh, and ran an unsteady hand through her hair. "My parents were never married, you know. There was a front-page story when my mother was killed. Inevitably, people would find out. In the circles you move in, I'd be so much of a liability—"

"Liability, hell! That's no excuse at all." He sighed wearily and got to his feet. "It's because of what I did to you, isn't it?" he asked in an odd voice. He wouldn't look at her. He lit another cigarette, took a few draws and, as quickly, put it out. "It's because I humiliated you. You think I might do it again."

"No!" Her head came up. "No, it isn't that, truly it isn't! It's just that you'd—oh, Thorn, you'd be so ashamed of me."

His eyes closed. "The only person I've been ashamed of in recent weeks is myself." He moved restlessly toward the door. "I need to do some paperwork, I'll see you later."

She stared at his broad back, half puzzled, half certain. Did he care? Could he care that much and still not believe her reasons for rejecting his proposal? Her heart raced wildly.

She took a gamble, the maddest gamble she'd ever taken in her life. If he rejected her, she'd never get over it.

"Thorn!" she called.

He paused with his hand on the doorknob. "Yes?"

She gathered all her courage and held out both her arms to him.

He hesitated for an instant, and her heart began to throb. She feared that she'd misread the entire situation. Then his face changed. He moved back toward the sofa and suddenly dropped to his knees and clasped her hard enough around the waist to hurt her, burying his face in her breasts.

She held him, feeling the tremor in his body, her hands tangling in his dark hair. She sat disbelieving, trembling with new emotions, with shared emotions.

"I love you," he managed in a broken tone. "Oh, God, I love you, and I didn't know it until that night, until it was too late, and I wondered how I was going to live if I'd caused you to do something desperate. I called to make sure Jessica was with you because I was afraid. After that, I could never get close to you again. I knew I'd lost you. I knew I had..." His arms tightened and he caught a savage breath, while Sabina stared down at his dark head in shocked delight. "I kept up with you, I followed your career, I even paid for that damned video," he added, stunning her. "But nothing compensated me for you. I haven't been near another woman since you left. I've hardly eaten or slept...and then that damned light fell on you, and I paid for sins I haven't even committed yet. I sat by your bed and held your hand and knew that, if you died, I might as well lie down beside you, because I wouldn't have had a reason left to stay alive myself."

"Oh, Thorn," she whispered, pulling his head closer. "I love you so much . . ."

His head lifted, his eyes unusually bright. "Do you? Even after all I've done to you?"

Her fingers touched his face wonderingly. "I understood even then, you know," she whispered. "I knew you so well. It frightened me sometimes, especially when I was pretending to be engaged to Al, because you were like the other half of my soul. I even knew what you were thinking."

"Yes, I felt that," he sighed. "At the church, when you said I never let people come close, you hit a nerve, darling. I hated having you know that, hated being so vulnerable, so readable. If it's any kind of compensation, I've paid for what I did to you. Being without you was more than enough punishment."

She bent down and kissed his mouth tenderly. "I want a child with you."

His breath held, and his eyes were gloriously loving. "I want one with you. I did even that first day you came to the ranch. You mentioned having babies, and I looked at you and wanted to see you big with mine. It scared the hell out of me," he said with a chuckle. "After that, all I could think about was getting you pregnant. That was when I realized how committed I was." His smiled faded. "Marry me, Sabina."

"There'll be gossip," she cautioned.

"Darling, there'll always be gossip. I love you. What else matters?"

"You're hard to argue with," she murmured.

"So they tell me." He kissed her gently. "Marry me. Give me some children. I'll buy you a new bathrobe and let you sing in my nightclub."

She laughed at his phrasing. "How can I sing when I'm pregnant?"

"Listen, lady, you can even sing while you're getting pregnant, for all I care."

"Thank you," she murmured demurely, batting her eyelashes at him. "Thorn, I hear that new vocalist is doing great with the band. And if you'd let me study opera in my spare time, and let me teach voice . . ."

He looked shocked. "What are you offering to do?" he asked. "Give up everything you've ever worked for?"

She slid down onto the floor in front of him and linked her arms around his neck. "I have everything I ever wanted right here," she said solemnly. "There is nothing I want more than you, and that includes a career. Later, when the children are older, perhaps. But being on the road was already beginning to pale, and I'm terrified of large crowds. I want to live with you and travel with you. I love you."

"Darling," he breathed, searching for words.

"Shhh," she whispered, putting her mouth against his. "Lie down, darling," she murmured wickedly.

"Like hell." He chuckled. He got up, smoothing his hair. "You're not getting me into bed without a wedding ring."

"Tease," she said accusingly.

He made a mock bow and helped her to her feet. "We'll set a wedding date. Meanwhile, don't you want to know who all those presents are for?"

She stared past him at the tree. "Who?"

"I got Mr. Rafferty a warm coat, and the twins some new shoes, and their mother a coat . . ."

Tears welled up in her eyes. "My friends. . . ."

"The whole world is your friend," he whispered. "But I'm your best one. Between us, we'll spread a little comfort, okay?"

She reached up and pressed a warm kiss against his chin, her eyes brimming with love. "Okay."

He smiled at her. In his eyes, she saw the sweetness and laughter of the years ahead. And she laughed, softly, wonderingly, just before he lifted her in his arms and carried her back to the sofa.

"I thought you weren't going to let me get you into bed until we were married," she chided.

"I didn't say one word about sofas, did I?" he murmured with a roguish smile. He put her down on the couch and let his eyes wander slowly from her toes up over her legs and hips to her taut breasts. His hand went to the buttoned cuffs of his shirt and he flicked the buttons out of the holes with deliberate slowness while she looked up at him, lips parted, body aching.

"The door's open," she whispered.

"For your sake, we'd better leave it that way," he murmured. His lips curved in a smile. "On second thought, to hell with it." He closed the door without looking out, locked it, and went slowly back to the couch. "Now," he said in a breathless, laughing tone. "Aren't you too hot, with all those clothes on?" he murmured, easing down beside her. "Hmmmm, your skin's hot, darling," he taunted, watching her as he lazily disposed of the robe and put it aside. His mischievous eyes went down to the taut outline of her breasts, which were moving with the torturous raggedness of her breathing.

"Thorn," she whispered in a tone that throbbed with hunger.

"I want you, too," he said in a whisper. "But I'll stop before we go too far. Lift up, darling, and let me get this gown out of my way.... Yes, yes!"

Old Juan, who'd been on his way to tell them dinner was ready, had watched the door close and simultaneously turned around on his heel, smiling, to go back to the kitchen. Time enough to eat, he told himself. There were more important things. He put the plates aside and began to hum.

PENNY JORDAN

A COLLECTION

Volume 2

From the bestselling author of *Power Play*, *The Hidden Years* and *Lingering Shadows* comes a second collection of three sensuous love stories, beautifully presented in one special volume.

Featuring:

FIRE WITH FIRE
CAPABLE OF FEELING
SUBSTITUTE LOVER

Available from May 1993   Priced: £4.99

W●RLDWIDE

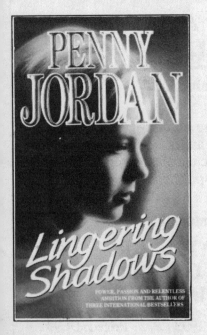